# SCIENCE and MAN

# SCIENCE AND MAN

*Twenty-four Original Essays by*

ALEŠ HRDLIČKA · REINHOLD NIEBUHR · JACQUES MARITAIN

ALFRED E. COHN · ARTHUR H. COMPTON · HAROLD C. UREY

WALDEMAR KAEMPFFERT · K. KOFFKA · BRAND BLANSHARD

JAMES T. SHOTWELL · CARL L. BECKER · JULIAN HUXLEY

BRONISLAW MALINOWSKI · FRANK KNIGHT · LEWIS MUMFORD

WALTER B. CANNON · KARL T. COMPTON · JEAN PIAGET

PHILIP C. JESSUP · HANS KELSEN · HAROLD D. LASSWELL

EDWIN G. CONKLIN · C. G. JUNG · RALPH BARTON PERRY

*Edited*
WITH AN INTRODUCTION AND CONCLUSION
*by Ruth Nanda Anshen*

*With a new prologue
to the Greenwood reprint by the editor.*

GREENWOOD PRESS, PUBLISHERS
NEW YORK

# ACKNOWLEDGMENT

I wish to express my profound gratitude to Jacques Maritain, Wm. Pepperell Montague and Waldemar Kaempffert for most important suggestions and criticisms; and also to my daughter, Judith, for invaluable and generous assistance in the preparation of the Index.

RUTH NANDA ANSHEN

# CONTENTS

## 1. INTRODUCTION

## 2. SCIENCE AND THE UNIVERSE

## 3. SCIENCE: ITS MATERIALS, METHODS, ENDS

## 4. SCIENCE AND SOCIETY

viii CONTENTS

# PROLOGUE 1968

After more than a quarter of a century, it is not only gratifying to the scholars constituting this volume in the *Science of Culture Series* (first published in 1942), but, I must confess, a confirmation to myself, as planner and editor of this Series, to note the continuing relevance of this book, SCIENCE AND MAN, to the compelling problems of our apocalyptic epoch in 1968.

It is of course impossible, not to say presumptuous, to speak for those who have made their distinguished contributions to this effort but who have, since its publication, passed into eternity. And yet, in rereading this volume, one is profoundly impressed by, and grateful for, a truth which these scholars, some still living, have defined with such intellectual cogency and such moral insight concerning the nature of science and of man.

The positive triumphs of the last quarter of a century are beyond question. The scientific vision has been followed wherever it led. The search for an understanding of the interrelationships and the interactions of knowledge and reality is at the heart of all scientific inquiry, of biology as well as of physics. The atom has been split; the neuron will inevitably be split. Perhaps there do indeed exist universes interpenetrating with the earth —perhaps even with a high degree of complexity, perhaps containing their own form of awareness, constructed out of particles and interactions which we do not now know but which are awaiting discovery.

In science, inquiry is not inhibited, but rather stimulated, by the conviction that generalizations now held to enjoy a high degree of probability may in the light of new evidence and new experiences have to submit to radical revision. Men of science take for granted that finality is a conception alien to their undertakings. It is often argued that finality is foreign to the spirit of science merely because the inductive method, supposedly the scientific method of ultimate authority, is such as to preclude the possibility of any generalization having more than probable validity. While this is true, it suggests that it does not express the most important aspect of the situation. The relinquishing of finality on the part of science is not merely a matter of method. For particular generalizations, those, for example, that have to do with the revolutions of the planets or the circulation of the blood, claims may be made that are tantamount to indubitable certainty. Such is the competence and seduction of the inductive method. The foe of finality is the spirit of science as such, irrespective of the method it may employ and regardless of the established verity of some of its conclusions. For nothing in science is ever so conclusive as to fail to entice the scientific spirit to further exploration, of which the result is always a crop of fresh problems and a harvest of unexplored insights.

In this respect the point of view of science presents an interesting contrast to that of art. The contemplative (not, of course, the creative) aspect of art is marked by an absence of doubt and perplexity. The work of art, when it is great, engenders repose and felicity. It does not trouble or strain. It does not ask to be solved. It appeals to our sympathetic imagination rather than to our analytical or critical prerogatives. And in the immediacy of the aesthetic enjoyment, the object, be it a product of art or, like a sunset, the work of nature, is felt to be a thing of joy forever — something unique, hormonious, self-contained. It is final. For in the total experience of artistic enjoyment, finality in the sense of completeness constitutes an essential ingredient.

However, the spirit of science is not a spirit of contentment and of peace, such as is afforded by the contemplation of art. It is a spirit of incessant search and endless struggle, of scrupulous criticism. The soul of science is a restless soul. Its temper is a temper aglow with defiance of all that limits and arrests inquiry, analysis, experiment. Ceaseless incursion into the unknown is its limitless task. And it is therefore in this sense that the question of finality is utterly incongruous with the critical and mobile spirit of science. The truths of art are ultimate truths, stated symbolically, metaphorically. But science has achieved its triumphs precisely by disregarding such truths, by not asking unanswerable questions, by sticking to the question: "how?"

The aim of this volume remains now as it was then, more than twenty-five years ago: the need for science to embrace not only the linearity of cause and effect but also the circularity of reason and consequence; the need for purpose, for teleology, which is not synonymous with function, since function can go in many directions but teleology only in one; the need to show that life processes transcend physics and chemistry, statistics and equations; the need to point to the error in Newton's *Celestial Mechanics*, in which he stated that man does not influence the objects of his observation. On the contrary, he is constantly influencing such objects since he brings his perception to them.

Yet the problem, basically, remains unsolved, in spite of the many efforts made to solve it, namely, that man is summoned to communicate values. And so we are reminded of the epistemological problem relating to the discovery of the proper balance between our lack of an all-embracing way of looking at life, our yearning for a thematic hypothesis, and our power to express ourselves in a logically consistent manner.

Nature operates out of necessity; there is no alternative in nature, no will, no freedom, no choice as there is for man. Man must have convictions and values to live for, and this also is recognized and accepted by those scientists who are at the same time philosophers. For they then realize that duty and devotion to our task, be it a task of acting or of understanding, will become weaker and rarer unless guidance is sought in a metaphysics that transcends our historical and scientific views or in a religion that transcends and yet pervades the work we are carrying on in the light of day.

For the nature of knowledge, whether scientific or ontological, consists in reconciling *meaning* and *being*. And *being* signifies nothing other than the actualization of potentiality, self-realization which keeps in tune with the conquest of the world, with one's inclusion in it, and with its continuous transformation. This leads to experience in terms of the individual, and to organization and patterning in terms of the universe. Thus organism and world actualize themselves simultaneously.

And so we may conclude that organism is *being* enduring in time, in fact, in eternal time, since it does not have its beginning with procreation, nor with birth, nor does it end with death. Energy and matter in whatever form they may manifest themselves are trans-temporal and trans-spatial and are therefore metaphysical. Man as man is summoned to know what is right and what is wrong, for emptied of such knowledge he is unable to decide what is better or what is worse.

This volume, SCIENCE AND MAN, continues to submit that human society is different from animal societies, which, having reached a certain stage, are no longer progressive but are dominated by routine and repetition. Thus man has discovered his own nature, and with this self-knowledge he has left the state of nonage and entered manhood. For he is the only creature who is able to say not only "no" to life but "yes" and to make for himself a life that is human. In this decision lies his burden and his greatness. For the power of life or death lies not only in the tongue but in man's recently acquired ability to destroy or to create life itself, and therefore he is faced with unlimited and unprecedented choices for good and for evil that dominate our time.

Our common concern is the very destiny of the human race, for man has now intervened in the processes of evolution, a power not given to the pre-Socratics, nor to Aristotle, nor to the Prophets in the East or the West, nor to Copernicus, nor to Luther, Descartes, or Machiavelli. Judgments of value must henceforth direct technological change, for without such values man is divested of his humanity and of his need to collaborate with the very fabric of the universe in order to bestow meaning, purpose, and dignity to his existence.

—Ruth Nanda Anshen
New York, 1968

# *1. INTRODUCTION*

# MAN AS AN ELEMENT OF EVERY EXPERIMENT

## by Ruth Nanda Anshen

THE Baconian prophecy has been fulfilled—the prophecy of power through knowledge. Such is the legacy of the advancement of science. Nature has been divested of its mysteries; its terrors have been overcome; it has submitted to the captivity of human research and has been transformed into what we term civilization. The apocalyptic character of scientific achievement has endowed man with a sense of ownership and superiority: Man has been able to arrogate unto himself the status of proprietor of the universe.

Science has made possible the transformation of life's motives from mere preservation to actual and benignant conquest, and man now anticipates the future with a fresh and infinite hopefulness. Even the ancient conflict between science and religion has been transcended and as a consequence science has been justly exalted, exalted through its relation to religion, and this reconciliation has evoked a faith in the power of life to establish and magnify itself through the progressive mastery of its environment—a faith which is perhaps the most messianic force of contemporary history. For the average man scientific ideas have an almost immediate intelligibility and appeal, a *prima facie* probability which philosophical ideas do not possess. When philosophers discourse on the good, the true, and the beautiful, intelligibility frequently becomes less lucid. The scientist alone seems to fulfill the needs of serious discourse. A certain consanguinity has been established between him and common sense, and both common sense and science have their being (the former consciously, the latter with an ever-increasing degree of consciousness) within the same peripheries. They mutually enjoy

3

the same unreflective categorization of experience, utilize the same axes of reference, define an individual thing in the same manner. Great and wonderful and continually expanding experiences lie before life. No, there is no bankruptcy of science.

Thought, during the past two centuries, has experienced a kind of historical revolt, the abandonment of the belief that the avenue to truth lay preponderantly in a metaphysical analysis of the nature of things, which thereby determine how they acted and functioned; the abandonment of this method and the embracing of the study of the empirical facts of antecedents and consequences. In religion this tendency was exemplified by an appeal to the origins of Christianity; in science, by the appeal to experiment and the inductive method of reasoning. Thus science has come to stir the imagination of men to an extent that is unparalleled. Every increment of science presents unprecedented possibilities. The miracles of yesterday are the undisputed commonplaces of today. Science commands reverent attention; it stirs the blood of man.

But thought, too, has its original sin, its line of least resistance, its inertia, its strategic power of rationalism, a rationalism which is the antithesis of reason. For example, it seems to be of specific significance that *knowledge* has no plural—a linguistic usage which follows a natural tendency to recognize that there is a unity and integrity in all knowledge no matter what its subject matter may be. What a curious oblivion to this fact seems generally to exist!

All disputes of antiquity and of modern times, up to the most recent moment, are caused by the division of that which in its nature exists as one whole. In the human mind, as in the universe, there is no top or bottom and all parts have an equal claim upon a common center which manifests its hidden existence in the harmonious relationship of the parts to it. In the final analysis as in the first, Man cannot be regarded as a creature, segregated from nature, in whom something was merely added to the animal, in whom rational powers were merely superimposed. The human intellect has unfortunately been too long considered as a separate force in the soul which Man obtained as a special dispensation in preference to all animals, as something super-added and disjoined from his animal life. This is of course ontological absurdity no matter how great the philosophers may be who promulgate this kind of thinking. If conceived as separated, all individualized powers of Man and animals are nothing but metaphysical abstractions. They are described as self-sufficient entities, abstracted by virtue of the fact that our weak intellect could not grasp their coherent activities all at once. They are treated as separate chapters, not because they operate compartmentally in nature, but because a textbook presents them with greater facility in this manner. Yet everywhere, the whole, undivided life is at work. Every segregated peculiarity is lawfully connected with every other.

But Man in his nature is differentiated from the animal in this: he possesses reason. If instinctive drives in man were simply of the animal kind, he would not possess this element of reason, and unless we wish to commit grave errors by false analogies, we must continually bear in mind this differentiation. It is reason with which this book is especially concerned: reason which is the only common ground for the solution of the problems of mankind; reason as finally revealing the nexus between thought and action, between empirical approach and speculative doctrine, between science and Man—Man who must be considered as an element of every experiment in science—for there are no antinomies in nature and no dichotomies either, and all of man—even his limitations—can be subsumed under the hierarchy of reason.

Science at the present time faces a crisis, a crisis which will discredit it as a theoretical discipline unless it resolves the paradoxes with which it is confronted. These paradoxes—these traditional oppositions of soul and body, the more recent dualisms of life and protoplasm, of energy and matter, *et alia*, will only be resolved when it is recognized that knowledge is possible because *thought and being coincide*, and when it is conceded that *Reason*, the highest part of the soul, has direct intuitions. Truth, then, will at last be held to be the agreement of these self-evident principles with the forms of reality.

Modern philosophy of science with its deadly atomization since the time of Comte has forgotten, nay, even repudiated

Man. It has de-ontologized him, de-anthropomorphized him. The purpose of this volume is to indicate how science may be returned to man, the body to the mind. The universe and the organism manifest themselves simultaneously and evolve from the sphere of potentiality into that of actuality. Life is positive in its character; it is never manifested in a negative manner. Every endeavor which necessitates an explanation of phenomena in negative terms, in such concepts as inhibition, struggle between opposing forces, negation of vital forces, is meaningless and unproductive. Whenever this negation seems to assert itself, wherever these negative factors seem to operate, this is the result of fallacious theory, or is the sad consequence of the false hypostatization of *processes* as being *absolute*, processes which actually refer to the field of performances.

Modern science has approached the dynamism of nature by means of artificial instruments and experimentation; hence its amazing mechanical applications and, when it is taken as ruling philosophy, its moral and pictorial myopia, and, at times, even blindness. It devotes itself with infinite intensity to methods rather than to objects; it manipulates without philosophical understanding and if it succeeds in its manipulations, it is content, it is imbued with a sense of victory and virtue. Science is indeed responsible for many beatitudes of human existence and of these mankind is gratefully aware; but science with its antiseptic objectivity and its subordination of reason to observation is too ready to burst with pride and vain satisfaction when it has traced some phenomenon or action back to its microscopic origins and dissected it into its original atoms. The realism of which these philosophers who replace philosophy so eloquently boast consists in proving over and over again that the miracle of reality is no miracle at all. Thus science may be said to be indulging in a kind of Sabine march; one step forward and two backward.

The common endeavor of the contributors of this volume to the problem of science in its relation to Man is to emphasize the fatuity of those "scientists," or metaphysicians of science, who always and everywhere explain Man exclusively on the basis of the things by which he is conditioned and hemmed in, who acknowledge the power of the hundred forms of gravitation by which he is bound to the earth, who hurl themselves with malicious and suicidal joy into the grip of a polyp-like determinism which holds them in its throttling embrace—a determinism which excludes possibility—while they paradoxically exhibit a kind of indeterminism denying human responsibility.

The scientist forgets that all causal explanations have no meaning whatsoever, and his statements no truth, and his universe no reality, if he and we do not postulate an idealistic and metaphysical belief in those absolute standards of eternal values by which we can discriminate the true and the untrue, the good and the bad, the real and the unreal. Despite this oblivion on the part of some scientists the integrity of science is nevertheless uncompromisingly acknowledged and whatever criticism is urged against science is urged against it as a system. It is a criticism not against science but against a philosophical system usurping the name of science.

The scientist proper, the man of special research, the scientist in the strict sense, is non-committal with reference to philosophical problems. He adopts and employs a technique which is authorized by the consensus of experts within the peripheries of his own field of endeavor. His problems are the unsolved problems of his predecessors and his colleagues; his method, a variation or refinement of methods which have already produced fruitful results. He is not concerned with—and is often impervious to—ostensible paradoxes of time and space, or with the problems concerning the unity of the world, the nature of causality, or the meaning of Truth. Teleological considerations are for him irrelevant to life. He moves within intellectual limits which he does not question and of which he may even be unconscious. But a scientist is also a man and hence may become a philosopher. On hours of unprofessional meditation the scientist may inadvertently direct his attention to those ultimate problems of morals, values, and destiny which perpetually clamor for recognition and clarification. If at such a critical moment our scientist asserts that the solution of these ultimate problems lies in the methodological applications of the discoveries of science, he repudiates himself—existentially and essentially—as a man and condemns himself as a scientist, condemns himself to that dubious heaven whence it is said science emanated on the inclined plane of Galileo taking root on earth.

Science is to be acknowledged as unimpeachable when it acts within its proper sphere, and is admitted to an amicable alliance with philosophy and all its imputations. But it is held to be inherently devoid of self-sufficiency and finality. It hypothecates something else; and that which it hypothecates is more fundamental and contains more *reality*. Science has to do with *appearance* or *phenomenon* rather than with reality, because of the very nature of its basic concepts, space and time. Without disparagement of the reality of physical nature, without prejudice to the truth of science or to the validity of its methods, or the reduction of it to dependence on consciousness, one can only conclude that science is not all of Truth, nor physical nature all of Being. That which distinguishes such a criticism of science is its recognition of science and nature in their essences. They are not partially true or real, they are simply parts of truth and reality. And the other parts, while they do not transmute or undo the fact, may nevertheless place the total situation in a new light. These parts abrogate every claim to the *exclusive* truth of science but they do provide part of the equilibrium.

In regard to logic, a phase of science which cannot be omitted from this consideration, and ethics which is correlated with logic, in the sense that logic deals with more elementary forms of being, it is prior to physics; and ethics is at least correlative with physics in that what it describes is as truly to be found in the world as that which physics describes. And logic and ethics, with other equally unimpeachable branches of philosophy in their devotion to and concern with the *nature of man* not only disprove the generalizations of positivism—logical and illogical—but afford a basis for metaphysics.

It is of the very essence of science to concern itself with *symbols,* which it substitutes for the objects themselves. These symbols undoubtedly differ from those of language by their greater precision and their higher efficacy; they are nevertheless limited to the general condition of the symbol, which is to denote a fixed aspect of the reality under an arrested form. The fatal legacy of science, as it is unfortunately interpreted in contemporary anthropomorphic culture, is the too frequent insistence that the symbols do themselves constitute a logically autonomous and self-sufficient system, and that in the syntactical structure of that system resides the logical reality that has formerly been supposed to subsist in the extra-linguistic entities symbolized by the system. Nevertheless, these symbols are indispensable. In order to think movement, a constantly renewed effort of the mind is necessary. Symbols are utilized to remove this effort by substituting, for the moving continuity of things, an artificial reconstruction which is its equivalent in practice. But what of the end? What is the essential object of science? It is to extend our influence over things. Science may be speculative in its form, disinterested in its immediate ends. But, at least if we consider the inspiring motive-power of the scientist, it is always practical utility that science considers. Even when it launches into theory, it is compelled to adapt its behavior to the general form of practice. Whatever heights it may attain it must be ready to return to the field of action. This would not be possible for it, if its rhythm differed absolutely from that of action itself. Action proceeds by leaps and to act is to re-adapt oneself. To know, namely, to foresee an act, is then to proceed from situation to situation, from arrangement to arrangement. Science may consider rearrangements that come closer and closer to each other; it may thus increase the number of moments that it isolates, but it always isolates moments, with a kind of Cartesian discontinuity (the discontinuity that was evidenced in the mind-body dualism of Descartes and his consanguineous predecessors. What a pity that his cosmology as expressed in his emphasis on continuity [plenism] in opposition to Gassendi and the atomists did not take more ubiquitous root! For even though attacked by Locke and the British empiricists or positivists, the rationalism to which the influence of Cartesian thought led was a rationalism antithetic to reason). With the significance of the intervals between the moments, science is quite unconcerned.

The preoccupation of science then is the search for simple statements which in their joint effect will express all things of interest concerning the observed recurrences. This is the saga of science; merely this and nothing more. It is the great positivist doctrine the remote origins of which may be found in the doctrine of Cartesian rationalism and separatism in which much of contemporary philosophy had its birth, the impulse of that torrential movement toward subjectivity which began with Luther and Descartes. This great positivist doctrine urges man to adhere with faithful and implacable tenacity to things observed, and to describe them with excessive simplicity. Laws in accordance with this doctrine are statements of observed facts. This doctrine can be traced even to Epicurus, and embodies his appeal to the common man, removed from metaphysics and mathematics. The observed facts of clear experience are comprehensible, and nothing else; and "understanding" is synonymous with "simplicity of description."

It cannot be denied that this positivist doctrine contains a fundamental truth about scientific methodolgy. But modern science, ignoring Man and his nature has committed the same sins and precipitated the same limitations from which the Hellenistic and the Scholastic epochs suffered. And modern scientists, as many of their predecessors, canalize thought and observation within predetermined limits, based upon inadequate assumptions dogmatically assumed. Modern science and its assumptions exclude from rationalistic thought the final values of existence. The apprehensive timidity of professionalized, specialized scholarship circumscribes reason by reducing its topics to triviality—to sense data and to tautologies. It then attempts to exonerate itself by dogmatically banishing the remainder of experience to an animal faith or to a religious mysticism, incapable of reason. The world must be saved from this form of rationalism—the rationalism which makes man more bestial than the beast, and to achieve this salvation the world must remember with Aristotle that to propose to Man merely human ends is to misunderstand the nature of Man.

The hope of the concilium of minds in this volume is that issues will be joined and discrepancies between the materialistic mechanism of science and the moral intuitions which are presupposed in the concrete affairs of Man, resolved. The common effort of these scholars is to point out that every nature requires a formal principle, but that not every form is living. Inorganic form is a principle of the structure and arrangement of energies but not a *source* of energy which is calculable or empirically demonstrable, nor an inner spontaneity giving rise to observable quantitative variations. Forever and forever the tight little island of empirical existence will be set within the vast sea of subsistence.

Never has science been more eminent as a method—but this technological organization of human activity, this child of science, may well be doomed to commit the sin of Oedipus, annihilating his paternal parent and extinguishing his own vision. The mentality of an epoch springs from the emphasis placed upon the dominant view and meaning of the world in that epoch. The diverse human interests which suggest cosmologies and are also influnced by them are science, esthetics, ethics, and religions and in every age each of these suggests a view of the world. Each age has its dominant preoccupation, and during the past two centuries the cosmology derived from science has been asserting itself almost to the exclusion of older and more ontologically sound viewpoints. Man can be provincial in time as well as in place and we may well question whether the preponderantly scientific mentality of contemporary life is not an eloquent example of just such provincial limitation, a limitation axiomatic to concepts based on a mechanical determinism, on a relativity of moral judgments, and on a naive belief in experimentation which disregards deductive principles on the exact predictability of human events and social transformation.

This book, as the second volume in the Science of Culture Series,[1] is an apostrophe to value, that is, to the meaning of value which is not to inform man how to achieve his ends so much as to inform him when his subsidiary, superficial, and immediate ends are in harmony with the primary, fundamental, and more ultimate ends—ends which are often too deep and broad for specific formulation. This book attempts to indicate the errors inherent in the failure to discern higher values which

[1] Vol. I, Science of Culture Series: *Freedom: Its Meaning*, New York, Harcourt, Brace and Company, 1940.

may be present in a situation, and in misunderstanding the ways and means to the achievement of the more ultimate ends and of the specific conditions that would constitute their realization. In brief, it attempts to point out the too often ignored or condemned fact that errors in value judgment are the result of misunderstanding of the *relation* of the value element in experience to other data.

Scientific epistemology can give to the scientist a view broader than his traditional view. That it is beneficial to the technical progress of science is undoubted. At the same time it affords a more just conception of the significance of physical knowledge in relation to philosophic thought,—a perspective which neither exaggerates nor underrates the physical aspect of the world forming a setting for the conscious experience of mankind. The realization that physical knowledge is concerned only with structure points the way by which the conception of Man as an element in a moral and spiritual order can be harmonized with the conception of Man as he is influenced by the forces of the material world.

Man is a totality; Man is a unity; and it is irrelevant to a true estimation of his nature to develop an infinite multiplicity of doctrines concerning his nature: a scientific one, a philosophical one, a psychological one, a religious one, a secular or a sociological one. All methods contribute (there may be many methods but only one doctrine) to one and the same realization: the indivisible unity of Man. Since Man is composed of every stratum of being, since Man includes every element of reality, every method must be employed in dealing with him.

Man is the microcosmos, the description of which should not neglect any instrument utilized in the description of the macrocosmos. In the ensuing pages the effort will be exerted to point out that it is a profound fallacy to insist that one method of approaching Man is the only one and to point out further that it is productive of tragic consequences to subordinate all other methods to a single approach whether it be a theological, a rationalistic, or an empirical one. The danger which it is our hope to indicate is the atomism of methods, and, in addition, to show that the empirical approach cannot be utilized without elements presented by the rationalistic method; and that this in turn postulates elements discovered by moral, and spiritual, by ontological values.

What is progress if it is a progress to the antithesis of human reason and sublimity. The ultimate purpose of Man is not merely to clothe himself, obtain food, shelter, employment, and reproduce his kind through endless generations of existence. If life had no other purpose and meaning, if existence were an epitome of mediocrity and hopelessness there would be infinite truth in Dante's inscription above the entrance to the infernal regions, "Ye who enter here leave all hope behind you." No, the purpose of life is the realization and fulfillment of Man in all his potentialities, the recognition that the entire synergy, the entire dynamism of the individual must be included in the evaluation of Man, of the human person, and that Being is interfused with nature as the "everlasting universe of things flows through the Mind."

# 2. SCIENCE AND THE UNIVERSE

# THE PROBLEM OF HUMAN EVOLUTION

## *by* Aleš Hrdlička

T HE PROBLEM of human origin is the culminating problem of natural history, of the history of living beings on this earth; and men doubtless began to reflect on it from the time they became capable of observation and thought. They have given collectively and in some form or other a vast amount of attention to it, formulating system after system of theories and dogmas for its solution. But none of these sufficed for any great length of time, yet the inquiries always revived, particularly after modern science was born, and they are carried on with ever more precise and deep-delving researches which will not cease until the subject is fully solved. Or rather until all the important details of it are thoroughly elucidated, for the main facts are already well established.

But the study of the problem has almost from the start met with unique and great difficulties. These were, the rooted older conceptions, at first a lack of material documents, and the well-nigh impossibility of dealing with the subject wholly objectively. Man until relatively lately had no actual remains of his past. And he was taught to regard himself not only as different but in essential respects, physically, morally and intellectually, as superior to all the rest of the living beings. He was "the lord of nature" on this earth, even though he saw his many resemblances of common origin—just as his own pharaohs and kings and hereditary chiefs were his "lords," who would not concede the same origin with the common elements of their people. Had there existed a race of beings superior to man, the solution of the question of his origin would have been quite obvious to such beings and would have offered no greater difficulties than that of any other species.

It was from these elements—the sense of superiority, and the lack of evidence of his past—that man eventually assumed the theory of separate, and that not very ancient "creation," in "the image of the creative deity," endowed with "a soul which he alone possessed," and with "immortality," which he denied to all other creatures. Before long his spiritual leaders —the priests—formulated these assumptions into fast bound tenets and these became the pillars of "religions."

But then came natural science and began to show the inadequacy of these beliefs. There also began to appear material remains of primitive human cultures, and eventually of various early forms of the human skeleton; and anatomy, physiology, chemistry, even pathology, showed gradually more and more similarities of the human body, functions, and even diseases, with the rest of the living forms. All of which carried with it the growing need of reconsideration of the older assumptions, and this, as compelled changes in all set mental habits do, generated resistance, antagonism to and even here and there a forceful conflict with the dawning of the new truths.

That phase of mental re-accommodation has stormed itself out and is now passing. The suspicions and great fears with which the new truths were met have shown themselves to be groundless. The new facts have neither debased man from his high pedestal nor demoralized him, but are paving the way for a rational, solid, hopeful, and even more moral attitude and behavior than those of his past. The teachers are more and more becoming acquainted with the facts, and preparing for the true spiritual leadership which must be their future function—leadership that will be able to explain man's shortcomings and imperfections by his past, satisfy his dignity by the knowledge of his ages-long struggles and sacrifices, and open an endless vista to him for genuine progress in the future.

## HUMAN ORIGIN

The very basic question that confronts the student of the human species is how Man came into being on this earth; and there are but two possible alternatives in explanation—the legendary one of a special creation, or that of a gradual development from the rest of the organic world. The assumption of the first is possible only by belief without present knowledge, that of the second by present knowledge freed from mere belief. The creation idea is incapable of explaining man's intimate similarities in structure, functions, instincts, with the rest of the organic beings, his bodily as well as mental imperfections, the many vestiges he carries and manifests of prehuman conditions, his varieties and variability. The notion of his early origin by gradual development from the organic kingdom removes these obstacles, is sustained by all the known organic laws, and the only difficulties that confront it are, on the one hand, the as yet incomplete material evidence of man's and his direct prehuman ancestry's past, and on the other hand, the great development of his brain.

Taking however everything into consideration and in the light of established knowledge, there is possible but one unbiased answer to the above great question, and that is, that Man originated from the rest of the terrestrial organisms, and that not by any sudden miraculous jump, but by the gradual natural process which accounted also for the rest of organic beings on this globe, and which in general is known as *evolution*.

What is *evolution?* The process may perhaps be defined most simply as a gradual differentiation of a better adapted, or a distinctly more able, organic species from a less adapted or inferior one.

One of the most essential properties of organic beings is that they are impressionable, sentient beings. This means primarily that they are capable of "feeling" everything that comes to act on them, and which broadly is known as the environment. Much of such feeling may be unnoticed, not conscious; but whether subconscious or conscious every influence that is felt by an organism arouses in the same a reaction, the object of which is accommodation; and if the agency keeps on acting and the organism cannot escape, there develops in it a gradual adaptation to the agency. Such an adaptation is realizable, however, only by some change, physical or chemical or usually both, in the organism—and such a change is the beginning of differentiation of that organism which, if sustained for a long time, leads—there are many examples of that—to a more and more "set" adaptation, which is one of the ways of evolution.

There are however also potent contributory ways, connected more directly with the hereditary-carriers of the organism, the most potent of which probably, in the widest sense of the term, is *hybridization*. Among the vast majority of organisms every individual is the resultant of the union not only of two different beings but of two lines of ancestry. Such lines carry family, tribal and even further hereditary differences. The combination and reactions of these in the new individual may make of this more or less a new creature and, if this turns out to be more adaptable than its kind, this creature may become an aid to evolution.

Evolution, therefore, as a whole is no simple phenomenon. It is a highly compound and complex natural process by which, especially under changing conditions, newer organic forms develop from old, newer forms of greater efficiency and survival values. Its whole substance is still far from being fully grasped by science, but its existence and its principles are evident enough. It is this process, progressing throughout ages in some already highly differentiated primate group or groups, that led towards Man. These are no theories anymore, but definite well-substantiated scientific deductions.

The human mind naturally would not be content with mere statements on so highly important a subject, however authoritative and plausible these might be. The individuality of every student demands, in a matter of such weight, such proofs as will enable him to reach his own conclusions. Gratifyingly the proofs of human evolution are now a legion in number, and they may be presented in a relatively non-technical language so as to be more generally comprehensible. Aside from the actual evidence, however, the subject also demands some further consideration, namely, as to the indications of future human evolution. Difficult as these problems are even they can now be dealt with to some satisfaction.

## THE EVIDENCE

The evidence of human evolution may be subdivided as follows:

A. *The Indirect Evidence*
   1. Analogies in inorganic nature.
   2. Evolution in all known organic forms.
   3. Man's appearance on the earth at the right time of organic advance.

B. *The Direct Evidence*
   1. Relation of various structures in the embryonic development of man to those represented by some lower vertebrates.
   2. Similarities with other mammals in mode of conception, processes of development, in all vital functions, in the whole life course, in senescence when continuation of the kind is assured, and in death.
   3. Physical similarities to identities in organs, limbs, and all other physical as well as microscopic parts of the human body.
   4. Close similarities to identities of the chemical constituents of the human body with those of other mammals.
   5. The presence in man of many vestiges of or reversions to features regularly present in lower animals.

C. *The Documentary Evidence*
   1. Man's cultural remains in relation to geology and paleontology.
   2. His skeletal remains in the same relations.

D. *The Observational Evidence*
   1. Man's changes, physical, functional, and mental, ob-

servable scientifically at the present time, with indications for the future.

## EVOLUTION UNIVERSAL

The process of evolution is now known to be a basic, universal phenomenon. Nature changes throughout, and these changes, taking place under definite laws, so long as they are constructive or progressive toward other "fitter" forms, can only be called evolution. The whole cosmos, each star, each organism, and probably each particle of matter is changing or is capable of change under proper conditions, stability being only relative. No living being, especially if it is well established, is immutable, but all are capable, within limits, of change in the form of "adaptation" to changing conditions. The possibility of adaptation is, in fact, seen to be one of the fundamental and vital properties of all organic beings. And every adaptation, every change of some consequence and duration in an organism, calls for adjustments which, if lasting, appear to bring about needed and eventually inheritable modifications in structure. To which must be added the potent influences of isolation, selection, and hybridization. The effects of all this are observable in many wild forms, and especially in the domesticated animals and in useful plants, where man is knowingly assisting nature. To exclude man· and his ancestry from these basic conditions and laws would be to exclude him from the range of organisms, which is impossible.

## THE EVIDENCE OF FOSSILS

Thanks to the work of Leidy, Marsh, Cope, Osborn, and other American as well as European paleontologists, it is now possible to follow, by whole series of actual specimens, not merely structural adaptations, but progressive evolution of an increasing number of phyla of animals over great lengths of geologic time. Perhaps the best example of this is to be found in the case of the horse, which is known in many stages, from an ancient little four-toed suggestion-of-a-horse to the fine racers and the other specialized equine forms of today. But a little less known is the evolution of the camel, and much has been learned already about the dinosaurs, the proboscidea (elephants, etc.), some of the carnivores, and still other forms; and there is much evidence of a similar nature pertaining to the invertebrates, such as the Ammonites and Nautilus among the Cephalopods; the Acatinelas and Partulas among the Mollusks; and also pertaining to plants (the Dicotyledons, the Conifers, etc.). Evolution, though not always of the same type or pace, and though greatly influenced by environment, is seen to be as universal a process in living beings as life itself, and no organism has ever been found that would be outside of its workings.

## THE CHRONOLOGICAL FACTOR

Man's appearance on the earth at the right time of organic differentiation is one of the most important pieces of evidence as to the nature of his origin. Like the top bough of a tree, he appears only after the preceding parts or forms have reached the proper grade.

The Tertiary era, the era essentially of the evolution of mammals, is divided by geology and paleontology into four periods, each of several millions of years' duration, namely, the Eocene, Oligocene, Miocene, and Pliocene. The oldest of these, the "Dawn" period, shows only the most primitive of primates, approaching lemurs and small monkeys; the Oligocene, and especially the Miocene rocks, give remains of the true lemurs, monkeys, and eventually of some anthropoid apes, such as the Dryopitheci of Europe and of the Sivaliks, foothills of the Himalayas; while the Pliocene is the age of differentiation of the apes and anthropoids toward such forms as we know today, with the probable appearance, in southern Asia and also in western Europe, of some superior creatures that can only be called human precursors. After which begins the era known as Quaternary, or the Ice Age, which is characterized by repeated coolings and consequent series of ice extensions over large parts of the Northern Hemisphere, with warm periods between; and about the beginning of this age there are found to exist already at least two undoubted human precursors, if not early men, namely, the "Pithecanthropus" of what is now Java, and the "Eoanthropus," or Dawn man, of what is now southeastern England. Of these science possesses in the first case parts of four skulls, one of which shows a remarkable near-human brain, and in the second case a portion of a highly interesting lower jaw, not to mention other parts that are attributed to each find.

At about the same time something wholly new begins to occur on this earth. In large areas of the Old World there begin to appear in the sands, clays, and gravels of those far-away periods, in company with fossilized remains of long-extinct elephants, rhinoceroses, and other animals, flints that show intentional, objective chipping. Some creature has developed "hands," full-fledged enough to do the chipping and to use the resulting tools or weapons, with mentality enough behind them to appreciate the advantage of such artifacts, as well as to make them and use them for definite purposes. There is a new form of existence, a beginning of beings with enough mentality to advance to "cultural" manifestations. From which time on evidence of these new beings never lapses, but augments step by step, extending over many lands. The artifacts keep on developing in workmanship and variety, until, well before the middle of the Ice Age, they reach a status that is clearly "human." There has definitely come into being a Man.

In all this there is in general a logical and orderly sequence which, of necessity, must be given great weight in the studies of Man's origin.

### EMBRYOLOGICAL EVIDENCE

The human being begins with two minute "germ" cells, that come from the two "sexes," and that have to unite into one unit, which then divides, grows, and develops in most intricate ways —all precisely as in the case of any other vertebrate. This beginning of the new being, and the following stages of embryonal development, constitute an array of conditions and processes so minute and so important and so thoroughly regulated, that they could never be duplicated accidentally. To the student with the microscope the organic unity of man with the rest of the living beings, and especially with the rest of the mammals, is indeed a profound fact, a fact so plain and complete and great that it alone is wholly sufficient for a conviction of unity. Even heredity, that vastly complex endowment of every organism, is now known to be carried by like clusters of molecules, known as "chromosomes" and "genes," in each germ cell, human or animal.

In addition, the human embryo shows at various stages traces of pre-human characteristics that disappear or are reduced to rudimentary condition in the course of subsequent development. These matters are too technical for a general discussion, but features that may be mentioned are the initial primitiveness of the neck, hands, and feet; the rudimentary tail which persists in the human embryo up to and even over the ninth week of prenatal age; the early hair covering the body and face; the presence of plain traces of the intermaxillary bone; the at first birdlike, entirely smooth brain. These and other similar features, taken together, are so impressive that the human embryonal period has been called the period of the "recapitulation" of evolution.

## THE PHYSICAL EVIDENCE

By this is meant the evidence of the human body. This body has an exceedingly varied and highly organized composition. It is constituted of many billions of different modifications of cells, which form its many organs and parts. These cells range from the quite "primitive" cells of the blood and lymph to the most highly differentiated and specialized ones of the central nervous system, the organs of the special senses, and the glands of reproduction. And the organs which many of them form are very involved. Nevertheless, a cell for cell, an organ for organ, every important part of every organ, and structure for structure, all are practically identical in man and the higher mammals. The cells or organs or parts may differ in form or size, or in other secondary features, but they are the same in all essentials. This applies even to the most differentiated features of organs, such as the fissuration and subdivisions of the brain. These similarities and identities alone, if dealt with in detail, would fill a volume.

The facts concerning the brain are the most striking and deserve a few words in addition. The brain, relatively to the mass of the rest of the body, is much larger in man than it is in any other creature; yet in all its essentials, even to the arrangement of brain cells and localization of the nervous centers, it is much like the brain of any of the higher anthropoid apes and other mammals. The brain subdivisions into cerebrum, cerebellum, medulla, and pons; the subdivision of the brain matter into the gray and white substance; the special brain "nuclei" and the cavities; and even the principal convolutions and furrows of the cortex, are substantially the same in man and the primates, as well as in many other mammals. The most striking, however, is the same location in all these forms, from the dog and the ape to man, of the various important functional areas, such as those of sight, hearing, association, etc., and of the series of clusters of cortical brain cells which control the action of various sets of muscles. The location of these centers has been learned through electrical experiments on the brains of the dog, the chimpanzee, and other animals, and then it was found that the same number, order, and location of these centers is present in man. This knowledge is constantly being made use of in diagnosing the location of lesions or tumors in the human brain and for successful surgical operations on the organ.

Man, anatomically, is truly a faithful image of his precursors.

### THE FUNCTIONAL EVIDENCE

The most important functional complex of every living creature of a higher order, is its life cycle. This begins with the exceedingly involved formative functions of the being, proceeds with those of infancy and childhood, reaches sooner or later the period of ripeness for the sexual functions, passes through a more or less prolonged period of child-bearing which assures continuation of the kind, and when this functional period is completed the organism passes gradually into senility, which is its preparation for elimination and ends eventually in its termination or "death." These several phases of the life cycle vary in different species, but they are always present and follow the same order. And these same identical phases, in the same order, exist in the human organism.

Of the utmost importance and intricacy are the functions of heredity. These functions reach to the very foundations of the being, and their gradual ripening and discharge throughout life in every feature, every action, are full of wonder, as well as precision. And all this in all essentials is the same in the animal and in the human species.

Still another great function of every higher organism, Man included, is the complex of the sexual activities, which assure the continuation of the kind. These functions are multiple, deep-set, peculiarly specialized and organized. Yet in every essential and even in many minute details they are the same or similar in Man and in all the rest of the higher vertebrates.

Further vital functions are digestion, metabolism, elimination, circulation and respiration. These functions involve whole chains of highly differentiated and complex activities, and they, with every important link of them, are the same in Man and in all the higher animals.

In general, in fact, there is not a single function of any importance that would be limited to Man and not shared at least by the higher vertebrates. Thus in physiology as in anatomy Man is one with the rest of the organic world, and can in no rational way be set apart from it.

## THE CHEMICAL EVIDENCE

The chemical elements and compounds of the human flesh, bones, skin, hair, and all other parts, are practically identical with those of other primates and higher mammals. And this closeness to identity extends to all the fluids of the body, even to the exceedingly complex secretions of the internal glands. The similarity of these secretions is such that those of various animals are effectively used in Man when he shows a deficiency of them. Extracts of animal blood and animal glands, which mean but very complex chemical compounds, are used on a great scale for protective vaccination of, or to supply defects of similar substances in, Man. Thus the pepsin of the pig, the thyroid of the sheep, the pancreatic extract (insulin) from these or other mammals, the extracts of suprarenals and even those of the sex glands of apes and other animals, with the immunizing sera from the horse, calf, rabbit, etc., are constantly being utilized to supply the want of such substances in our body and thus to prevent or cure our diseases. The common cod-liver oil is merely a carrier of certain organic chemical substances that are lacking for the time being or are being produced in insufficient quantities in some human children.

## MENTALITY

There are many who are willing to accept the similarity of the human and animal bodies and even that of their functions, but would draw a line between the activities of the human and animal brains. Yet if they would intently and impersonally analyze the mental qualities and performances of Man and at least the closer animals, one after another, they would find differences in degrees and quality, but they would also find such resemblances that in the end they could not but conclude that there is a great basic similarity. They would find that the animal brain is capable of receiving the same sensory impressions as ours, though the apperceptions may differ in acuity. Some, such as those of the smell of the dog, of the sight of many of the birds, etc., exceed by far these faculties in the human. The researches might even find some senses in animals that so far as can be determined as yet are not present in Man, but they would find none of those of Man absent in the animals.

Animals have memory, and many—perhaps all—when experienced, show judgment. As the human young so they learn by experience, and by instruction. They have patience, love, friendship, jealousy, enmities; and may show vengefulness. Some are brave and some are cowards. They know happiness, and also misery. Many seem callous, but some on occasion show definite grief or compassion. Animals do not talk in words, but they have their own sound and motion "languages" which they well understand; there are many who under proper conditions learn to understand, more or less, human words, and there are some who can even say such words and know their meaning. Animals dream; they know pride; and they will sacrifice themselves for their young as humans do. They plan, combine, obey "chiefs," show organized endeavors. And they manifest many other mental characteristics that are like those of humans, only in less or different degrees. They show joy, grief, hypocrisy, mischief, and some even turn criminals. And there are many grades in these qualities in the different individuals of every species, as there are in the humans. In only the highest mental functions, in self-consciousness, rational self-control, thinking, planning, idealism, intellectual feelings and pursuits, is Man, in degree at least, above all other forms of life. It is his intellectual entity and potentiality, this surpassing something that constitutes his "soul," that places Man above, but not outside, the rest of creation. For even in these most distinctly human lines it would be difficult indeed, if not impossible, to establish a radical distinction between Man and his natural smaller "brothers and sisters."

## THE VESTIGIAL EVIDENCE

The human body not only duplicates the bodies and functions of the higher mammals and especially of the primates, but it also carries, or occasionally reproduces, features or behaviors that are the remains of, or reversions to, conditions that existed far back in the animal kingdom, long before an immediate prehuman ancestry. Here again it would require a whole treatise adequately to present in detail such conditions and behaviors. Some of them become manifest only during the embryonal development of Man, or during his childhood, endure awhile, and then vanish; while others may appear later and endure throughout the life of an individual.

Some of the most striking ancestral features appear, as was already mentioned, for a shorter or longer time during the embryonal human development. The external caudal protrusion of the spine, or rudimentary tail, is one of these. This becomes covered generally by the third month, but the rudimentary bones of it, the coccygeal segments, persist in all of us; and in rare cases a rudimentary external tail without bones develops and lasts throughout life. The human embryo also, at an early stage, manifests in what is to become its neck certain lateral slits, which later on become depressions, the traces of which rarely may last to later life; and these it appears can only be reminiscences of the ancient gills. The primitive structure of the hands and feet in the fetus, with the nails, and the longer middle finger, are vestiges of the far past.

In certain instances the human mother will bear from two to six children at a birth; and several hundreds of instances are recorded in medical literature of women and even men who had supernumerary breasts or nipples, located more or less as they are in other mammals. The human baby will cling strongly to a rod, branch, beard, or the hair, as do little apes; and it manifests various actions that have remote prehuman connections (see literature on Atavism).

Some very remarkable and significant functional "reminiscences" of the prehuman past occur in the human child during infancy. No child, it seems, grows up entirely free from them, but in some they become much more manifest than in others. Not a few of the human infants between their 7th and 12th month will run on all fours.[1] This is no mere crawling, or learning to walk, but definite instinctive and very apt running on all fours, exactly like that of all the American and smaller Old World primates. There are infant climbers that frighten their mothers by their performances; while still others will show for a shorter or longer time different additional behaviors that reproduce similar actions of various animals, particularly those of other primates.

As the child grows, it develops two sets of teeth, exactly as do all the higher mammals, and there is the same differentiation of the teeth into incisors, canines, premolars and molars.

[1] See Author's *Children Who Run on All Fours*, New York, McGraw-Hill Book Company, 1931.

The human canines themselves are vestiges of the old canine-weapons of a great many of the animals, and now and then they will still develop to such prominence in Man that they will be called "dog teeth." Besides this, however, there appear in rare cases in the human denture, particularly among or in the vicinity of the incisors, extra or supernumerary teeth, which are reminiscences of the long lost additional teeth of those regions; and there are other dental "reversions."

In adults, the external ear shows in instances a little tubercle or a protrusion in the upper part of the helix. This is the "Darwinian tubercle," a vestige of the more pointed ear of many animals. In other cases, especially frequent in some races of man, there will be no lobule to the ear, another ancient animal characteristic. Obliquity of the eyes, marked in some human races, is a remnant of still another animal feature. There may further be found occasionally a webbing of the second and third toes; an extra lobe at the lower end of the right lung; a division of the left lobe of the liver; remnants of the ancient platysma (muscle of the skin) and of the ear muscles; and now and then there will be certain fissures in the brain which reproduce those common to some of the higher mammals.

The hairiness of the body in some of the males of the White race, and also occasionally in the Negro, will be excessive. On many animal arm bones (humeri) there is found above the lower extremity of the bone a characteristic large bony arch known as the supracondyloid foramen, serving as the protection of the main artery of the part and a nerve. The same foramen is still found in some of the South American monkeys, but in the majority of the apes the formation has long since disappeared. As a rule this foramen is also absent in Man; but in many human arm bones on closer examination a roughness will be found or a slight ridge in the place where the arch existed, and in between 2 and 3 per cent of human humeri there is a more or less marked bony process in this location which reproduces a part of the ancient bony arch. Finally, in at least one case, a specimen reported by Dwight and preserved in the Medical Museum of Harvard University, there is a complete bony arch in a human arm bone, like that in animals.

And this list could be greatly extended. Every part of the human body, every organ, manifests in some cases some such vestiges or reversions. They are useless to Man today, may even be disadvantageous, but they recur now and then to remind him of his prehuman ancestry.

## DOCUMENTARY EVIDENCE

When Darwin wrote his epoch-making books on the *Origin of Species* (1859) and *Descent of Man* (1871), Man's prehistory was barely beginning to be known.

Since then the cultural remains of early man, consisting of his stone implements, and of the bones of extinct animals on which he fed or left his traces, reach literally into millions; and skeletal remains of ancient man himself have reached such numbers that only a few students are able to master the vast richness.

The cultural objects occur in quantities in ancient caves, deposits, and river terraces, especially in western and central Europe, but also in many other parts of the Old World. The cave of San Brelade, on the island of Jersey, has yielded to Professor Marett and co-workers approximately 20,000 stone objects showing the work of man; the site of La Quina, in Southern France, gave Henri Martin over 100,000 specimens, many of which were whole implements; the Viestonice site in Moravia, of which only a small part has been excavated thus far, has already given to Absolon over 300,000 objects showing the work of later early man; and the Musée de St. Germain, near Paris, the Institut de Paleontologie in Paris, the National and Cinquantenaire Museums of Brussels, the British Museum, the Territorial Museum at Brno, and many other institutions, in Spain, Germany, and elsewhere, possess collectively vast quantities of such remains, with more coming to light every season.

These stone implements and other cultural objects are found associated with the bones of various extinct animals, which help to date them. These animals range from ancient elephants, rhinoceroses, lions, leopards, hyenas, etc., to the mammoth, cave bear, reindeer, extinct horses, stags and bison. They show warm and cold periods, corresponding with the subdivisions of the Ice Age. And the stone objects show definite phases or fashions of workmanship which, together with the criteria of age, enable the student roughly to classify human prehistory into a number of cultural periods. The chief ones, proceeding from the past toward our time, are:

The Old Stone Age (Paleolithic)
The pre-Chellean and Chellean
The Acheulian

The Mousterian (or Neanderthal) { lower middle upper

The Aurignacian { lower middle upper

The Solutrean, the Magdalenian
The Mesolithic
The Neolithic, or New Stone Age

Here is comprised a great mass of evidence that may be consulted in European and even American museums, or in the field where, especially in France, under government regulations and guardianship, whole sections of the implement-bearing strata are left as archeological monuments. Moreover, the old implements, animal bones, etc., may readily be collected first hand.

However, there is much more than this. In addition to the innumerable cultural remains of early man, the Old World scientific institutions also now possess the skull fragments of complete skeletons of over 200 prehistoric men and women that may safely be dated at more than 20,000 years of age. These precious documents are held as national treasures in France, Belgium, Holland, England, Germany, Czechoslovakia, Croatia, Italy, the Soviet Union, and Peking in China. They range from a portion of a lower jaw, with perhaps a few pieces of the skull, as in the case of the already mentioned Piltdown find in England, to most of the parts of 18 skeletons discovered at Předmost, Moravia, the series of highly valuable

specimens at Peking, and the even more valuable and growing
series of Java. They come from ancient gravels, sands, loess,
or volcanic muds, from old caves and rock shelters, and even
from the depths of hard stone, as in the quarries of Ehringsdorf near Weimar, in Germany, near Barcelona in Spain, and
at Choukoutien in northern China. They are associated with
and in instances overlaid by the bones of ancient mammals.
They show various grades and forms of petrifaction; and, in
general, the older they are the more primitive is their form
and the farther away they are from the modern human. (See
writer's *The Skeletal Remains of Early Man.* Smithson.
Misc. Coll., LXXXIII, 1930, 379 pp.)

Here we have before us a most weighty evidence of human
evolution, and in a large measure even an actual illustration of
the process. When an observer regards such specimens as the
several now known skulls of the Pithecanthropus, the skulls and
other remains of the Sinanthropus, the Piltdown, the Heidel-
berg, the Krapina or the Ehringsdorf jaws, the Neanderthal,
the La Chapelle, the Gibraltar, the Spy, la Ferrasie, the Gali-
lee, and the Rhodesian skulls, and even some of the later crania
and skeletons, he sees forms that he could hardly believe were
truly human; yet some of these skulls already show fairly large
and distinctly human if not superior brains, and the teeth, with
the bones of the body, even though more primitive, are nevertheless already clearly those of Man—or, in the case of the
Pithecanthropus, a close precursor.

The originals of these precious skeletal remains are scattered
over the Old World, but the main part of them may be seen
collectively in perfect replicas in two of our foremost American institutions, namely, in the National Museum in Washington and the American Museum of Natural History in New
York, while more limited series are possessed by several larger
American museums that include the subject of Anthropology.

To this invaluable material further originals are being added
every year through new discoveries; and as conditions for scientific research will again grow more propitious, it will be safe
to expect an ever-increasing flow of accessions in this field.

THE EVIDENCE OF MAN'S CONTINUED EVOLUTION

This important phase of the subject has so far been dealt with but little by the students of human evolution, due mostly, perhaps, to a lack of perspective.

There are thinkers, occasionally even among the foremost men of science, who are inclined to regard organic human evolution as practically at an end. They observe that the potent natural factors of evolution, such as isolation, natural selection, and the influence of the environment, have nearly ceased to act on Man. Man in a large measure has neutralized these factors through ever freer communication and self-protection, and through many artifices, in the way of housing, clothing, heat, food, and other agencies.

Every generation, every year in fact, Man is making himself more and more independent of the very influences that forced him on in the past; and as no changes can be expected in nature to which Man could not more or less readily artificially adapt himself, it is easy to conceive that he has reached, or nearly reached, a sort of equilibrium with nature and hence presumably the end of his personal changes. The future evolution of Man, in the opinion of those who hold these views, will be of a social rather than of an organic order.

These views fail, however, because of two vital conditions. The one is that according to all the tests Man is still as plastic —that is, impressionable and changeable—as he ever was, if not more so; while the second is that Man is developing new and powerful evolutionary factors of his own.

That Man is still plastic—reactive to all changed or new influences by proper accommodation—is plain enough, especially to the medical observer and the anthropologist. In pigmentation, in stature or strength, in form and size of the teeth and jaws, in the dimensions of all other organs, including the brain, and in his functional qualities and effectiveness, including those of the mental powers, he is seen to respond to changing conditions; and these reactions are observed to be the more prompt and effective the higher in civilization and refinement is the individual. It may be stated, as an organic law, that every reaction, whether in the direction of more or of less, unless artificially counteracted, leads, if repeated often enough and within the healthy limits, to an organic habit and organic modification. And such habits in the course of time lead, in some way that as yet is not fully understood, to more or less hereditary traits—which are items of evolution or devolution.

Acquired characteristics, the influence of which does not reach deeply enough to the trophic centers of the brain or nervous system and the germ cells, are as a rule not inherited. But there are many functional acquirements that evidently in time do reach these depths, as a result of which they tend to become fixed and hereditary in families or even in large groups of men.

Studies on the descendants of the older American families have shown conclusively that stature in these families has materially increased since their coming to this country.[2]

The form of the head has been slowly changing within the last thousand years, as shown by the works of Matiegka, von Luschan, Keith, Fleure, and others, in Bohemia, Austria, England, and Germany.

Changes in pigmentation have greatly affected, and have become more or less fixed in, the Aryan population of India since their coming to that country; while others of opposite nature, i.e., in the direction of lightening, may now, according to various indications, be slowly proceeding, as in the Eskimo, the civilized American Indian, and the North American Negro.

The civilized white male shows everywhere an increasing weakness of the hair, and early baldness is already a hereditary trait in the males of many otherwise normal families.

There is perceptible in the civilized man of all races a progressive refinement of the physiognomy, with diminution of the protrusion and size of the cheek bones, lessening of the size and massiveness of the jaws and teeth, and more generalized beauty. These features, or a tendency toward them, are being transmitted to the progeny.

[2] See Author's *The Old Americans*, Baltimore, 1925; also *Observations and Measurements on the Members of the National Academy of Sciences*, Third Memoir of the N.A.S., 1940, XXIII, 108 pp.

The teeth of the more highly civilized white man, through less use, have not only become smaller, but especially less resistant, and some of them, at least, tend to a tardier eruption, causing many difficulties and irregularities. Other changes in size or shape have, under the influence of other factors, taken place in the teeth in various groups of the human being. All these changes have already become more or less hereditary.

The higher civilized man besides this has, it seems certain, advanced in the lines of human endurance, due to the stresses of civilization and the calls for endurance. He may not have the more automatic strength of some primitive people, but his eyes, ears, body, and, above all, the brain are evidently capable of greater conscious exertions, and endure longer. The last war taught much in this direction, and on every side may be seen the great endurance of the financier, the industrial leader, the intellectual worker. The amount of labor they are able to perform, the strain endured by eyes, all the senses, and above all by the intellectual powers, are at times astounding. Nothing of that nature is evident in the old times except in rare individual mental giants. Qualities are now manifested by multitudes which in the past were barely manifested by individuals.

Therefore, it seems safe to say that the human frame and, above all, the human brain, are still quite plastic and respond, by strengthening or weakening, to all sorts of influences.

On the other hand, the natural laws conditioning evolution are still acting, except for man's interference. Natural selection still eliminates the incurable and unfit, and gives the leadership in progress to the strong and fittest. Fault, weakness, transgression of all nature's law, must still inexorably be paid for by the defective or culpable. Nevertheless, the evolution of man today is being more and more directed or led by forces different from those in the past. Even though nature is still acting, it is being left behind by the human factors, by Man himself. Man is beginning materially to supplement and partly to replace nature in the process of his own evolution, as he has in the case of domesticated animals, and is advancing upon nature.

He is using more and more, and ever more effectively, self-protection. Survival of the fittest does not apply to Man as it once did. Natural selection has been modified, so that it no longer means the survival of the fittest alone, but preservation as well of all who can be preserved. Fear is not seldom expressed that this preservation of the weaker will have a deleterious effect upon Man's future; but fortunately these fears are not well grounded. Many of those who are preserved are not unfit except in some particular, as in a predisposition to or lack of immunity toward one disease, such as diphtheria or tuberculosis. And with the really weaker who are preserved there enters into play a most beneficial agency, the old but ever potent complex of natural factors known to our forebears as the *vis mediatrix naturae*, the healing and strengthening forces of nature.

Were it not for this important factor, whole groups of mankind would probably have perished in the past, as after the epidemic of syphilis in Europe in the sixteenth Century. Many families have certain infections or weaknesses, but we see that in the majority of cases the family does not perish; instead there is a gradual restitution, and in a few generations through this and strengthening by marriage with healthy stock, the bad effects may disappear entirely.

Through continuously more effective self-protection Man counteracts the hard mastership of conditions. He is replacing their tutelage by more and more correct self-training and education. Children, on the whole, are ever more carefully trained, and adolescence is turned more effectively in a fit direction—periods of demoralization, such as those of the world and present wars, notwithstanding.

The white child and adolescent of today lead, in general, a more normal and healthy life than did the child and adolescent of any time in the past. Growing girls and boys are taught that it is not desirable to mate with the sick or mentally unfit. More rational and scientific care is taken of the defectives, in this way eliminating one of the most serious disgenic features of the past. Pre-school, school and college life are being regulated ever more rationally. Hours of labor are reduced to avoid physical and mental exhaustion, and harmful labor of children is largely eradicated. In many factories the workmen are already being taken care of as valuable assets of the concern. Men in the mass, soldiers and employees, are being restored to health, strengthened, and instructed in hygiene. All this together is certain to have a large and wholesome evolutionary influence upon future generations.

New ambitions and necessities, new inventions, and especially new and intense competitions, are acting powerfully upon present man in highly civilized societies—much more so than they have ever acted in the past. When we weigh the effects of the automobile, movies, radio, the daily newspaper, etc.; when we contemplate what groups of competing business men or any other men go through; when we feel man's utmost efforts in all directions—we cannot but recognize that new and very potent agencies are developing in human relations, which must have an effect upon man's further evolution in a mental as well as in a physical direction.

About the greatest factors of contemporaneous and future progressive human evolution, however, are the thirst and striving for the better, for something ever higher and more distinguished in every line. This means a desire and striving for ever greater strength, beauty, bodily and mental effectiveness, for mental freedom, ability and power, and true happiness. The more man is developed intellectually the more there is of this striving for a higher state, for happiness, progress and intellectual freedom.

This great factor was not so manifest in times past. A man then was too often satisfied to serve another provided he had enough food and a little leisure. This agency has already had, and is bound to have in the future, a very considerable effect on man's evolution. Notwithstanding the difficulties, it is steadily refining Man's mental actions, making more out of humankind in every way. And with it will proceed a progressively more intelligent and discriminating sexual selection, which has been in the past, and promises increasingly to be in the future, a potent aid to favorable evolution.

These factors and agencies, and still others, are plainly acting on civilized man today, and are largely taking the place of the older natural agencies which gradually have been losing their power on the direction of Man's evolution. They may prove equally, and in some respects even more, effective. Their promise is a gradual further evolution of man in the right direction, physically, as far as this may still be possible, but above all intellectually; evolution toward beings ever freer from imperfections and limitations; an evolution in general ever more guided and safeguarded by and through increase in knowledge.

But this promising road is not without many obstacles, and even serious dangers. A sober view of the human future envisages, indeed, further evolution, but evolution amid and through difficulties. As in the past so in the future, Man must pay for his advance, pay by the innumerable victims who will not be able to keep the pace. Some of the obstacles may here be enumerated:

*Modern diseases.*—There is no record in the distant past of tuberculosis, and it was very scarce even in the time of dynastic Egypt. There is little if any evidence of cancer until fairly recent times, and none of rickets. As animals in confinement develop diseases unknown in freedom, so with men, domesticity brings new infirmities. These are often now connected with overexertion and exhaustion. Where Man is forced beyond his powers he falls more often a victim to diabetes, heart and lung trouble, nervous disorders, insanity. Some of these diseases are, however, also connected with Man's lengthening life period. Medicine is trying to overcome them, but so far has not been very successful. They constitute serious impediments to human progress for the future. There is, however, no perceptible need of apprehension that diseases of the civilized man —barring the psychoses—will further increase, or that new and uncontrollable scourges may originate.

*Great wars.*—These constitute an obstacle of Man's own making. Great wars are unquestionably deleterious, and the disgenic influences of the last as well as of the present war will be felt for a prolonged time to come. The underlying cause of wars, however, is increasing density of population, just as it was in the old invasions; and the remedy for wars lies essentially in that direction. Unless some as yet unknown agency of nature develops that will by itself restrict human multiplication, one of the main problems of the world before long will be the control of its population—unless Man's inventiveness frees him still further from his dependence on nature.

*Idleness, luxury* are perhaps even more deleterious than war. It is a truism that as soon as any being, or any group—be this a family or a nation—ceases strenuous endeavor and·yields to comfort and indolence, or from other causes falls into demoralization, he or it commences to retrogress and lose in physical and mental standards.

*Excesses* and *strains,* due to the very exacting and irregular modern life, produce weaknesses that call for stimulation by coffee, nicotine, alcohol, or drugs. Some excesses and strains were, of course, always present and always disgenic; but they are growing more common and new ones are being added. Repeated excesses lead to overstrains, and result not only in the diminished potentiality of the individual in every way, but also in poor progeny. They lead to the generation or retention in the system of poisons that may and often do affect the germ plasm. The child of an overstrained or neurasthenic individual cannot be absolutely healthy or fully efficient.

*Poisons* in mines, in chemical and manufacturing plants, and elsewhere, must also be considered. His multiplied and widely differentiated occupations and even his needs and pleasures bring Man into contact with many new poisons. Such poisons, too, acting deeply, must often affect the germ plasm. Man is using his growing knowledge to counteract these poisons, but this knowledge is not yet sufficient.

Then there is *mechanization.* It is estimated that approximately 8,000,000 men, women, and children in this country alone are for seven to eight hours a day doing semi-automatic work that calls for but little mental exercise and brings but little satisfaction. This in the course of time can hardly fail to have a disgenic influence upon the mental, if not also upon the physical, life of many an individual, and in the long run cannot but be harmful to the race. The automatic work of the day is often compensated by harmful excitement or excess afterwards—also a disgenic factor. Fortunately, as the recognition of these dangers increases, they can to a large extent be properly counteracted.

Finally may be mentioned misapplied *birth restriction*. The principle of birth restriction is sound and necessary, but the trouble is that the very people, the morons and defectives, who should practice birth restraint most, do so least, while those who ought not to practice it, the intelligent and well-to-do, are those who put it most often into effect. This danger can be counteracted by the better bringing up of the youth; by rational regulations as to the defectives; and by such measures as the furnishing, together with and as a part of the marriage license, to every marrying couple a treatise of a high order on health, eugenics, and happiness in the family.

Thus it is seen that on the one hand Man is supplementing nature and helping himself on his way, making errors only through ignorance or abnormality, and with an advance of dependable knowledge, is becoming more and more a factor in his own evolution. On the other hand, there are still many agencies that are retarding and may in places or at times even threaten his progress. These may gradually be neutralized or eliminated. Largely the question is again one of knowledge, which, translated into practice, means more research, instruction, genuine enlightenment. As true knowledge will advance, men more and more may safely be expected to proceed gradually toward rational and eugenic self-regulation and self-direction; for that will, according to indications, be the road toward happiness, progress, and propitious further evolution in the future.

## CONCLUDING REMARKS

This, briefly, is the scope of the scientific evidence of Man's evolution, and of its indications. A true appreciation of the subject carries with it not disillusionment but clarification, and a sense of deep gratification. To be the chief product of a great life-tide of millions of years' duration, looms as an achievement of the highest order, and one that at the same time furnishes a substantiation of Man's supreme position in the organic world.

If ages have labored and built to produce Man, a recognition of the fact is bound to be full of proud consciousness, as well as deep responsibility. With the knowledge of his past, furthermore, and with that of his present, Man can well feel that ages of further development are still ahead of him, so that he may reach eventually the highest legitimate aspirations.

# RELIGION AND ACTION

## *by* Reinhold Niebuhr

MAN, as a living creature, driven by the necessities of nature is forced to act. Action is the essence of his existence. But Man is no simple creature and is not simply contained within, and limited by, nature's impulses and necessities. He is a creature who transcends the natural process to which he is related. His rational freedom over natural processes forces him to think as well as to act; to think in order to bring his action into conformity with some general scheme of purpose and some coherent system of ends.

But the freedom of Man is not limited by the freedom of his reason over the processes of nature. It includes the spiritual freedom to transcend himself as well as to transcend nature. This higher freedom of self-transcendence may be included in what is usually designated as rational freedom. But if it is included, it must be clearly understood that the capacity of self-transcendence is a special dimension of freedom. Man as self-transcendent spirit stands outside of himself and his world, making both himself and the world the object of his contemplation. This higher dimension of freedom is the source of all religion. It forces human beings to relate their actions in the last resort to the totality of things conceived as a realm of meaning. Action which has become emancipated from nature's necessities remains incoherent until it has found a final anchor and source of coherence in a total realm of meaning. For this reason all action proceeds from and is oriented by a conscious or unconscious, an implicit or explicit religion, an overt or covert presupposition about the meaning of life.

The freedom of Man and his capacity to make himself and the world the object of his thought not only constitutes his nature as "incurably religious" but it also forces him to seek for

44

a center and source of his system of meaning beyond himself and the world. Every system of meaning is rooted and grounded in a principle of meaning which is not the object but the presupposition of thought, which is not the consequence but the principle of rational analysis. This transcendent principle is the god of religion.

To be sure it is possible for men to conclude that "nothing but" the causal sequences of nature give the world meaning. In that case we have a religion in which "nature" or "causality" is in effect God. It may be asserted that a rational analysis of the world has forced us to the conclusion that nature is God. But a careful scrutiny of the processes by which we arrive at this conclusion must lead to the conviction that the presupposition that nature is God was subtly involved in the reasoning by which we arrived at the conclusion. The system of nature is regarded as the ultimate principle of meaning. Such a conclusion is naturally subject to criticism. Is the system of natural causality really the ultimate principle of interpretation? Does it do justice to the element of novelty in the sequences of nature? Above all does it do justice to human freedom, to Man's transcendence over nature? Does it not exclude what is most significant in human life from the system of meaning which has been established?

In the same manner it may be asserted that life and the world are meaningful only in terms of rational coherence, in which case it is reason rather than nature which is regarded as God. Certainly there is no possibility of elaborating a realm of meaning without engaging the rational faculty. But if the rational faculty is itself made god the question arises whether it is sufficiently ultimate to bear the burden of divinity. Can a man who transcends his own reason to such a degree as to be able to ask the question about it, whether it is the ultimate and essential principle within himself and whether there is a significant coincidence between the processes of nature and the processes of mind, so that one may be sure that the mystery of mind unlocks the mystery of nature, can such a man really make reason into God? He may of course declare that it is not his reason but a more transcendent reason which is really God. But in that case he would have to be sure that what is connoted by "reason" were able to explain the world not only as a system of coherence but also as a realm of vitality. Premature identifications of rationality and meaningfulness always tend to depreciate action and vitality in favour of an imperturbable realm of forms.

There is no action without religious orientation and no religion without God. There are, to be sure, many actions prompted by immediate necessities which are not consciously related to a total scheme of meaning. But every man, in so far as he lives in some degree of freedom over nature, is bound to construct some kind of universe of meaning and to conform his actions to this universe.

## I I

*Ideally* religion is the force which brings all individual actions and vitalities into a total harmony by subjecting them all to the realm of meaning. *Ideally* religion is the principle of harmony which must be substituted for the harmony of nature, once Man's freedom has broken the latter and made the equanimity and order of nature unavailable for him. Yet religion is frequently (and some believe always) the force of disharmony in life. It accentuates conflict, generates fanaticism and aggravates the pride and arrogance of individuals and groups. *How is it* that a principle of harmony should become a force of disharmony and conflict in actual history? Why is it that Man has such great difficulty in bringing his actions into conformity with a total scheme of values? The simplest answer to these questions is that while religion is *on the one hand* the force which subjects all actions and vitalities to a total realm of meaning, it is on the other hand the force which creates false ultimates. Religion relates the immediate to the ultimate; but when it centers life around a false ultimate, when it seeks to organize life around an inadequate center of meaning, a false god, it brings chaos into the world. The basic and perennial problem of religion is, in other words, *the problem of idolatry*. Men are not persuaded by religion in general to worship false gods. They are tempted by the situation in which they stand to use religion for the worship of false gods. The situation in which they stand is this: They are on the one hand involved in the flux of nature and bound by its limits. On the other hand they transcend the flux of time and the limits of nature. They transcend their immediate situation to such a degree that they cannot act in it without bringing their actions into relation with some total structure of meaning. But they do not transcend their immediate situation sufficiently to be able to envisage the ultimate center and principle of meaning without filling it with content and connotations drawn from their immediate situation. *In short,* they conceive God in their own image.

The anatomy of idolatry can be analyzed most clearly in the study of primitive religion. All primitive religion, whether animistic or totemistic, centers life prematurely around some vitality or unity of nature or history, which is incapable of serving as a final center of meaning. Indeed primitive polytheism in its earlier forms has only an inchoate sense of a comprehensive system of meaning. In the religious systems of the earlier empires of Egypt and Babylon a certain order and comprehensiveness emerges out of the primitive chaos. In their pantheon of the gods one god assumes a chief place. What gradually emerges is a form of idolatry in which the god of Egypt, let us say, is assumed to be something more than the god of Egypt. It is assumed that in some sense he is the transcendent source and end of all existence. This god is indeed more universal than the totemistic divinity of the primitive tribe; but he also makes more pretentious universal claims than the tribal god. The gods of the early empires clearly reveal the ambiguous compound of universalism and imperialism, which is the perennial problem of Man's spiritual life. That the god of Egypt is something more than the god of Egypt, is the symbol of finite Man's recognition of a center and mystery of existence beyond the confines of his collective existence. Yet he *is* the god of Egypt and what lies beyond Egypt in terms of life and value must be subordinated to Egypt by means of *his* universal claims. This is the symbol of finite man's effort to comprehend the ultimate in terms of the immediate.

This ambiguous character of religion is basic to all primitive brutalities and the fanaticisms of imperial conflicts. These brutalities and conflicts are never merely expressions of natural vitality. Primitive man is brutal toward his foe, just as a modern self-righteous moralist is cruel toward his adversary not simply because "animal" passion has not been sufficiently disciplined by reason. This brutality in human history is spiritual and not natural. It results not from the chaos of impulses which have not yet been brought under the discipline of mind. It results from a spiritual chaos. Various vitalities and forces of nature and history are brought in conflict with each other because each seeks to usurp a position of superiority and centrality which is incompatible with its conditioned and finite character.

Religion is so deeply involved in the brutalities and conflicts of society that one can quite understand the viewpoint of rationalistic anthropologists, or for that matter rationalistic social scientists of any kind who, since the eighteenth Century, have asserted that religion is a force of chaos and social disorder which must be eliminated from human history. But while one may understand such a viewpoint it is nevertheless a very superficial one. Religion is not some artifice of priests; and idolatry, the worship of contingent elements in history as the ultimate centers of meaning, is not some aberration of religion which could be eliminated if religion were destroyed. What is known as religion is simply Man's effort to come to terms with his situation of finiteness and freedom. Since Man transcends both nature and himself he is bound to seek for a principle of meaning which will give coherence to his world, beyond nature and himself. Since Man is finite and involved in nature he is bound to express his sense of the ultimate in less than ultimate terms. That is, he makes god in his own image and his god therefore comes in conflict with other gods made in the image of other men and other civilizations and cultures; (and the conflict is brutal beyond the brutality of animal life because unconditioned claims are made for these conditioned values. This is a permanent and perennial problem of human history and it reveals itself with equal clarity whether the religious element is explicit or only implicit and whether men are consciously religious or have consciously disavowed traditional religion.)

## I I I

All high religions represent varying strategies for solving this problem of overcoming the chaos of human history and of bringing human actions into conformity with a general realm of order and coherent meaning. High religions may be divided into three types with reference to their solution of this problem. The first two of these three types are two versions of what may be generally designated as "culture religions" in distinction to the third type of religion, which is religion of revelation or prophetic religion. Culture religions seek by some discipline of heart or mind to extricate the soul and the mind from the welter of passion and the conflicts of nature and history in which they are involved. Both types of culture religion are united in their belief that the conflict of interest and the chaos of human action are due to the self's involvement in the passions and the necessities of nature. Both derive the evil in human history not from the freedom of the human spirit but from the inertia of Man's physical nature. Both define the religious task as the extrication of the self from its involvement in nature by some internal discipline, whether rational or mystical, so that it will achieve perfect harmony or even identity with the eternal and transcendent realm of source of meaning, with God. The more rational versions of culture religion regard human reason as the agent of universality and order. The more mystical versions believe reason itself to be involved in finiteness and seek to cultivate a discipline above the level of reason which will emancipate the soul from its involvement in nature, from its dependence upon the necessities and contingencies of the natural order. Despite the wide variety of mystical religions, the mystical technique may without unfairness be defined in comprehensive terms. It is the technique of introversion by which the self cuts its contacts with the outside world and centers consciousness upon the unity of consciousness in the belief that this inner unity of consciousness represents the divine principle within the self. The self achieves divinity, and finally even absorption into the divine, by destroying or obscuring the multiplicity, variety and particularity of the finite world.

While a distinction must be made between the mystical and the rational versions of this ascent from particularity to universality, from finiteness to eternity, from confusion and conflict to order and peace, this distinction is neither absolute nor of primary importance. The more important distinction is between the *pessimistic* and *optimistic*, between acosmic and the cosmic versions of this strategy. There are pessimistic and world-denying forms of rationalism and mysticism which rest upon the basic assumption that the finite world is, as such, evil and that the evil of human life is the inevitable consequence of the contingent, dependent and insufficient character of human existence. What is born and derived is evil, according to Buddha. The finite world is either evil or illusory. Salvation is defined as emancipation from this finite world. The orient has developed this type of acosmism most consistently. Buddhism with its doctrine of Nirvana as the final goal and end of life reveals the logic of acosmic mysticism most clearly. Nirvana is significantly a state which can be defined neither in terms of existence nor non-existence. It hovers between them. It is a state in which all desire has been stilled and in which selfhood has been destroyed and all particularity has been transcended.

In all acosmic mysticism the soul uses the technique of introversion to *project a ladder into the eternal*, into the realm of undifferentiated unity of existence; and then it seeks to draw the ladder up after it. The finite world is regarded as evil by reason of the particularity and individuality of its discrete forms of life so that extinction is the only possible salvation.

In the western world culture religions have never been able to reach a stable equilibrium between the pessimistic and the more optimistic versions of the belief that Man's involvement in the necessities and contingencies of nature is the cause of evil and pain in human life. The more optimistic version does not seek flight into an undifferentiated eternity. It seeks rather to establish the eternal and the universal in history. It believes that human reason, or some mystic capacity above the level of reason is capable of freeing the self from the bondage of nature. It does not regard contemplation and passivity as an end in itself. It believes that thought and contemplation may lift the self above the welter of passion and conflict of interest. It believes in the self-emancipation of Man by the power of his rational faculties.

The classical culture of Greece betrays a significant ambiguity in its analysis of this problem. It is both pessimistic and optimistic, both world-affirming and world-denying in alternate moods.

Plato wants reason to govern the world and the philosopher-king to bring order out of chaos in the city-state. But he has moments of pessimism in which he confesses that whether such a city as he envisages exists on earth or not does not matter. The roots of neo-Platonic world-denial are in Plato himself. The sober and naturalistic Aristotle, for whom nature is the footstool of the ultimate perfection, nevertheless defines the final blessedness as the contemplation of perfection. Here contemplation ceases to be preparation for harmonious action and becomes an end in itself. In the same way there is an equivocal note in Stoicism. It is on the one hand a rationalistic pantheism which seeks by the discipline of reason to bring all actions and passions into a system of harmony; but on the other hand Stoic mysticism despairs of the world and prompts the self to withdraw into itself to secure that perfect imperturbability, that ATARAXIA and APATHEIA which is the consummation of Stoic spirituality. (Bergson)

The note of ambiguity and equivocation between life-denial and life-affirmation, between contemplation as a method of extricating the self from the world and as a method of conquering the passions and the chaos of the world is a basic aspect of classical culture. To a certain degree it has been transmitted to our western culture. Yet on the whole the western world, has chosen the optimistic as against the pessimistic form of culture religion. The basis of its affirmative attitude is confidence in reason as a force which will bring all the activities and vitalities of life progressively under the dominion of a universal harmony. The rational optimists agree with the pessimists in regarding Man's involvement in nature as the cause of his ills. But they disagree with the pessimists in their estimate of reason, which is for them not involved in finiteness and nature but the force of universality by which man in history is extricated from the partial and the particular.

We do not understand the history of our culture, particularly since the Renaissance, if we do not recognize to what degree *ratio* is really the god of modern western man. Reason is the principle of meaning. It is also the force which subordinates all vitalities to this principle. In the impressive system of Hegelian idealism the whole of human history is conceived as a process of Man's gradual spiritualization. The essential conflict in human nature is defined as the conflict between the self as imbedded in "nature-necessity" and the rational and universal self which must and can extricate itself from the too narrow and limited objectives of nature. Hegel does not shrink from identifying the element of universality in human reason with the Absolute itself. In his thought the logic of rationalism becomes crystal clear. Reason is not only God but the effective agent of subduing all recalcitrant vitalities of history and nature to its order and harmony. The tragic inadequacy of this solution of Man's spiritual problem can be measured by analyzing the social theories which flow from Hegel's thought. He finds the state to be the real instrument of human salvation because he regards its collective and comparatively universal character as the historical expression of the universal principle in conflict with particularity and individuality. *Yet it is precisely in Man's collective life that human conflict and fanaticism become most destructive.* Collective man engages in idolatrous self-worship and makes pretentious denials of the contingent and partial character of his existence which individual man cannot allow himself because it would be impossible to make such idolatry plausible. The realm of collective behavior is the very point at which the spiritual pride of man makes its final most desperate and most pathetic effort to obscure the weakness, dependence and finiteness of human existence.

The worship of reason as God is not confined to idealistic rationalists. The most significant characteristic of modern culture is its tendency to press even naturalistic philosophies into the service of this religion. The naturalist may seek to interpret Man primarily in terms of his relation to nature and may minimize his rational transcendence over natural process. Yet he curiously places his faith in reason as the seat of virtue. Thus in the philosophy of Professor John Dewey reason has only a limited freedom over the impulses of nature but that does not prevent him from manifesting the most touching faith in the ability of "free co-operative inquiry" to achieve a vantage point of disinterested intelligence from which it can arbitrate and harmonize the conflicting interests of men. In effect, even the naturalist regards the limited ends of natural impulse as the cause of confusion in human life and hopes that the more universal objectives of reason will bring harmony and coherence into all human activity.

It must be observed that there has always been a note of skepticism in modern culture about this worship of reason. The romantic movement has been the bearer of this skepticism. In some of its forms (as for instance in the philosophy of Bergson) it calls attention to the fact that nature has its own system of harmony which the "divisiveness" of reason destroys. It discovers, in other words, that human freedom breaks the harmony of nature and does not find it easy to achieve a higher and better harmony. In some of its forms romanticism expresses the fear that a rational harmonization of impulse will destroy and enervate the vitality of natural impulse. This is the burden of Nietzsche's protest against rationalism. This form of romanticism is afraid that the "harmony of the whole will destroy the vitality of the parts" (Santayana), that "Fleiss in den Formen kann zuweilen die massive Wahrheit des Stoffes vergessen lassen" (Schiller). A third form of romantic protest, as it is developed by Marxist materialism and by psychoanalytic psychology particularly, expresses no fears that reason may enervate impulse; it has the contrary conviction that reason is really the servant of impulse and that its pretensions of mastery are bogus. The Marxist calls attention to the ideological character of all human culture and to the intimate relation between interest and the supposedly transcendent and disinterested conclusions of philosophy, religion and law. The psychologist reveals this same tendency toward rationalization in more intimate and individual terms.

There is a *negative* validity in all these romantic criticisms of rationalism. It is not so easy to lift human action into a realm of complete harmony with all conflicting vitalities as rationalism assumes. The bigotry of cultures is not due merely to the limited vision of ignorance. Race prejudice is not simply dissolved by enlarging intelligence until it envisages the values and interests of other races. Injustice is not merely the consequence of the failure to include the interest of the other in the field of vision; or of a faulty logic which fails to concede a value to others which it claims for the self. The romantic protest (in which Marxism must be included despite the fact that it is only provisionally romantic and ultimately develops a rationalism of its own) rightly calls attention to the fact that human reason is never the transcendent force of disinterestedness which it pretends to be. It is more intimately and organically related to human passions and interests than the rationalist realizes. Reason, like idolatrous religion, does not simply subordinate the immediate to the ultimate and the partial to the universal. Its effect is always partly to give the immediate the prestige of the absolute and to veil the partial behind the universal. The idolatrous tendency of man to make his own life, culture, civilization, race, nation and interest the premature center of the whole world of meaning is not so simply overcome by *rational contemplation* and discipline as the optimistic version of rationalism assumes. This is proved by the fact that a rationalistic bourgeois civilization which began with such high hopes of achieving a universal culture and establishing universal peace is perishing today in a welter of bigotry and international anarchy.

Yet the romantic protest against rationalism does not solve the problem of human spirituality. If the vitality of nature is asserted against the enervation of reason we are *left without a principle of harmony to discipline the supernatural vitalities of Man*. Some romanticism leads to *nihilism*. If the *unity* of nature is asserted against the divisiveness of mind we are left with no principle of harmony but the limited forces of cohesion in nature itself, the principle of consanguinity in politics for instance. This form of romanticism leads to *primitivism*. If romanticism merely challenges reason's pretensions of mastery over natural impulse, the question still remains unsolved how Man is to achieve either internal or social harmony.

These weaknesses of romanticism prove that it is not possible to solve the human problem by emphasizing the sub-rational vitalities and unities in Man, once we have discovered that we cannot explain human behavior merely by emphasizing his rational faculties. The fact is that the confusion in human life is not due to the limited objectives of natural impulse as rationalism assumes; but neither can it be cured by a simple disavowal of the freedom and capacity for the transcendence involved in Man's rational faculties. *The real situation is that Man does transcend nature but he also transcends himself*. He is therefore capable of using and debasing the universal aspects of reason and of making them tools of his own interest. The sense of coherence and consistency in reason is, therefore, no adequate guarantee of a disciplined human freedom. *The man who transcends nature is not so simply the servant of reason as rationalism assumes*. Reason is on the one hand a force of transcendence which brings the interests of the self into a field of coherence with the interests of others. It is on the other hand an instrument by which the self makes itself the center of such a system of coherence. Immanuel Kant recognized this in his theory of "radical evil" though this recognition stood in contradiction to his total system of thought and would have annihilated his whole philosophy of morals, had he elaborated it.

There is in short no solution for the human problem in terms of so-called "culture religion." Pessimistic culture religions are really closer to the truth than the optimistic versions because they recognize that the same *ratio*, the same principle of *logos* in Man which presumes to achieve universality and transcendence is itself involved in finiteness and actually aggravates the human problem by pretending a degree of transcendence which is beyond the capacities of finite man. But pessimistic culture religions have no solution for the historical problem of

Man. They merely negate history. The optimistic versions of culture religion betray us into utopian illusions, which historical reality consistently disappoints. We are now living in a period of history in which we are subjected to the most tragic disillusionment of these utopian hopes.

## I V

Is there any escape from the dilemma of either disavowing the world of historical reality because it is involved in contingency and finiteness or of establishing false and premature absolutes in it, thereby aggravating its chaos and confusion? In answering that question we must look finally at Biblical religion which belongs in a separate category of religion. It not only *offers a different* solution for the problem of human spirituality but it defines the problem in very distinctive terms. For Biblical religion, God who is the source and end of all existence is more completely transcendent than the God of culture religion. He is not merely the *logos,* the principle of form which brings the formless stuff into order. He is the Creator who is the source of both form and vitality. His *word* is not an impersonal form and principle of order. It is a creative act. *"God spake and it was done."* "God said, let there be light and there was light." These assertions reveal the typical Biblical conception of divine nature. God created the world. The world is not, as in neo-Platonic mysticism an emanation from the divine and transcendent unity of life. *The world is therefore not evil by reason of its involvement in contingency and finiteness.* Man is not evil by reason of his physical existence. Sin does not spring from nature. Human acts are not involved in evil because they are bound by the limits of nature.

The Biblical conception of God as Creator and the doctrine of the goodness of creation lead to very significant consequences in the definition of the human situation. Man is a creature but he is not evil by reason of the finiteness of his existence. He is a creature in every sense, which is to say that he is not divine in his rational life and a creature only in his physical life. His rational capacities are not an eternal element which must be extricated from the finite and the natural element. Yet Biblical religion does not conceive *the human situation as modern naturalism does*. It does not define Man primarily in terms of his relation to nature. It declares that Man is made in the image of God. While the term of "imago Dei" is variously defined, sometimes in terms which equate it with the mere idea of "reason" the general tendency of Christian thought is to emphasize that the image of God in Man is a capacity for transcendence. Man is, in other words, a creature who cannot understand himself either in terms of his relation to nature nor yet in terms of his rational transcendence over nature. *He can understand himself only as he is understood from beyond himself, from the standpoint of God.* His capacity for self-transcendence in infinite regression means that he cannot comprehend himself without a principle of comprehension which is beyond his comprehension. Yet it is believed that the God who is this principle of comprehension makes himself known to Man. That is why Biblical religion is a religion of revelation. It does not believe that it is possible for finite man to comprehend the transcendent and eternal. But it does believe that finite man is able to accept by faith the significant revelations in time and history of what lies beyond time and history and gives history meaning.

Ideally this would mean that men are able by faith to bring all their impulses into conformity with one another and to relate their interests and actions harmoniously to the interests and actions of others when they had found the transcendent source and center of life's meaning which can alone dictate this harmony. All lesser centers of meaning create confusion in human life and action because they lift a finite and contingent factor or force into the false eminence of life's center. There are forms of Christian gnosticism which regard this ideal possibility as a simple possibility. To them Christ has revealed God to Man; and Man once in the possession of the knowledge of the true God henceforth lives in obedience to his will. Most forms of modern liberal Christianity are touched with this gnostic heresy.

Christianity in its profounder forms does not regard this ideal possibility as a simple possibility at all. For it historical reality must be defined not only in terms of the two categories of Man's creatureliness and his freedom ("imago Dei") but also in terms of a third category, *that of original sin.* Man is *child* of God, *creature and sinner.* His sin is not the inertia of his physical nature upon the universal and inclusive ends which his reason projects. His sin springs from his spiritual capacities and is defined as pride and self-glorification. *"He changes the glory of the incorruptible God into the image of corruptible man"* (Romans 1). Unfortunately the concept of original sin has been confused in all Christian orthodoxy by the literal interpretation of the Fall as an historical event. But this literalism cannot entirely obscure the profound truth which underlies the Biblical conception of sin. Sin is not the *inertia of the partial* against the claims of the universal. Sin is not the *limited objective of nature* against the inclusive end of spirit. Sin is the pride of finite man, who is not altogether finite but forgets how finite he is. Sin is not Man's ignorance but his refusal to admit his ignorance. Sin is not Man's dependence upon natural necessity but his refusal to admit his insecurity in nature and his consequent effort to establish complete security, that is, his lust of power. Sin is occasioned by the paradoxical human situation of finiteness and freedom, of involvement in nature and transcendence over nature. Sin is not expressed in the fact that no man is universal Man but *American* man or *bourgeois* man or *western* man. Sin is revealed in the fact that western man, or bourgeois man or American man refuses to admit the partiality of his viewpoints and the contingent character of his existence. The human act is brutal not with the brutality of nature. Its brutality has a spiritual source. Man is ruthless with his foe because he regards his relative standards as absolute and must therefore regard the standards which do not conform to his own as evil.

It may be possible for Man to be conscious of this dilemma in moments of transcendent contemplation. He may have an uneasy conscience when he contemplates the implicit pride and arrogance of his life. But this does not prevent him from continuing to sin in his actions. *No rational universalism can save*

*Man from the sin of imperialism in action.* The fact is that all actions are curiously compounded of universalism and imperialism. Man actually uses the universal perspective of his freedom partly as a false front and rationalization of his partial interest in action. This is the element of original sin in all historic activity. It is easy to see that Biblical religion defines problems of historical action in more tragic terms than any culture religion. It declares in effect that Man is involved in a situation from which he cannot extricate himself by his own power. Every effort on his part to do so actually involves him more deeply in sin, since every such effort will merely insinuate the partial and particular perspective of finite man into the concept of the universal or the eternal which he projects. This process may be pitched upon higher and higher levels of culture. A genuine difference between primitive bigotry and civilized tolerance cannot be denied. But there is no level upon which Man escapes the vicious circle. At the precise moment when he claims to have escaped the vicious circle he is most deeply involved in it. This is the tragedy of self-righteousness to which Jesus calls attention in the parable of the Pharisee and the Publican. It is the tragedy revealed in modern communist spirituality in which the communist begins by calling attention to the element of pretension in burgeois culture and ends by claiming to have achieved a transcendent and absolute form of social justice.

*What is the solution* which Biblical faith offers for this problem? What possible solution is adequate for a problem so grave? The solution for Biblical religion is to be found in its doctrine of "grace." "With Man this is impossible, with God all things are possible," said Jesus when his analysis of the situation of the rich young ruler had prompted his disciples to the despairing exclamation: "Lord who then can be saved."

The Biblical doctrine of grace is corollary to the doctrine of original sin and has meaning only in relation to it, which is why it has no meaning for modern Christians of the liberal tradition, who do not take the doctrine of original sin seriously. According to the Bible, history and revelation reach their climax in Christ in whom the mercy of God is revealed. Christ is the final revelation of God because his suffering is a revelation of a redemptive resource in the heart of the divine which transcends punishment. All human history is involved in punishment because every culture and civilization, every individual and collective human enterprise "exalts itself above measure" and is destroyed. This tragedy of human history can be resolved only if the Eternal takes the contradictions of history into Himself. God suffers with and for Man. Christ is thus the act of self-disclosure of God in history. He is the divine *Logos*. At the Cross human history comes to a full realization of the perennial contradiction in which it stands. Man recognizes not only that he cannot be his own end, but that he cannot be saved from the abortive effort of making himself his own end without a divine initiative which overcomes this rebellion in his heart.

According to Biblical doctrine Christ becomes not only the "wisdom of God" which fully reveals the meaning of life. He also becomes the "power of God" who fulfills life's meaning. It is possible if man is able to comprehend his situation in faith and repentance to appropriate resources beyond himself, by which the sinful contradiction of his life is overcome. The emphasis upon *"grace"* in Christian thought is always an antidote to the emphasis upon *gnosis* in classical and mystical thought. The difference between the two is twofold. On the one hand the power of redemption is believed to come from God and not Man in the doctrine of grace. On the other hand it is power and not knowledge which is desired and obtained. The prayer of the modern poet:

> "Knowledge I ask not, knowledge thou hast sent
> But Lord the will, there lies my bitter need"

is completely orthodox. It analyzes the human situation exactly as St. Paul does: "The will indeed is present with me, but how to perform that which is good I know not." The claim of the Christian doctrine of grace is that the soul which has become contritely conscious of the fact that the deed always falls short of the intent, that the justice which we achieve in action always corrupts the scheme of justice which we conceive in contemplation, that the soul which knows itself incapable of transcending the contradiction within itself between the divine will and self-will, is given a measure of power not its own. The self as centered in itself is destroyed so that the self which is centered in God may arise. St. Paul explains the process of regeneration in the words: "I am crucified with Christ, nevertheless I live." This is to say that redemption consists not in the destruction of the self and its absorption into divinity or transcendent unity. The particular and individual self is not destroyed. The self, on the contrary is more fully realized as it ceases to realize itself too narrowly with its self as the center. The self as infinitely self-transcendent can realize itself fully only as God becomes the center of its life.

All Christian doctrines of sanctification rest upon this Scriptural, more particularly Pauline, *doctrine of grace as power,* of the divine fulfillment of life. *Yet it must be noted immediately* that there is another emphasis in Pauline thought from which the Christian doctrine of justification, in distinction from the doctrine of sanctification, is derived. According to this doctrine Christ is not so much the power in us as the revelation of the divine mercy toward us. The symbol of salvation is not "Christus in nobis" but "Christus pro nobis." The relation between a divine power which overcomes sin in actual history and of a divine power which overcomes sin by taking it into itself is not completely clear in Pauline thought. The proof that this is so is that St. Paul is the fountain and source of sanctificationist and perfectionist interpretations of history just as much as he is the source of the Reformation emphasis upon justification.

The conflict between these two interpretations of sin and grace, which came to a head in the Reformation is of tremendous importance for an understanding of the human situation particularly in our own day. It has not been understood or considered important for the reason that modern forms of Christianity, following the general utopianism of modern culture, are so simply sanctificationist and perfectionist that the problem which the Reformation raised is completely irrelevant to them. The Reformation was a protest against the Catholic doctrine which subordinated justification to sanctification and claimed that whatever the sin of natural man might be, the redeemed man who had benefited from the infusion of sacramental grace was essentially perfect. It was not claimed that he achieved completion but that he "walked perfectly toward perfection" (St. Augustine). Catholic conceptions of redemption and sanctification establish a place in history, namely, the Church, in which sin is actually overcome. It is the contention of the Reformation that whenever such a claim is made the sin which is ostensibly overcome is actually expressed upon a new and more subtle basis. An historical institution, involved in the relativities and contingencies of nature and history claims to have achieved a position of complete transcendence in history and by that very claim reveals the character of original sin in its most essential form; for it obscures partial and relative interests behind the aura of ultimate sanctity. Both Protestants and secularists, when observing the Papacy operating in the relativities of current European politics, and being tempted to come to terms with fascist tyranny if only· this tyranny does not try to destroy the Church, think they can detect a striking verification of the Reformation criticism in current history. No religion lends itself so completely as an instrument of human pride as a religion in which this pride is broken in principle but in which the principle is used by finite man to make claims that he has overcome sin in both principle and fact.

It is the affirmation of the Reformation on the other hand that the Church, that the center of Christian faith, is the locus in history where the sin and pride of man are broken in principle but not in fact. This affirmation rests squarely upon those elements in Pauline thought in which grace is interpreted not as a power which overcomes the contradiction of sin in Man but as the divine mercy which accepts Man despite his sin. "The just shall live by faith." There is no locus in history where sin is overcome except in principle and in intention. There is no possible goodness in Man which can give Man an easy conscience. An easy conscience which rests upon moral achievement leads to moral pride on a higher and more terrible level.

This Protestant doctrine is the stone which the builders have rejected and which must become again the head of the corner. Modern liberal· Protestantism has rejected the doctrine much more completely than medieval Christianity ever did. As a consequence it is involved in all the utopian illusions of modern culture. It regards perfect love as a simple possibility of history. In consequence it is always tempted either to Pharisaism or futility. Either it must say, as liberal Christianity said in the World War, that democracy is identical with the Kingdom of God, or it must say, as it is inclined to say now, that we cannot defend democracy because it is not just enough to deserve defense. Utopianism must either persuade itself that it has achieved a vantage point of perfection from which it can act, or it cannot act at all. This is to say that it is a source either of fanaticism or futility in the relativities and contingencies of history. Modern Christianity thinks it makes a tremendous contribution to politics when it insists that no one comes to the struggle against modern tyranny "with clean hands." Such an assertion can only imply that it were possible for some individual or nation to achieve guiltlessness. This is exactly what is not possible.

All human actions remain within the limits of sin. "Every deed," says Nietzsche, "must be loved more than it deserves to be loved in order to be born." Nietzsche of course glorifies the sinful element in the deed because he is afraid of the enervation of moral scruples. In this he is wrong but no more in error than those who think they can achieve guiltlessness by just a little more contemplation.

Whatever decency we establish in history and whatever justice we are able to maintain against the threat of tyranny on the one hand and anarchy on the other, must rest upon a religious interpretation which refuses to make sin normative but which also refuses to withdraw from history because all history is sinful. "Sin bravely," said Luther. While it must be admitted that the evils of antinomianism lurk in this advice of Luther, it must be recognized that the evils of utopian Pharisaism and futility are implicit in perfectionist doctrines which do not understand the truth in this advice.

The Reformation doctrine of justification by faith is important in our day because without it we are threatened by the illusions of a moralistic Christianity to which our American churches because of their sectarian background have already largely succumbed. Instead of understanding the common tragedy in which we are all involved, augmented by the misapplications of science, we try desperately to separate ourselves from that tragedy in the hope that we may also separate ourselves from the sins of the world. We try to achieve perfection but it is a pitiless perfection. We believe that our loyalty to the ideal of love is best served by remaining free of conflict. But our love is a loveless love which refuses to assume its fair share of responsibility for the relative justice and relative peace which is possible in the world but possible only in relative terms. The most pathetic religious and moral figure in the world, as Christ has taught in the parable of the Pharisee and Publican, is the good man who does not know that he is not good, and who becomes the more evil by the very sweat of his self-righteous labors. Without a profounder understanding of the insights of the Christian religion than American Christianity reveals today we cannot extricate ourselves from the alternate moods of fanaticism and cynicism which assail all utopians. There is no guiltlessness in history. The only possibility of action is the possibility of acting in the contrite knowledge of the guilt of our action, in which case it is possible to have some knowledge of a divine mercy, which overcomes the sinful hurt of our action. "With man this is impossible."

# SCIENCE AND WISDOM [1]

## *by* Jacques Maritain

IS THERE a distinction of nature or of essence between Science and Wisdom? This is a fundamental question not only for human intelligence but also for human culture and for the destiny of civilizations. In truth, it may be said that all men are in agreement regarding the answer, whether they believe in the existence and reality of wisdom, or give it up: the skeptic who denies the value of knowledge or the possibility of truth considers skepticism to be wisdom. The positivist who believes in science and denies metaphysics affirms in the sharpest manner the distinction between them. So does, in an opposite way, the visionary who despises science as an illusion of human pride, and believes only in mystical insight. The Platonist, the Aristotelian, the Spinozist, the Hegelian, expound a wisdom which considers itself as distinct from science and, at the same time, as establishing foundations of science.

Pythagoras attempted to build up the realm of wisdom itself in the radiance of mathematical knowledge. Yet Plato willed that geometry be only the threshold of wisdom. Generally speaking, for Greek classical philosophy, the distinction between science and wisdom was to be the distinction between mathematics and metaphysics. For modern classical philosophy this distinction is, above all, the distinction between physico-mathematical or empiriological knowledge and metaphysics. But what is the meaning of such a distinction? Why does not mathematical or physico-mathematical science constitute a kind of wisdom?

A first observation, in this connection, concerns the relation of both science and wisdom with human conduct and human destiny. Mathematics provides man with the means of action, so

[1] Translated and adapted by Miss Dorothy Rothschild.

does the science of phenomena. Neither gives rules for human life itself. Wisdom, on the contrary, has a basic practical value, it claims essentially to govern our existence. We ask advice of him we deem to be a wise man, we feel inclined to entrust to him the most difficult problems which make us anxious about our moral conduct. Science puts means in man's hands, and teaches men how to apply these means for the happiest outcome, not for him who acts, but for the work to be done. Wisdom deals with ends in man's heart, and teaches man how to use means and apply science for the real goodness and happiness of him who acts, of the human person himself.

But how is human life to be conducted without knowing the truth about man and man's destiny? This is the very privilege and the very ordeal of the human being. Bees need neither wisdom nor the advice of some wise bees. For the conduct of bees science is enough, that science which is their instinct, animal science. Man needs to know the very roots of his own life and the very aims thereof. Is man therefore endowed with intelligence and freedom? But what is intelligence and what is freedom? Does man truly enjoy free will? These are questions which belong to wisdom. There is no good in mathematics, Aristotle said, because mathematics deals only with formal structures and relations of mathematical entities, it ignores all which pertains to efficient causality and to final causality, and the notion of good is but one with the notion of final cause. Because wisdom obviously has a practical function in relation to human life, wisdom must also possess, and this first and foremost, a speculative function in relation toward everything concerning the fundamentals of human life, that is toward the nature of the cosmos and the place of man within it; wisdom must know that which *is*, it must know truth about the world and the world's causes. What is truth? Is truth attainable? These are also questions belonging to wisdom. And similarly: what is the cause of the world, is the world without cause, that is to say, is the world its own God, or does it depend on a separate and transcending cause? Does God exist; and what is God? Hence, there is—if philosophy is to exist—a speculative philosophy distinct from the practical rational wisdom. Hence, theology—if theology is to exist—has a speculative function as well as a practical one, and must know the things of God before knowing the things of human salvation. Hence, mystical wisdom—if mystical wisdom .is to exist—is also speculative as well as practical, and is able to rule human life according to divine rules and inspiration only because it penetrates to the depths of God. Everywhere what is speculative—that is, what is concerned with truth—comes first and matters more than what is practical, that is to say, what is concerned with man.

According to the scholastic textbooks which summarize in a modern way the teachings of perennial philosophy, the notion of knowledge (or the notion of "science" taken in its broadest sense which means *knowing in a firm and stable way*) involves both wisdom and science; and science (in the strict sense of the word) is distinguished from wisdom in this, that science aims at the detail of some special field of knowing and deals with the secondary, proximate or apparent causes, while wisdom aims at some universal knowing and deals with prime and deepest causes, with the highest sources of being, attained through the simplest enlightening media. This distinction is valid, on condition that the word "cause" be understood, not in the sense of a Spinozist concatenation of "modes" expressing the hidden unique Substance, nor in the sense of an empiricist stable link between antecedent and consequent, nor in the sense, proper to the sciences of phenomena, of a mathematical function between variables, but in the general sense of raison d'être or principle of explanation. Yet this distinction seems to me to be not sufficiently illuminating. What are the conditions of mathematical knowledge? Exactly because it does consider neither efficient nor final causes, it is detached from real being; the entities it deals with may be either merely ideal or capable of existing. What are the conditions of physico-mathematical knowledge, or more generally, of the sciences of phenomena? They detach from reality what is measurable or, more generally, what is observable, they conceptualize these data in concepts relating, in their noetic structure, not to any intelligible essence, but to sense-observations and to numerical indications given by measuring instruments, and they seek the deductive systematization of such concepts in a texture of mathematical entities and mathematical laws, more generally in a texture of explanatory symbols: they know the universe—the phenomena —to the extent that things have been phenomenalized and de-ontologized by means of mathematical or symbolizing thought. Let us say, therefore, that science, in the modern sense, in the strictest sense of the word, is a non-ontological knowledge, while wisdom is an ontological knowledge. Being, taken in its own reality, Being as not phenomenalized, is the object of wisdom. Being is the oxygen of wisdom; wisdom is the breath of human intelligence within Being. In Being, wisdom lives, moves and exists.

A consequence of this is that while intelligence is the proper power or organ both of science and wisdom, yet intelligence in science functions, so to speak, separately, as detached from the personal roots of the thinking human subject, or as itself phenomenalized, exactly in the same manner that in science, the object of intelligence has been detached from the internal roots of being and phenomenalized. On the contrary, intelligence in wisdom functions in actual unity with the personal roots of the thinking human subject, in actual unity with the whole man; in this sense Plato was right in saying that we must philosophize ξὺν ὅλῃ τῇ ψυχῇ; moreover, the entire being of the wise man is engaged in the work of wisdom, his body as well as his soul needs therefore a certain purification (at least as regards the conditions of development, if not the formal medium of knowledge). On the other hand, because it is essential to wisdom to have a practical or ethical function, the practical implications of the outlook of a wise man may reverberate, more or less unconsciously, upon the speculative outlook of the same, and determine or disturb, in an effective, not a logical way, those speculative convictions which by themselves are prior to the practical ones. Briefly, the *status* of human intelligence, its existential conditions of exercise, must here be taken into account as well as its *specification* by its object. The notion of a Christian or Buddhist mathematics has no sense, except a merely accidental and historical one. But the notion of Christian philosophy has an intrinsic and constitutive meaning. Not only because that which pertains to wisdom is by itself so arduous that objective guidance, danger signals or stimulating utterances of revealed truth are needed for securing in this domain a completely true knowledge, without mixture of errors; but also because, from head to foot, the human person, existing in such or such an ontological status, is involved in wisdom's achievements.

There are many prejudices against wisdom in the modern world. I should like briefly to examine three of them.

The first prejudice emphasizes the seemingly insuperable contradictions that are revealed through the ages between the great metaphysical doctrines. If a stable agreement among men, a general intersubjectivation is not possible in this domain, is it not that some hidden root of illusion or some essential character of subjectivity permeates every attempt toward metaphysical wisdom? On the contrary, a character of objective necessity, causing universal assent and enabling men to use a common fixed vocabulary, appears to be the brilliant privilege of science. This argument has been largely exploited even by great philosophers, by Kant, for instance, who nevertheless sought to save metaphysics by new means, but who was fascinated by the glamorous appearance of infrangible fixity and universality offered by the mathematics and the Newtonian physics of his day. Yet such an argument is by itself strangely weak. In order to possess conclusive force, it should first have established that the oppositions in question are not the effect of the weakness of human nature rather than of a constitutional impotence of the intelligence with regard to metaphysical truth. Difficult are the beautiful things, Plato said. They summon us to beautiful dangers. And Heraclitus: "If you do not expect the unexpected, you will not attain truth, which is difficult to discern, scarcely accessible." If the intrinsic arduousness of metaphysical wisdom is such that, according to Aristotle, we can attain it only in a precarious manner, as something which is lent to us rather than as something we possess, and if on the other hand this wisdom requires, at least indirectly, the whole dynamism and synergy of the human person together with a real purification of his voluntary and affective powers, then the

fluctuations and contradictions with which metaphysics is re-
proached appear as quite natural and comprehensible; they are
only a ransom for its superiority. What is surprising is that
sometimes, by a happy fortune, mankind has been able to conquer this kind of knowledge.

Moreover, the progress of modern knowledge has broken
down the beautiful fixity and universal coherence of classical
mathematics and Newtonian science. Not only has mathematics
been immensely changed and enlarged, and physics submitted
to an extraordinary crisis of growth; but the internal conflicts
between axiomatic and intuitive thought with regard to the
foundations of geometry, the seemingly insolvable discussions
concerning the principle of *tertium exclusum* applied to the
theory of Numbers, and the internal contradictions which contemporary physics endeavors to solve have shown that oppositions between schools of thought and apparently insuperable
antinomies adorn the "exact" sciences as well as metaphysics.
(In both cases, yet in different ways, antinomies are in reality
superable.)

Finally, when things are carefully considered, the whole
argument haughtily emphasized in the *Prolegomena to All Future Metaphysics* can be reversed. It suffices to take into account
the agreement of intelligences and the power of making men
unanimous not only with regard to the extension in space at a
given moment, but with regard to the dimension of time: we
shall see that metaphysical wisdom enjoys, much more than
the sciences of phenomena, a character of relative universality,
continuity and human consistency, and a power of provoking
the assent of the intelligence. Between the mechanical, astro-
nomical, chemical and biological conceptions of an ancient Greek
or Hindu, a medieval thinker and a modern scientist, there
are infinitely fewer common features than between the intuitions and utterances of metaphysical thought at these three
moments. Not only does there exist a perennial philosophy,
prepared by the pre-Socratics, founded by Socrates, Plato, Aristotle, assumed by the Christian tradition, lifted by Thomas
Aquinas to a high point of organization, and still improving
and progressing throughout centuries, but every metaphysician

worthy of the name has a feeling of citizenship, of mutual stimulation and exaltation and of deep understanding toward his fellow-hunters of all times and toward his sharpest enemies in the metaphysical field, and rejoices in discovering a kind of community among them, which is so hidden in the profundities of human thought that it paradoxically endures among absolute oppositions of doctrine and despite a radical incommunicability—which has become truly babelian in modern times—between the vocabularies and the very meaning of the words employed by everyone. Here we realize that the intersubjectivation managed by a well-established vocabulary—however important and desirable it remains—is not the only possible intersubjectivation; not only this kind of intersubjectivation is possible in philosophy (in a determined school of philosophy)—where it relates to intellectual perceptions—as well as in physical sciences, where it relates to sense-statements, but another kind of intersubjectivation exists at the elementary basis of human knowledge, relating to that obscure and still unformed life of the intellect, which precedes words and conceptual expression. We also realize that the intrinsic arduousness of the things of wisdom is compensated by the long-lived accumulation of common experience which is conveyed in man from generation to generation.

The second prejudice which deters many modern people from wisdom is of a psychological order. Thanks to the characteristics of empiriological science which I indicated above, and to the kind of intersubjectivation it implies, there is a sort of equality among the immense folk of honest, patient, laborious minds which constitutes the working army of science. Everyone feels he is participating in and co-operating toward an invaluable collective task; he feels that, even if he spends his life in securing a single humble bit of scientific data, his work and his devotion will have been useful and dignified in the common edification of science; he feels that even if his own intellectual powers are middling, he stands in true solidarity with the discoverers and theorists of genius in whose conquests he shares in some way. This is the privilege and glory of Science, which Wisdom may envy, and must not deny. But this is no reason for denying the ways of wisdom and its own privileges. Everywhere in nature the gifts and the tasks are diversely distributed. The philosopher, the metaphysician, he who pursues wisdom, is more solitary than the scientist; he feels alone in the face of being and of mystery, he knows he is lost if he misses the mark. Yet his joy is greater and his achievements more useful, if it is true that what is of no immediate usefulness and application is what mankind needs the more, and that, as Aristotle said, there is more joy in catching an imperfect glimpse of what is most universal and divine than in perfectly possessing what is particular and poor in intelligibility. Doubtless misunderstandings and conflicts will always endure between scientists and metaphysicians, they are the price of human status. During the major part of the Middle Ages wisdom was both imperialistic and patronizing toward science. From the time of Roger Bacon, particularly of the other Bacon and the great discoveries of modern ages, science has become contemptuous of wisdom, repudiating its very existence. Contempt and mutual exclusion contribute neither to the progression of humanity, nor of knowledge.

The third prejudice against wisdom in modern times depends on a curious and truly unreasonable rebounding of sociological feelings upon the very field of knowledge. If wisdom exists with its own domain and its own rights, wisdom is not only distinct from but also superior to science. In what sense? In the sense that its object is more universal and more deeply immersed in the mystery of things, and in the sense that the function of defending the first principles of knowledge and of discovering the fundamental structure and organization thereof belongs to wisdom, not to science. Yet, just as there exists a hidden imperialistic bias which unconsciously rejoices in every phraseology connoting power or domination, there also exists a pseudo-democratic bias of aversion regarding every kind of hierarchy. If wisdom is superior to science, will not science be treated as an inferior thing, a servant, a slave? Will not feudalism and the Inquisition and all the old exorcised tyrannies come down upon the earth enveloped in the dangerous folds of that self-styled superiority? Hence the sacred fears and the eloquent warnings of Mr. Sidney Hook. I do not despise this kind of argumentation, even if it seems to me meagerly philosophical. Scientists are right in remembering the abuses of authority of the theologians of old, and in suspecting also that such abuses will always be a temptation, not for theology or for metaphysics, but for the weakness and bitterness of theologians and metaphysicians, even when they are not simple parrots of wisdom. Yet the fact remains that a good theology and a good metaphysics, consciously and publicly acknowledged as such, and aware of themselves, are the best protection against bad, unconscious, larvated metaphysics and theology. Racist and totalitarian enslavement and depravation of science are an outstanding example of such underground and perverted metaphysics and theology, born of the rejection of wisdom and of idolatrous worship of science and technique.

In truth, the prejudice I am discussing and the argumentation it implies lie entirely in the realm of the accidental. And every student of philosophy has been instructed that no reasoning in merely accidental matters is valid. May it please God that the words superior and inferior be liberated from any sociological connotation! We are obliged, however, to use words of human language, just as they have been used for human things,—and even when in so doing they have sometimes degenerated—in order to express things of the intellectual life, not of the human and social one.

Is it possible to avoid this difficulty by imposing upon human language some ugly technical deformations? I myself tried to replace the words superior and inferior by the savory words "supra-valent" and "infra-valent," but I harbor no illusions about the results. The truth is that, considering things in themselves, it is absurd to apply sociological or political criteria to spiritual matters. Democracy is the best way of political life, citizens have to build up and improve a genuinely democratic society of human persons; yet democracy has no meaning as a method of finding the solution of a geometrical problem or of discerning the main lines of the structure of the mind and of the internal organization of knowledge. Philosophers and scientists do not have to build up a democratic truth, they have to see and affirm that which is.

On the other hand, a genuine democracy does not exclude the notion of ordering, any more than the reality of social differentiations; rather it demands that social differentiations and orderings emanate from the very bosom of the people and postulate an equal opportunity for everyone to attain, according to his condition, his full human flowering, in such a way that social authority be exercised by those whose personal merit is greater as regards common utility. Now, the authority of men, even of great men, is the lowest and weakest means of achievement in intellectual matters, and if a knowledge exerts "authority" upon another knowledge, this is in a merely analogical sense, as contemplating and explaining some truths regarding which the other knowledge has no competence. Thus mechanics or chemistry has authority with regard to metaphysics, if metaphysics deals with matters of mechanics or chemistry, and metaphysics has authority with regard to mechanics or chemistry, if the latter deals with matters of metaphysics. Doubtless it may occur that "inferior" sciences, unaware of their genuine boundaries, interfere with questions belonging to the metaphysical domain and express certain statements which, taken in themselves, endanger or deny some metaphysical truth. In fact, it often happens that these statements, taken in the context and the conceptual vocabulary proper to the particular science in question, have quite another meaning. In any case the "authority" of metaphysics will then consist in maintaining its own statements unshaken, in making clear the proper bearing and the limitations of particular sciences, in refuting the false metaphysical conclusions seemingly involved in the scientific conceptualization or generalization of new data, and in knowing and affirming that this very conceptualization or generalization will be given up or reduced to more modest proportions by science itself, progressing in its own way, in the course of time.

Moreover, to deny the diversity of the degrees of knowledge, the autonomy of each species of knowledge in its own plane, and the hierarchical organization of them within the life of the human mind, would be to break down the unity of this mind and to throw knowledge into a deadly atomization. Learned robots would then work on the disintegrated elements of a rotting corpse of knowledge. Human persons are equal in specific nature, yet they fulfill organically diverse functions within the social body. But the virtues of the intellect and the degrees of knowledge, receiving their specification from the object they tend to grasp, differ among themselves as to their specific nature, their very essence. With still more reason it is necessary to recognize among them an organic hierarchy which is, this time, a natural one.

I I

It is to the honor of pagan antiquity always to have understood that wisdom is a science (in the broadest sense of the word), a form of knowledge, a perfection of the intellect, that it brings into play the highest energies of the intelligence, yet never for a moment to have dreamed that science, in the sense of the special sciences, could claim to prevail over wisdom and enter into conflict with it. For the ancient world always realized that wisdom was sovereignly to be desired, that it is a knowledge of freedom, a knowledge which makes man akin to the divine. But what is this wisdom, and in what does it consist? In a general way what we find in the ancient world is what might be called the competition of wisdoms.

It is impossible to speak, however briefly, of the great pre-Christian forms of wisdom without attempting first of all to sketch the attitude of oriental thought, and above all of Hindu thought. But how can a Christian approach this question without asking also why a world so wonderfully gifted, so far as its natural disposition is concerned, for contemplation and "the better part," remained so long remote from the explicit revelation of the divine Word? Perhaps we may think that here too God preferred to choose the *infirma mundi,* and to spread the teachings of the Gospel first of all amongst us active barbarians of the West, who were destroyers and heirs of the Roman Empire, rather than amongst cultures which were so rich and so luxuriant that, had they been activated by the ferment of revelation, they might have run the risk of delivering up the deposit of supernatural faith to an unbridled and discordant intellectualism. The experience of the neo-Platonic *gnosis* and of Byzantine theology may perhaps lend some support to such a way of conceiving the problem of East and West.

However this may be, it would seem that India dedicated itself to that contemplation and experience of the Absolute which depend on our natural powers alone. And thus held in store, so to speak, under a regime in which, as St. Paul says, the just man is a law unto himself, India remained in a state of expectancy, a mighty witness to the supreme natural aspirations and the inherent failings of the human spirit.

India always conceived of wisdom as a wisdom of deliverance and salvation. This is so true that her immense metaphysical speculations never quite attained a purely speculative *mode*, involved as they were in a practical science of perfection and holiness.

But this wisdom of salvation, India did not learn from the prophets and the Messiah of the people of God. She struggled to reach it by a desperate urge which sprang from the depths of the soul, a sort of tidal wave of the divine energies poured out onto the universe and concentrated in man. How should India have been able to distinguish as the Judeo-Christian does, between the natural order and the supernatural order—that is to say the order of participation in the intimate life of an absolutely transcendent God, who created all things *ex nihilo?* In her eyes nature itself, freed from the constraints of illusion and the power of causality, must transcend itself in a perfection which we may call supernatural in quite another sense. Wisdom, the wisdom of salvation, the wisdom of the saints, is to be achieved by the ascetic and mystical effort of human nature.

I am fully aware that India bases all her philosophy on a sacred revelation, and that the idea of divine grace is not absent from her thought. I am fully aware that in the sort of prefiguration of an unknown truth, the fervor of *bhakti* brought to India, mercy and love were conceived as descending to us from on high. But the theism and the doctrine of piety of *bhakti* are only one aspect of Hindu thought, and one, moreover, which is far from having retained its purity. And even if grace were conceived as coming from above, the significance of such a gift remained implicit and unexplained. As for the sacred revelation upon which all Hindu thought depends, it is not the living voice of a God telling of himself through His Son and bringing to the heart of humanity His truth which tolerates no immixture. It is a holy literature inherited from the wise men and deposited in the shelter of a ritual tradition: from which each dharsana, each human school of thought will derive various truths, glimmers of wisdom at variance with each other.

Thus we can well say that India conceived of the wisdom of salvation and of holiness as of a supreme good to be achieved by an upward effort of the energies immanent in nature, and by a supreme tension of the capacities of our spirit. Such a concrete designation, in terms of the direction of a movement, seems to me much more important than more analytical designations which have to do with hidden structures. I am not examining here what in this movement answers to nature and what to grace. But, as I see it, the essential characteristic of this wisdom, and of oriental wisdom generally speaking, is this: it is primarily and above all an *ascensus,* an *upward movement,* whereby man wishes to pass into superhuman conditions and enter into divine freedom. From this point of view we can see the full significance of the athleticism of mortification, the strained asceticism and plethora of means and of recipes, of methods of perfection and contemplation which can be observed so often in the Orient.

And the rush of the crowds throwing themselves beneath the car of Juggernaut also takes on a special symbolic value. For the wisdom of salvation cannot be taken by storm. We do not carry the key that opens heaven. Heaven itself must open the gates. And though a grace whose true name they did not know may have raised to great heights the souls of good faith and of good will who sought that wisdom, still Hindu wisdom itself was finally bound to fail as wisdom. It was bound to remain without reaching its goal, struggling endlessly to escape from monism, yet unable to take definite form without laying itself open to it; aspiring incessantly for deliverance in positive beatitude and only succeeding, after Buddhist experience, in explaining Nirvana in terms that more and more approached pure negation. If India knew her own soul she could but sing: *Expectans expectavi*.

Greek wisdom is quite another thing. It is a human wisdom, a rational wisdom. It is not the wisdom of philosophy aspiring to be a wisdom of salvation. It is a wisdom of philosophy with an order of its own, following its own line of *perfectum opus rationis*, a perfect work of reason. But here is no longer any question of a wisdom of salvation and holiness, a wisdom of eternal life. It is a wisdom of here below, an earthly wisdom. I do not say a rationalist wisdom, but a rational wisdom, turned toward created things.

Here again it is necessary to make distinctions, and to understand in a very unmodern sense (in a "pre-Cartesian" sense) the word "rational" which I have just used. I am aware that sacred traditions never ceased to move in the background of Greek thought and that the reason of the ancient world was a reason naturally religious and which took form in a climate of natural piety haunted by many terrors. It knew good and bad fortune, believed in inspiration from above and in demonic influences. The idea of Fate and the jealousy of the Gods, the superstitious fear of admitting happiness, the very worship of divine similitudes wide-spread in nature, bear witness to a profound sense of the tragic element in man's estate, and to a religious feeling for the suprahuman energies at work in the world. For all that, Greek wisdom is not constituted on the basis of hieratic and priestly traditions like the wisdom of the Orient, but outside them and sometimes in opposition to them. Greek wisdom does not start out from the Supreme, from the absolute Being, as the Vedanta does, asking how anything can exist which is not God and finally renouncing hope of finding a reply which is not Maya. It starts out from things, from tangible and visible reality, from becoming, from movement, from the manifold which with such scandalous energy exerts its being.

Even if it failed to hold to it, Greek wisdom experienced at a decisive moment a sense of the real which is offered to our human mind and experience, and of the *existence* of that which is not God. This was its peculiar merit which perhaps explains the strange favor bestowed by Providence on these frivolous and noisy folk. For Providence seems to have no liking for angelism. It is not good to despise the creature of flesh and blood. A certain affirmation, though it be frivolous and disordered or even pagan, of the ontological gifts at work in nature and in man has less of pride in it than the refusal to accept the human condition. Here lies the significance of the honor that history has paid to the Greeks for having, in the face of the crushing divinities of the East, lifted up the image of man.

Greek wisdom has the common measure of man. It is a strictly philosophical wisdom which does not pretend to set us free in a union with God, but merely to lead us to a rational knowledge of the universe. What it achieved best was to disengage the idea of itself, and that point I specially desire to stress. It had of itself and of the rational process an admirably just idea which has entered for ever into the heritage of mankind. Doubtless it sinned by philosophical optimism, but it knew what it means to philosophize. It discerned with sureness the fundamental distinction between speculative philosophy and practical philosophy, the object and nature of metaphysics, physics and logic, the hierarchy of the sciences and the subordination of the special sciences to the simplest and most universal science, the science which is the most highly speculative and the most disinterested, which has to do with being as such and with the causes of being.

And it touched on the beginnings of everything. The human wisdom of the Greeks not only had the idea of what it ought to be, but in addition it succeeded in setting itself up and coming into existence: in outline and in promise. The outline itself is so beautiful that optical error of retrospection might easily deceive us into believing it a completed work. . . .

The beauty peculiar to Greek wisdom is a beauty of outline, of some masterful sketch in which the essential points of appeal are suggested with infallible art. It could not be completed, it is nowhere complete. Nor was it complete on the metaphysical side—we know well enough how Aristotle, faced with questions concerning the supreme spiritual realities, hesitated and shut his eyes; we know into what errors he fell and what a meager following his speculative discoveries won for him in the world of antiquity. Nor was it complete on the side of science—for although the physico-mathematical method was successfully applied in certain particular domains, it never did lead to a general knowledge of natural phenomena; and although physics was well founded as far as philosophical principles are concerned, it led to major disasters in the detailed explanation of phenomena. Nor was it complete on the moral side, for neither the ascetic cultivation of pleasure nor that of virtue reached any conclusion other than despair of the existence of the wise man.

And when this human wisdom tried to accomplish its own perfection, to complete itself by its own devices, it took a bad turn. It was not content to affirm the ontological consistency and value of creatures, as was its mission. Instead of paying honor to the principle of created being, as shown in created things themselves, it divinized them. For this it earned the condemnation of St. Paul. In the end it called in vain for the help of the East, of a syncretism without existential roots, and sought a remedy for the great melancholy of paganism in mystagogy and magic. Its original strength had lain in orienting thought to existence: it renounced existence, and contented itself with a substitute, a dialectical world in which the search is only for an ideal procession of essences, and for an ecstasy which lies beyond Being. The neglect of the singular, and, more profoundly, of existing things, the primacy of the generic and the logical which it is the fashion (quite wrongly) to blame on Aristotle—really represents what was a temptation for Greek philosophy and finally brought about its defeat when it showed itself no longer capable of sustaining Aristotle. The Renaissance of Platonic idealism during the Alexandrian period was a punishment of human wisdom which had gone to seed. And I am not sure that the same cannot be said of every Platonist revival during the course of history.

But in the ancient world there is a third wisdom, the wisdom of Moses and the prophets, the wisdom of the Old Testament. This is not human wisdom like the Greek. The Jewish world until Philo seems to have even ignored or despised all strictly philosophical and metaphysical inquiry, every search for human wisdom. This is a wisdom of salvation and holiness, of deliverance and freedom, of eternal life—but unlike the wisdom of the Hindus, man cannot conquer it by his own effort. *Quis ascendet in caelum*, who will ascend to heaven and look for it? [1] The heart of Israel knew that no effort of asceticism and of mysticism could *force* that wisdom. Wisdom must give itself, must itself open the gates of heaven and descend.

Here we have the peculiar mark of the true wisdom of eternal life. As it is a matter of entering into the depths of God, how would it be even conceivable if God Himself did not take the initiative with a free gift?

The long unwearying impatience of the Jews beseeches God to give Himself—God whose only wish is to give Himself, and yet who hides Himself. And He will come even in person and in the flesh, and descend lower than all so as to save all. Wisdom itself will bear our sorrows.

Nowhere is wisdom spoken of more gloriously and more mysteriously than in the Bible. It appears as increate and yet created, it is identified with God and is yet the first creature, the maternal form, so to speak, in which all things are planned and formed. So much so that in our time certain Orthodox Russian theologians have tried to turn Sophia into some sort of hypostasis intermediary between the uncreated and the created. Catholic theology is aware that this expression moves analogically from God to His consubstantial Word made Flesh and to Her who, inseparable from Him, and reflecting God as perfectly as a pure creature can, was Herself, too, and for this reason, foreseen from the beginning.

The wisdom of the Old Testament is bound up with the most inflexible idea of divine transcendence, and of the abyss of glory of an uncreated life whose thoughts are not like our thoughts, and whose initiatives and sanctions intervene per-

---

[1] Deuter. xxx. 12; Rom. x. 6; Baruch, cap. III.

petually in our history. And it is bound up with the idea of creation *ex nihilo*. It seems to me very remarkable that while we have here a conception as opposed as possible to any immanentist monism more or less endangering the divine personality, we have at the same time a conception of the creature as far removed as possible from an effacement of created being, of its human reality, of its personality and freedom in face of the divine. This perishable and corruptible flesh, this very flesh will arise again—an idea that Greek wisdom never even suspected. History is an unimaginable drama of confronted personalities and liberties, of the eternal divine personality and our own created personalities. And how real are the being and existence of these created personalities! If we wish to get beyond the nightmare of a banal "indefinite pronoun" existence, of "one" instead of "I"—by which our imaginations are oppressed in the conditions of the modern world; if we wish to awake to the consciousness of ourselves and *our* own existence, we may indeed read Heidegger, but we would surely do better to read the Bible. The behavior of the patriarchs, of Moses, David, Job and Ezekiel before God will teach us what personal existence, as distinguished from "anonymous" existence, is; the existence of an Ego. They have no shame in existing and in existing in their own name precisely because they are in the all-powerful hand of Him who made them. Everything in Holy Scripture is dialogue: it is always a question of "Thou" and "I."

The wisdom of the Old Testament cries out that our personality exists ultimately only in humility, and is only saved by the divine personality. For the One is a personality which gives and the other a personality that is given.

And here is the chief point I wish to make. This supernatural wisdom is a wisdom which gives itself, which descends from the Author of Being like a torrent of generosity. The wisdom of salvation, the wisdom of holiness is not achieved by man but given by God. It proceeds essentially, not from an ascending movement on the part of the creature, but from a descending movement of the creative Spirit. And that is why it is essentially supraphilosophical, suprametaphysical, and really divine. Prior to any more detailed specification we must see the difference between the wisdom of the Ganges and of Tibet and the wisdom of the Jordan in terms of the opposition between these two movements of ascent and descent. The wisdom of the sapiential books like the wisdom of the Gospel emanates from the depths of the uncreated love, stretches from one shore to the other and descends into the deepest being of the creature. And that is why it cries out in public places, and on the house-tops, knocks at the doors and is freely given. What is essentially secret it proclaims: if anyone thirst, let him come and drink; a secret so hidden that it hides within itself him to whom it is made known.

At one moment, with Philo, an effort was made to conciliate this wisdom and the wisdom of the Greeks. But such an eclecticism, from which St. Justin and several of the early fathers were not exempt, was bound to be vain. There was an inevitable warfare between the wisdom of the philosophers and the wisdom of the saints. The former, as I have pointed out, claimed to be complete in itself and to suffice for mankind. It raised a mountain of pride, and united the energies of paganism in *gnosis* and its factitious mysteries. The latter at last uncovered its face, inclined its head crowned with thorns, a scandal to the Jews, a folly to the Gentiles. This conflict of wisdoms marks the ruin of the ancient world. St. Paul was its great witness. St. Augustine, who experienced the conflict and resolved it for himself, was its doctor and arbiter.

Later centuries were to live on Augustine's doctrine of wisdom and knowledge. Augustine taught them that between wisdom which knows by "higher reason" in the day-light of divine things, and science which knows by "inferior reason" in the twilight of created things, there is an order of preference for or against which souls and civilizations must choose. For science is good and worthy of love, but it is not above wisdom. If not in its very nature, at least in its human dynamism and in its relation to human life, it belongs to the sphere of *uti*, and it is absurd to take the useful as an end. An end is that which is truly ultimate and delectable, and wisdom belongs to the order of *frui*. If the three divine Persons are the supreme object of man's fruition, wisdom is so to speak a foretaste of the Trinity. But it is clear that the wisdom of which St. Augustine speaks is first and foremost the wisdom of grace. The wisdom of this world is overcome, and subordinate to it. And it is a victory without loss or harm, either for the conqueror or for the conquered, because in ridding itself of the mixtures of syncretism and pride, the wisdom of the philosophers recovers its true nature and *its own* truth.

### I I I

Thus, if the ancient world appears as the world of the competition of wisdoms, the Christian world will appear as the world of synthesis and hierarchy of wisdoms. This order, which is the very order of the soul, is for human beings order par excellence. All other more visible orders, social, political and economic, important though they be in their place, are secondary to it and even depend on it. That is why, in spite of its failings, medieval society was in its way an outstanding success. It knew this order of wisdom.

But we must understand the basic facts. We are not dealing here with a simple and, so to speak, architectural arrangement. In this order everything is movement, life, inspiration. It proceeds from love. "Deep calleth unto deep at the noise of Thy waterspouts." [1] Two deeps call one unto the other and rush one into the other. But it is from on high that all begins.

I spoke just now of a descending movement in connection with the salvation-wisdom of the Old Testament. It is time to call the law of this movement by its proper name. It is the law of the Incarnation. St. Thomas formulates it in a text valid not only for the head but alike for the whole body. "In the mystery of the Incarnation the descent of the divine plenitude into the depths of our human nature matters more than the ascent of human nature toward God." [2]

Thus there is a double movement in the Christian universe. And the movement by which it mounts upward to God is only a consequence of the primary movement by which God descends into it. And the more it opens itself to the movement by

[1] Ps. 42:7.
[2] *Sum Theol.*, iii, 34, I, ad. I.

which God gives Himself, the more is awakened in it the movement by which it gives itself to God. For grace vitalizes and is not, as Luther thought, a mantle thrown over a corpse. Stirred to his depths the creature emerges from sleep and becomes the image of vigilance and activity: in the end, activity par excellence, activity of love and contemplation, and of superabundance. But also, on the way, and as a mean to the end, moral and ascetic activity, practical and militant.

Perhaps we can see here the deepest motive of that historical dynamism which so strangely marks the Christian West, and that efficient energy which, when it has denied its first principle and rule, could only lead to the distraction and destruction of the human being. In any case, as soon as man came to believe that the *second* movement was the *first*, when in the age of anthropocentric humanism, and its practical pelagianism, he forgot that the first initiative in love, as in goodness and in being, comes from God, and behaved as if the progress of the creature was prior to the "descent of the divine plenitude into it," then the Christian world, worked on by the threefold ferment of the Renaissance, of rationalism and of its Calvinist or Jansenist opposite (which, in annihilating man on the side of divine things, exalted him in equal measure on the side of earthly goods), was bound inevitably to dissolve.

But here I want to offer another observation. In the internal life of Christian souls it may happen—for the workings of grace are hidden—that the ascending movement of the creature to God, his effort—and remember it is absolutely required and indispensable—to arrive at spiritual perfection, may hide from one's eyes the descending movement, the self-giving of uncreated love. If this happens there will be a growing discord between the reality of Christian life and the way one is conscious of it, the way one believes it ought to be lived. Religion will become less and less real, appearances will become more important and one will live by them. One will retain one's belief in grace but one will behave as if it were only a façade on a monument, as if, supposing by chance it ceased to operate, things would still hold together without it, with the help of purely human precautionary aids and props. Such epochs work against the grain of grace, and there is no reason to wonder at their ineffectiveness.

The Middle Ages were anything but such an epoch. Their vast human activity, which may perhaps deceive the historian, did not deceive the medievals. They knew that this constructive work only masked an invisible mystery of love and humility. They obeyed the law of the Incarnation, which continued to accomplish its effects within them; they obeyed that folly by which love desires at whatever cost that the divine and the spiritual should descend into the temporal and the human and there take flesh. Medieval Christendom knew that the Word became Flesh, and that the Holy Spirit follows this movement and also descends. It opened out the universe of knowledge to the stream which ran through it from one level to another. And thus it is that this universe came to know the order of wisdom, and saw accomplished in itself, for a while, the peaceful conjuncture and harmony of wisdoms.

According to the doctrine made classical by St. Thomas there are three sorts of wisdom essentially distinct and hierarchically ordered. Infused wisdom or the wisdom of grace, theological wisdom, and metaphysical wisdom.

They differ from one another by their objective light and their formal object. The first has for its own special light the kinship of love with the supernatural. It attains God in an experimental and suprahuman way, in its intimate life and according to its *deitas;* and it attains to created things in so far as they refer to God so known. It is a wisdom of love and of union. As its principles theologians enumerate faith and charity and the gifts of the Holy Spirit acting under God's present inspiration and illumination. And this wisdom knows what it knows according to something that is itself divine, according to the very gift that God makes of Himself to the soul, according to the effusion of which I have already spoken, according to the descending movement in us of divine plenitude. Hence though it is the supreme actuation and activity of the soul, it consists first of all in receiving, in yielding to an all powerful influx. If it is completely enveloped in God, and is superior to concepts and images, it is truly mystical contemplation. Yet being sovereign, it can make use of everything. It may use the treasures of the imagination and of creative intuition, and the stammerings of poetry: and then it sings with David. Or it may make use of the ideas and treasures of the intelligence and the stammerings of the philosophers: and then it teaches with St. Augustine.

The second form of wisdom is theological wisdom. Its special light is the communication of the knowledge which God has of Himself, which is made to us by revelation, and which offers to unfold its content to the effort of our intellect. In a human and discursive way it knows God in His intimate life and in His divinity, and it knows created things in their relation to God so known. This is a wisdom of faith and reason, of faith making use of reason. It is natural in the sense that it proceeds according to human logic and is constituted thanks to the labor and equipment of reason; it is supernatural in its roots because it exists and lives only through faith. Thus in it the movement of divine descent and communication must be considered primarily, but not exclusively. In addition, progressive work and human toil and technique have their place. This wisdom is divine in its object and suited by its mode to our natural manner of working. The bread it provides is gained with the sweat of our brow. Some people are impatient of it because they know and prefer the peace of divine things, others because they do not like work and are lazy.

Metaphysical wisdom has for its own special light the intelligibility of Being perceived for its own sake (i.e. without intrinsic reference to a construction in the imagination or a sense experience), at the highest degree of abstractive intuition. Its formal object is not God in His *deitas*, but Being in its own proper mystery, *ens secundum quod ens*. It knows God only as the cause of Being. It is a rational wisdom, and is natural in its essence. It is wholly resolved in natural and rational evidence. In itself it does not imply the divine communication and supernatural descent of the Godhead of which I have spoken, but only natural communication and that initial creative generosity, by which the supreme Intelligence enlightens every man coming into this world. It is entirely contained within the order of the progressive movement of human reason toward the supreme truths which are accessible to it of themselves and by rights.

By virtue of a dynamism consubstantial with the spirit, and which was never lived more intensely than by St. Thomas Aquinas, wisdom of lower rank aspires of itself to the higher wisdom. Not that it is by itself impotent with regard to its particular object, which would be absurd, but because the better it reaches its object, the more this object awakens the desire for a higher form of knowledge and creates a void which this form of wisdom is incapable of filling. It does not aspire thus to a higher form of wisdom because it knows its own object wrongly, nor does it do so according to the measure of its incompetence. On the contrary, the reason is rather that it knows its object well; and it aspires according to the measure of this very knowledge. Thus, the more it drinks, the more it thirsts. The more metaphysical wisdom knows Being, the more it would like to see the cause of Being, and in expectancy to pass beyond rational discourse, and even within the discoursing order itself, to keep at the highest point of its spiritual domain (of which it knows the gods are jealous) of definite data and absolutely certain landmarks, points of crystallization more incontestable and more stimulating than those which the senses furnish to physical science. Theology will supply them. The more theology knows God from afar, the more it would like to know Him through experience. The more mystical wisdom knows God through experience, the more it aspires to the vision of Him. And it is always the wisdom of the higher degree which gives the soul what the wisdom of the lower degree caused it to desire . . .

But how are these desires fulfilled if not by the vivifying gift which overflows from the Pure Act? Not only does He fulfill them, but He enlarges their scope and vivifies them ceaselessly. In any case it is clear that the more the soul welcomes this vivifying gift, the more there awaken in its depths the energies by which this soul can mount toward it. Thus theology is activated by contemplation and metaphysics by theology.

And this is not a violent or despotic rule, but a natural and spontaneous one, like that of the tides and the seasons.

At this price only, with this condition *sine qua non*, order and harmony, unity of life, force and suppleness are maintained in the spiritual universe between the three concurrent and synergic wisdoms. The spiritual unity that medieval Christendom knew was made possible only because and in so far as medieval Christendom understood (as it sang in its hymns to the Holy Spirit) that nothing in us is purified or strengthened or made more supple in any permanent way if the Supreme Giver does not make firm and strong the frailties of our being.

I have spoken of the harmony of the various sorts of wisdom. But there is need to talk, too, of the harmony between wisdom and science or the special sciences, as this harmony was conceived by the Christian Middle Ages. It is important to point out how the activation of reason in the Christian regime, the scientific traditions of the Greeks and Arabs, the discipline and objectivity of scholasticism, and the deep realism of the Christian soul with its characteristic inclination to come to terms of brotherhood with created nature, all combined to arouse a powerful scientific urge from which the modern era was to profit.

Notice the significant delay which caused this urge to be manifested most visibly at the moment when medieval wisdom was beginning to decline and nominalism was becoming stronger. In truth, modern science was opened up not only by empiricist-mathematicians like Roger Bacon and eclectics like the fourteenth-Century doctors of Paris, but also by theologians like Albert the Great. But still, in a general way wisdom showed at that time a spirit of imperialism, and pressed its yoke too heavily on science—a mistake for which it was to pay dearly. It loved science and it had an inquisitive spirit. But it made science work in the livery of philosophy and believed, alas! in Aristotle's mechanics as much as in his metaphysics. If philosophy suffered as a result of this state of affairs, science suffered much more. And science could only reap its harvest in the field of experience when it had removed and smashed the marble slabs on Aristotle's tomb.

At the same time it is worth asking whether the technical poverty of the Middle Ages did not help to preserve its spiritual hierarchies against danger and temptation. For medieval man was as frail and ambitious as we are. Unable even to dream of reigning in godlike fashion over external nature with the help of mathematical science, because of his lack of means, he found it easier to keep his soul uplifted toward eternal things. . . .

## IV

It is from the sixteenth Century onwards that we get the reversal which is characteristic of the modern world. The intellectual order of the Middle Ages was broken up. The modern world has not been a world of harmony between forms of wisdom, but one of conflict between wisdom and the sciences, and it has seen the victory of science over wisdom.

The order of medieval thought was not achieved without struggle and conflict, without discord and contrast. It was constantly threatened from without, and only achieved historical realization in a precarious way. From the thirteenth Century onwards it was shaken by a violent crisis, the Averroist crisis— which still continues today. Averroism really meant an effort to separate philosophical wisdom from theological wisdom. It tried to tear it away from the synergic movement from above, of which I have spoken, and to set it up in perfect isolation. It thus cut man into two parts, one being man according to pure nature, with his philosophic wisdom: the other being man according to grace and faith, with his theological or even mystical wisdom. The myth of the two truths—and it is really a myth, is an adequate symbol of this duplication.

This effort at separation was centered on metaphysics. It failed, for a time, as is well known, thanks to St. Thomas. But the drama was more violent and the action of Siger de Brabant was of deeper significance than is usually imagined. Etienne Gilson recently pointed out the theological-political Averroism of Dante's *De Monarchia*. The revival of Averroism in the sixteenth Century was a cause which prepared for quite another revolution.

By this I mean the Cartesian revolution. I have spoken of it so often that I will mention it only very briefly here. The Cartesian revolution also derives from an effort to separate philosophical wisdom from theological wisdom. But this effort was centered on physics rather than on metaphysics, and it succeeded.

As I have tried to show elsewhere [1] Descartes' achievement, whatever may have been his personal intention, was to deny the possibility of theology as a science or as a way of knowledge. Without such a denial the separation I have spoken of would have been impossible. Strictly speaking Descartes deposed wisdom—and the result, if what I have said concerning the dynamism of Christian thought is accurate, could not fail to have an immense effect on philosophy itself.

Henceforward philosophy became separated from the stream of truth and spirituality which came down to it from the heights of the soul. And its own proper order was reversed. It became, as Descartes said, "practical"; and its goal was to make us "masters and owners of nature." Metaphysics ceased to be a summit and became a beginning: and this obliged philosophers after Descartes to proceed in angelic fashion, beginning with God and with thought. And why, and with what object? So as to found physics, science and the mathematical possession of nature.

In this way everything is at once turned upside down and pulled to pieces. There is no longer any vital ascending order in the three wisdoms: and as the two highest ones are no longer forms of knowledge, how can they remain forms of wisdom? The name of wisdom can only properly be applied to philosophy. And the internal order of philosophy is turned upside down in a similar way. Metaphysics grows in ambition, takes the place of Theology, installs itself *a priori* in the heaven of pure intelligibility, even of the intelligible in Pure Act. But at the same time it diminishes in strength, it is ordered toward science, and (without being conscious of it) constructs its vast arbitrary systems in dependence on the positive science of a period, and its passing states. Science is the real winner. That

[1] *Le Songe de Descartes*, Paris, Correa, 1932.

philosophical wisdom which believes it is supreme has already been beaten.

Also, the success of the Cartesian revolution was the expression of a great movement not only of human intelligence, but also, and primarily, of desire. Science was able to be preponderant over wisdom because generally speaking the classical humanist world was subordinated to created wealth as its final end. And such an event was entirely new in the history of civilized mankind. One and the same desire, one and the same mystical covetousness turned the human heart toward the possession of things by way of material control, and by way of intellectual control. The sense of the value of man's natural energies, even working with poor equipment, gave way to the worship of all-powerful equipment and to a sort of universal gluttony. It is very significant that the reign of a divinized science and the reign of money were rung in at the same moment, at the dawn of the modern world.

So the story continued. Kant had only to deduce the consequences of the Cartesian revolution. Just as Descartes separated philosophy from theology, so Kant separated science from metaphysics. As Descartes denied the possibility of theology as a science, so Kant denied the possibility of metaphysics as a science. And now that metaphysics in its turn was no longer a form of knowledge, how could it be a form of wisdom? It tried to defend itself, without success. After the great effort of German romanticism and idealism and its failure, metaphysics centers upon psychological and moral reflection. There is no longer any metaphysical wisdom.

But Kant still believed in a philosophy of nature, which was identified in his mind with Newtonian physics. Can we take this as a form of wisdom?

Tradition teaches that the philosophy of nature is a form or aspect of wisdom, wisdom *secundum quid* or in a given order. For the moderns of the classical period the philosophy of nature was one and the same as the mathematical knowledge of nature, as Cartesian and Newtonian science. At the end of the eighteenth Century and during the first three quarters of the nineteenth Century it was believed that science itself was wisdom—science as the science of phenomena and factual detail, the science which counts the pebbles in the torrent. The age of Auguste Comte and of Herbert Spencer sought wisdom in science.

But this illusion was soon dissipated. Mathematics has devoured every trace of philosophy that remained in the structure of science. The mathematical and empirical elements have driven out ontology. Thus science (in so far as it is distinguished from philosophy) is tending more and more perfectly to its pure type, which implies essentially that it is *not* a form of wisdom. It implies that in the very measure in which it constitutes an autonomous universe of explanation, a conceptual symbolization which saves sensible appearances: and though it tends wholly towards the real and attains the real, it does so in an enigmatic way and in the half-light of the *ens rationis* founded *in re*. (By *ens rationis* we mean an ideal entity which is constructed by the mind and which cannot exist outside of the mind; this ideal entity is founded *in re*, has its ground in reality, when it has been constructed, not in a fancy-framed manner, but in order to know and to express a reality which is by itself too poor in intelligibility,—or, as regards our means of knowing, too hidden and unseizable,—for us to be able to form a proper and direct concept or intellectual image of it. Thus we know the non-being, not by itself, but *ad instar entis*. The myths of the *Timaeus*, the phlogistic of the pre-Lavoisier chemistry, the transfinite number, the space-time of contemporary Einsteinian physics, are *entia rationis* founded *in re*. Thus mathematical thought grasps, by means of symbols, what is ontological and as such directly unseizable by such a thought. The great weapon of conquest of the supreme physical syntheses of our day, and at the same time their definitive giving up of any ontological apprehension of nature, is the systematic use of mathematical ideal entities grounded in reality, that is, in the real measurements and observations which the real events and agents of nature enable us to collect.) But then there is no longer any wisdom whatever, which is not of good omen either for science or for the world.

We are not forgetting that science is good in itself. Like

everything else which derives from spiritual energy in quest of truth, science is naturally sacred: and woe to those who fail to recognize its proper dignity! Every time that the fragile representatives of wisdom thought themselves authorized to despise science and its particular, experiential truths, in the name of a higher truth, they have been severely and rightly punished. But science is like art in this that though both are good in themselves man can put them to bad uses and bad purposes: while in so far as man uses wisdom—and the same is true of virtue—he can only use it for good purposes.

I speak here of that practical function of wisdom which I emphasized at the beginning of the present essay. The absolutely primary division of knowledge being the division between speculative knowledge, for the sake of truth alone, and practical knowledge, for the sake of action, the whole field of practical wisdom, that is, of moral philosophy, is radically distinct in essence from the whole field of speculative wisdom or speculative philosophy: moral philosophy and speculative philosophy are two distinct genera, developing apart from the very start (whereas, for many modern thinkers, morality is only an application of speculative knowledge to human conduct). On the contrary, theological wisdom and the wisdom of grace, being participations of uncreated wisdom, enjoy the transcending unity thereof, and are at once,—formally and eminently—both speculative and practical; moral theology is not a typical knowledge different from speculative theology, both are only two aspects of the same knowledge. Now, in any case, practical wisdom—either moral philosophy, or the moral implications of theology and of mystical wisdom—deals with the ends themselves of human life, and not with certain particular means, as does science. A man who possesses philosophical or theological practical wisdom, that is to say, who has his mind established in truth as regards the ends of human life, can do evil if his will is not straightforward, if he does not possess and use prudence (and charity)—the devil is an expert theologian—; but this man cannot do evil if he uses his wisdom practically, that is, in extending it, thanks to prudence (and charity) up to the point of the concrete action to be accomplished. A man who possesses the wisdom of grace, or rather who is possessed by it, cannot do evil if he uses this wisdom, which, being an experiential knowledge through union with God, supposes charity, and with charity that prudence and those moral virtues which the theologians call "infused," and which are given by grace, together with charity and with the gifts of inspired freedom. Such a spiritual organism cannot be used but for the good. That is why, as Léon Bloy said, "il n' y a qu' une tristesse, c'est de n'être pas des saints." "Amidst all our grief there is only one sadness—not to be saints."

Of course, there is no question of returning to the Middle Ages, and of denying the huge and magnificent development of the sciences during the course of the last centuries. On the contrary, the peculiar problem of the age lying ahead of us will be to reconcile science and wisdom in a vital and spiritual harmony. The very sciences themselves seem to invite the intelligence to take up such a task. Today they are ridding themselves of the remains of a materialist metaphysics which disguised their true features, they are calling out for a philosophy of nature. And the admirable renewal of contemporary physics gives to the scientist a sense of the mystery which is stammered by the atom and by the universe. Evidence of that is to be found in the books of the great physicists of our day. They are looking anew at the "mysterious universe" as at an immensity of inexhaustible being, of hidden and swarming spontaneity, of intercrossed energies arising and dying by turns, of infinite, fortuitous and unforeseeable events, an immense republic of activities which moves as a whole and changes in time, which really has a history, an evolution, a destiny, and which foils all the representations of our imagination and breaks down all the frameworks of mechanistic reasoning. It is highly noticeable that in proportion as modern physics must have recourse to a more and more elaborated and extensive mathematical symbolization, at the same time it longs for the cosmos in its most intimate, substantial and qualitative reality,—a longing which gives birth to inevitably disappointing attempts at interpreting physico-mathematical science in terms of natural philosophy, and which can be satisfied only by a genuine philosophy of nature. Science inspires the scientist with a thirst for the mystery of the cosmos which is his true heuristic stimulus, and which, if its real nature were revealed to him, would appear to him as an ontological thirst; yet for all this, with the aid of science alone, the scientist cannot arrive at an ontological knowledge of nature.

The condition of such a work of reconciliation is in my opinion the establishment of the critique of knowledge in an entirely new spirit, in a truly realist and metaphysical spirit. With such an approach it will be possible to distinguish, in the depths of the spirit, the specifically and hierarchically distinct degrees of knowledge, and show that they correspond to primal types of explanation which cannot be substituted one for another. It will become apparent that one selfsame urge, which, though it is transformed on one plane and another, is never other than the urge of the spirit in quest of Being, traverses these heterogeneous zones of knowledge, from the humblest laboratory experiment to the speculations of the metaphysician and the theologian—and even further, to the supra-rational experience and the grace-endowed wisdom of the mystics.

Thus the sciences and philosophy will no longer be as they were so often in the Middle Ages, in a position of subservience to theology. The full and effective recognition of their autonomy is a precious historical gain made by the efforts of recent centuries. It is an established thing. But at the same time this recognition of the autonomy of science will also involve a recognition of its just place as regards the order of values of the higher forms, that is of the sapiential forms, of knowledge.

# NO RETREAT FROM REASON

## *by* Alfred E. Cohn

IF FREE MEN are to survive in a free society a retreat from reason is unthinkable. Only if free societies cease to exist, can the use of reason be abandoned. The choice, freedom or no freedom, is fundamental and anterior, and depends on what kind of life, in what kind of society, we choose to create. The choice cannot be made decently without experience—our own or that of others. In that background we exercise our choice. Nor can a choice be made successfully without the use of those powers given to us by nature. If we do not possess these powers the retreat from reason is not a choice but a necessity. One hundred and fifty years of history must have assured us that we can manage—that in some measure our abilities are equal to the demands on them—not without difficulty, not without danger. But danger is inescapable; it is the price of free choice, the price of reason.

I propose to argue that to reason it is essential to know what we are to reason about, that the only thing about which we can reason is this world, that after reason comes action—to go along with reason; or to retreat. I propose to examine the meaning of four words—reason, science, civilization, society. We are experienced enough to know that no word has the same meaning for all men. We must examine the meaning, therefore, of these words. I have chosen them because they symbolize, it seems, the storm centers about which the very proposal to retreat from reason rotates. Only free men, after they have faced the realities implicit in these meanings, can choose how to act. The misuse of that opportunity, you must be acutely aware, may turn into disaster.

Reason itself is, it is unnecessary to insist, merely a function of the mind. The use which is made of this instrument

97

gives us no assurance that the result will constitute correct judgment or indeed only correct judgment. Reason is solely a technique for examining situations and ideas, of attempting to estimate aspects concerning them such as their inner consistency and their cogency. Reason itself does not choose the premises from which an argument flows. It attempts to see though that the flow makes sense. The premises of any society are the assumptions, the axioms, the postulates which underlie all our arrangements—derived in the first instance from the recollection of experience.

Because I am a medical scientist you will expect, correctly, that I shall be arguing for the positive value of science or at least for the value of its outlook and its method. But life is a whole. It is the sum of all the currents of our interests; these run through it, sometimes parallel, sometimes at angles. We do not lead scientific lives, and then social lives, and then economic lives and then political lives. We lead life as a whole, all these lives at the same time; if not, we lead it in such a way that life becomes confused and unbalanced. We cannot permit a minor current to stand in the place of the whole stream. Science must fit into life.

If you read what is being written in increasing volume about how science is not doing enough to make available for everyone the social goods which it contributes, and read also about how many of its discoveries and advances turn out to be destructive to the very existence of human society, you must appreciate what is meant by making science fit into the whole pattern or scheme of life. The dangers into which science has been running society have caused thoughtful people, including scientists, to take alarm. How great a place science has come to occupy in communal life cannot escape anyone's observation. For example a knowledge of the intricate constitution of protein molecules will alter, sooner or later, more profoundly even than rayon has done, the entire silk industry and the lives of the great variety of persons on two continents at least, dependent upon it—from growers of silk worm cocoons to manufacturers and distributors of silk fabrics. Is this result the consequence of the application of a single simple scientific principle or scientific discovery? By no means. The final stage was taken by Carruthers in utilizing certain chemical properties of certain protein molecules. But the idea that that could be done rested on other investigations—painstaking and very time-consuming earlier discoveries of the arrangements and qualities of the constituent molecules with techniques like X-rays and the analysis of the structure of crystals. In the production of a pair of silk stockings, themselves wanted for intricate emotional and esthetic reasons, lie interconnected the lives of men, women and children, devoted to purposes apparently, but only apparently, as unconnected as seem to be the lives of physicists, chemists, agriculturists, manufacturers, financiers, builders, stevedores, sailors, real estate operators, and locomotive engineers. Where the work of a scientist, no matter how pure, ends, from the point of view of a society in which he flourishes, is a problem by no means simple to define. If the end result of the process, possessing a pair of silk stockings, were decided to be too unsubstantial a good to warrant waging a war, where, in the course of the very long train of events from chemist to manufacturer, is it possible to call a halt? Stop it at the level of research in protein chemistry, a level where you deal with relatively a simple organization of things, and you interfere with advances in knowledge issuing in improvements in genetics, in the manufacture of countless articles which have a use in peaceful pursuits—the making of foods, of clothing, of glassware, of drugs.

Obviously, scientists do not live unto themselves alone. Being parts of Society, every act of theirs is reflected somehow in the course of the lives of other men. Desirable as it may be to put brakes on any of the processes of the living social organism, associations for the advancement of science seem likely to encounter difficulties almost insurmountable in separating what they decide to regard as socially desirable from things socially hostile. Difficult as the separation undoubtedly is, no one can look upon the chance of failure with equanimity. I mean to return to a further consideration of this problem. Science and scientists are embedded inextricably and very naturally and desirably in the matrix of the whole of our Society.

I am taking the view that the ties which bind science to life are inescapable and the influences which life exerts on scientists, determining.

Two views have been taken of the interrelation of science and Society. The older view was held without challenge almost to our own day. It was the common impression that novelty in thought, invention in technology, discovery in science, depended on the initiative and thinking of private scholars. Unlike artists they had no private patrons—they performed what they were driven to perform in institutions of learning or, presumably, with resources of their own. Sight should not be lost though, of the opportunities and facilities placed at their disposal by the Academies and Learned Societies. These were fostered by rulers and the rich and powerful beginning in Florence with the Accademia del Cimento (1657-1667) as is so admirably narrated by Martha Ornstein (in *The Role of Scientific Societies in the Seventeenth Century*). To a large extent they may be regarded as having been private scholars. With few exceptions that day is all but gone. What they did, so ran the general belief, contributed somehow to the development of the social structure. The result was an aid to what was designated as progress. Because what they did seemed to make sense, in that one step led to another, logic, whatever that is, was supposed as a thread to run through their acts. It was also believed, no doubt more or less unconsciously, that what was contributed was motivated toward realizing what Aristotle would have called a final cause—an objective toward which, in the words of *In Memoriam*, "all creation moved."

In the absence of any other formulation, no one troubled particularly to explain how so random an attempt, or better no attempt, at orderliness was to achieve an unpremeditated desired end. The system seemed to work though there was no pattern to show how it did so—it required no one's thoughtful attention, it was a part, unrecognized and not understood, of the system of *laissez faire*.

It is well known that under many circumstances, in many environments, there are spirits who regard themselves as wholly free to think what they please, to pursue what interests them, to believe that a new direction of thought is, or can be, of their own making. This view is part of the conventional idea of the habit of genius. Genius works, not by passing stepwise slowly and painfully from point to point but by great leaps from lofty crag to lofty crag—without signposts, without evidence, without intervening stages but under the influence of what is called, roughly, intuition, itself a function, if it exists at all, vaguely understood. In point of fact in the evolution of ideas steps are taken but they are rather of a different nature, small though radical, such as Einstein described as involving the differences between Aristotle and Galilei regarding the nature of motion. Genius in short, at least in the more or less popular view, is a possession that permits sudden overturns in conception, or revealing expressions, in extraordinary form possessing extraordinary content. Newton and Shakespeare are our outstanding examples.

I think there can be no doubt—at least there is no reason for entering a discussion—that men can be wholly unconscious of any motive driving them to their acts outside their own volition. That, as I have said, is the traditional view. As a view, it has scarcely been contested until our own time. But recently, at the Second International Congress on the History of Science and Technology in London, in 1931, another view was offered by a Russian scholar interested in the history of science and the history of scientific ideas. His is an arresting notion. Serious students have not dismissed it. So weighty a scientific journal as *Nature* has devoted space to its analysis. Volumes on science, both natural and political, have since been published which profess to have been influenced by Professor Hessen's contention. More recently, in 1937, G. N. Clark, an Oxford scholar, reviewed Hessen's argument. He found in it, I think, no essential fault. He discovered errors in detail which cannot be regarded as seriously damaging. He has taken too narrow a view, however, of what is meant by the interaction of social influences and science. He has divorced more sharply than seems possible, personal motive from social motive, and economic motive from the totality of social interest and necessity. Hessen was analyzing the background and development of the thought of Isaac Newton. The correctness of all the details of the analysis need not concern us but for the purpose of this argument his general insight concerning the dependence of originality, even of men of genius, on the influence of the past and knowledge of the present is illuminating. The view is that Newton's interest in such problems as the general law of attraction, the tides, determining longitude, a lunar theory, in gravitation, were no accident, but had their origin in compelling contemporary requirements, such as finding one's position at sea and in such other subjects as warfare and especially ballistics. Ballistics was important in the study of the trajectory of cannon balls. And cannon balls were important as a means of helping on the political and economic interests of the rapidly growing British empire. The degree of certainty with which it is possible to derive Newton's interest in this fashion is relatively unimportant, but of this one can be certain. However unformed the motives may have been and however inchoate the accumulations of natural knowledge, search for such knowledge was regarded as urgent. For this, founding the Royal Society, devoted to fostering advance in natural knowledge is good evidence. There was little doubt in the minds of the Fellows or in that of the British Government which gave the Society its charter in 1662, that its deliberations whether of pure or applied science were destined to give the commerce of Great Britain an advantage in the struggle for power in which the nation was already engaged. I can quote an observation of Bishop Sprat, the earliest historian of the Royal Society, to this end:

By their *naturalizing* Men of all Countries, they have laid the Beginnings of many great Advantages for the future. For by this Means, they will be able to settle a *constant Intelligence,* throughout all civil Nations, and make the *Royal Society* the general *Bank* and Free-port of the World: A Policy, which whether it would hold good in the *Trade* of *England,* I know not; but sure it will in the *Philosophy.*

Of this Society, Newton was a member.

In our own day there is further evidence for the view that

scientific enterprise is not always a spontaneous movement but often has its origin in the deliberations of thoughtful and far-seeing laymen in efforts to plan for the welfare—and the warfare—of their communities. The many activities of the National Research Council in its several sections—on public health, the physical sciences and the social sciences are evidence how organization is provided on a national scale to substitute for haphazard reliance on genius. The extent to which the great philanthropic foundations propose, foster and support programs of research illustrates the same principle. The almost countless prizes for essays, scholarships and fellowships, research institutes, scientific expeditions, devoted to the advancement of knowledge in directions regarded as wise and desirable by donors and founders are eloquent evidence that the mind, unlike the wind, bloweth not always where it listeth. On the contrary it takes advantage often of the direction given to it by shrewd and far-calculating men.

In two senses, therefore, the very existence of the scientific enterprise suggests that the time is not ripe for retreat. Scientists push forward in purposeful directions and Society, if scientists themselves were not ready to do so, would put pressure on them to see to it that they proceed with furthering the choice to which that Society is committed.

Now the methods of science can easily be misunderstood. I have already explained how the subjects which are investigated originate, how they do not arise simply or solely in the imaginations of scientists. Scientists know more or less the histories of their subjects and receive suggestions there for further researches. Very frequently, especially in these latter days, the requirements of industry or the demands of national defense suggest to them what had best be done. What has surprised historians is how rarely forward steps are taken without traversing intermediate ground. There are, as I have said, no great leaps; there are no great primary originations. Implicit in a current situation is almost always something that has pointed the way, usually only a short way. It is one of the great hazards of the game that rarely, on looking forward, can there be any certainty that the step about to be taken is necessarily correct.

The forward movement in science is usually tentative and is dependent on what is known as the technique of trial and error. In philosophy this is known as empiricism. Knowledge and a sense for possibility, narrowed to probability, are the aspects through which mental processes pass in attaining advanced positions. Knowledge and the need for reducing possible courses to probable ones involve the operation of reason—searching, testing, and discarding many methods and finally adopting a likely one. Unless the function of reason were orderly and were capable in some way of running parallel with and, in a sense, of testing its performances against the operations of nature, we might still be in the stage of witchcraft, alchemy, and astrology. In science, what we do in order to succeed must fit somehow into the processes of nature. Reason, the ability to select likely ways of accomplishment, goes a long way toward making possible solutions of value. Looking backward after a successful campaign, the elements which have facilitated the result have the air, even if they are known to have been selected haphazardly, of having fallen inevitably into place, so pat is the design. Unfortunately much of the history of discovery is written as if chance had played a minor role. Actually any candid investigator, who has the ability accurately to recapitulate the course of his thinking—and such men are rare—would confess to how checkered and how fortunate, how lucky, his course had been. To what extent reason takes part in this process is far from certain. It operates on proof. Experience is necessary. But experience may not be able to suggest what plan, in reason, must necessarily be followed. For this, the ways of nature are far too subtle. What can be asserted is that whatever is done, will subsequently conform to reasonable process.

I want to return to the phrase I regard as central to this discussion: reason is the operation which issues in choice—choice being witness that we have the opportunity and the obligation to behave as men who have and must shoulder responsibility. In this light I want next to examine the meaning of the word "civilization." In these days we are being told that this is something we are on the verge of losing—as if it were a substance, some concrete thing which exists in its own right, in a recognizable form, of which we are presumably actually possessed. But whether we have it or not, it is necessary to discover and to describe what the order is of the thing we hold so precious. The word is used to connote many situations—ancient and modern, Oriental and Western, European and American, Baltic and Mediterranean, Greek, Roman and medieval, Christian, Hebrew and Pagan. These words all denote civilizations. When we speak of losing our own, is it any of these we are losing, one or all or none, but instead something peculiar to ourselves, the product of our own manufacture? Is a civilization something which follows an already existing pattern, or a series of patterns, or is it an agglomeration, an accumulation, a deposit, fortuitous, unpremeditated, amorphous, like a paleolithic kitchen midden? Or is it just born, born spontaneously, or something that grows, or something that like one's clothes is made to suit—either a time, or a nation, or a people, or a climate? How do we recognize whether somewhere, at some time, there is or has been such a contrivance? Toynbee has been in process of writing thirteen volumes in which are to be accumulated specimens to which this word can be applied. Toynbee's is a very ingenious notion. If you can accumulate enough specimens you can examine them at leisure to study their construction and to see whether they contain elements common to them all. If you find a common thread you have a guide to their nature. You can then learn, perhaps, whether there is a course all of them follow, discover the respects in which they resemble one another and distinguish wherein they differ. To assemble the specimens means, of course, that a way exists of identifying them. That means, no doubt, possessing rough preliminary specifications to which all of them conform. To find the specimens is itself an exciting adventure as anyone who has entered upon it knows to his delight. To know that there are many has this importance—it assures us that we too can have one suited to our needs—that there is no ironclad inevitability about our own. Toynbee is not the only modern historian who has entertained himself with this fascinating search. Spengler's study suggests a related conception.

Whether there is an historical process and what is the nature of its mechanism has often enough been the subject of vigorous and penetrating discussion. Its mechanism is far from having always been regarded as identical. For some thinkers a civilization is something like a play in five acts, having a beginning and a middle and an end. With the last act the play ends. There is no provision for a next play. There may not even be a next play. For others, it has no end but passes to and fro from the rule of the many to the rule of the few. Sometimes a simple but important modification is introduced which transforms the circular conception into a spiral—ever on a rising incline, because time enters the picture as an inescapable element. In this plan too, there is a system of returns to points resembling the earlier positions. In the age of reason, in the 18th Century, quite naturally, the idea dawned that history could describe a course of continuous more or less uninterrupted progress. It was Professor J. B. Bury who called attention to the *Observations on the Continuous Progress of Universal Reason* which the Abbé de Saint-Pierre published in 1737. That was the first time, Bury tells us, that "the vista of an immensely long progressive life" was placed "in front of humanity." But it was far from the last. In the past century, both in Europe and in America, almost everyone was immersed in ideas originating in the doctrine of evolution. We were persuaded that civilization is a continuous process, passing onward from stage to stage, losing nothing, every discovery and every conception being added to all the preceding ones with the hope that, whatever the current vicissitudes, we were becoming better and better. We were so convinced that this was so we ceased even to trouble to inquire whether we might not be mistaken. We were convinced. We went so far as to omit teaching the history of the struggle for the attainment of freedom. We took it for granted. We needed no further persuasion that we were in fact becoming better and better. I remember, as a small boy, to have been vastly comforted because I heard my father confide to one of his friends that he thought on the whole the world was getting better. We were forgetting to ask, "Better than what?" or "Better toward what end?" Quite obviously toward what end might make a difference; better at an insight into the nature of God; or better in a knowledge of the liberal arts; or better in the use of the materials which the operation of the scientific process puts into our hands. We should be asking, "Better than what?" Better than a civilized Athenian of the 4th Century? We are in no doubt now whether the successors of the Greeks, in the German woods, say in the 4th Century of this era, were superior to their Greek predecessors. We no longer agree with Rousseau. The Golden Age, even if it does not lie ahead, certainly does not lie behind us.

What else can all of this mean than that the conception, civilization, is not a definitive arrangement, cut to a predetermined pattern, valid for all time, to be taken down from the shelf of history, to be fitted together, to be applied and lived whenever we choose to live it. There is nothing it seems that can, offhand, be called civilization, to be gained or lost, in some arbitrary way. It is more likely that a civilization is life in being, constantly becoming, and ultimately forming a structure with characteristic local features. The pattern arises under circumstances into the conditioning of which we need not now inquire, except that we know that its being our own, made by us and suiting our tastes and our nature, decides us in our loyalty to it. In the United States we have relatively little difficulty in identifying its elements. There were Greek elements and Roman elements. There is a powerful element derived from 17th Century England, especially the scene of religious, political and economic wars, inhospitable to persons of dissident religious faiths. Dissenters, many of them, emigrated, preferring life on an untrammeled and politically free continent, by good fortune recently discovered and opened for settlement. Out of that episode grew tolerance. The 18th Century contributed still another element. Facts and theories of politics and economics developed in a direction to make possible a fresh choice to those to whom the exercise of free will and the opportunity for free choice had become not only congenial but necessary. When all of this had been assimilated, more or less, what we call our civilization started off in a series of revolutions both here and abroad. Fresh choices were made. Men asserted opposition to ways of life habitual to Europe but becoming uncongenial. They initiated their new governments with declarations in which the words life, liberty and the pursuit of happiness appeared; or their French equivalent liberty, equality and fraternity. The former was our Declaration of Independence. Then came the first amendments to our Constitution. We now know such pronouncements as bills of rights. They declare the right and the wisdom of withdrawal from ancient and outworn ways and the adoption of new ones —not wholly new as those who recall the Annapolis and other spirited and learned debates of that day remember. They established the framework within which the first century and a half of the history of the United States evolved. The choices, the precise forms, that were offered to the citizens of the late 18th Century and the early 19th, were not simple, even if they were not new. Plutocracy, oligarchy, democracy, even monarchy were advocated and carefully examined as the Jefferson-Hamilton controversies and the papers in the Federalist amply demonstrate. As the century wore on, the interests of industry as against those of agriculture became intensified and were ever more fiercely asserted until there was no escape from or, to put the issue from the point of view I am urging, there remained no other *choice* except civil war. It is an important speculation whether an act like the Wages and Hours Bill, if enacted in the year 1850, might not have provided a technique in the domain of reason for avoiding that conflict. We have chosen now to enact that Bill with the ultimate, perhaps unexpressed intention, of forestalling a comparable controversy and of solving an issue which involves the economic future of the country. What it is important to understand is that within the framework of our basic beliefs, reason and, therefore, choice can enter into our decisions. The vehicles are education, the ballot, legislation, administration, and the courts.

Meanwhile industrial organization instead of remaining simple has become ever more complex. From being small it has become great, from having grown powerful, it came in the time of Theodore Roosevelt, to dominate government. Against this power, the natural reaction has been, through organization, increase in counter power of workers and smaller people on farms and in towns. Government itself has developed techniques to meet these issues until it has become necessary to look forward to a time when choice is removed from the simple direct volition of the many, the individual citizens, to a concentration of their wishes expressed through their own large and powerful organizations.

Because these issues are great they do not become less grave. They are grave because they are still in the region where decision is possible or where we must behave as if this were still the case. How they are decided affects the well-being of every citizen. To retreat, under these circumstances, from the effort at understanding the argument through becoming acquainted with the relevant factors involved in a situation which is intricate but not too intricate to be understood, is to sell one's birthright. The issues are grave, but they need not be beyond, indeed I think they can be brought within, the comprehension of the average citizen. He must take part in the debate, learning the nature of the issues. If he neglects engaging in it, he contributes conceivably to his own undoing. He must not complain if advocates of a program or of a solution place their views before him in a form calculated to obscure his vision, in order to win his approval. We need to become fully instructed in the form of debate. We need to learn the *meaning* of the arguments that are used. We need to inquire about the consequences of the possible decisions. Greek sophists have explained what an advocate in a debate must plead and how an opponent must meet his attack. The facts must become known. The arguments of both sides must insist on whether a statement based on the facts is probable. But to be vigilant about the form of the debate is not enough. More, much more is needed. Among the things that men say, wheat must be separated from chaff. We must be prepared to understand the meaning of plans and of arguments. If you are told a thing is "good," you must ask "good for what?" If you are told the assertion of individual rights leads to fascism, you must be very certain what the exercise of individual rights implies, you must know precisely what this particular advocate means by fascism, whether it is rule by the few or rule by the many, and if by the few, whether they be rich or poor and in whose interest they wish to rule, in yours or in theirs. You must be certain concerning your interests. You must know whether the two are identical. If you are told rule must be exercised for the good of the nation, you are entitled to ask what is meant by the nation and what role you play within its structure. If you are invited to wage war, your thinking and your training should have prepared you to inquire to what end that war is to be waged. Is it to ward off an enemy, or to capture another people to enslave them, or to capture a market; is it to defend the exercise of your beliefs or to impose your belief on other people? Designing men attempt to confuse our counsels. But we can be certain of this, unless we have a plan of life, unless we have decided on our objective, unless we understand how our choice is likely to operate, unless we perceive as clearly as may be, whether a procedure will accomplish our aim, wariness and further inquiry are necessary. We have for example, for very good and sufficient reason, come to believe we wish the way of our lives to be the ways of freedom. We have come to rest our faith in the belief that the best way to maintain freedom for individuals is by the use of the ballot, by the organization of great political parties. We may have perceived that a multiplicity of parties, though certain ends are served, such as a more exact expression on the part of a few of their desires, has worked abroad in such a way as to confuse the presentation and deliberations of major issues, and has worked in the end to the undoing of orderly democratic procedure and of the attainment of desirable democratic ends. Competent critics declare that the techniques of proportional representation, good as it may be for some purposes, worked in Germany under the Weimar Constitution, in so far as an administrative instrument can be regarded as contributing to the sequel, to the destruction of the German Republic. Professor Hermens of the Catholic University of America has written powerfully in advocacy of this belief. The use of reason requires an exploration of such an issue. If we are told proportional representation is good, we must ask, let me repeat, "good for what?" If we are told it is good because through its use we can destroy the republic, we may think twice before, in an unguarded manner, we introduce it into the national procedure. It may be necessary to decide whether, in order to secure a desideratum, the price exacted is not placed too high.

And so constituting this civilization there are, it appears, a multiplicity of elements, the accumulations or the deposits of time. In the very language of that civilization may be found a guide to the many peoples who have contributed to its form. Greek, Roman, Hebrew and Arabic are scattered thickly through almost every extended utterance. And so also are ideas, of God, of marriage, of law, of goodness, of tolerance, of freedom, whether of speech, of press, or assembly; of the right of every man to the benefits of the Bill of Rights; of the value of education, to Jefferson most important perhaps of all; of justice, and of how to attain it. Taken in the large, recognizable threads run through its texture and give it cohesion and consistence. In order that the scheme shall work, one without the other may turn out to be impracticable or, perhaps, impossible. Certain ones, the organizers of the Nation chose to write into our Constitution. What has clustered legitimately about it, as its irreducible essence, we in this society call our civilization.

Even so, many men would say, "This is not enough; that is not all." Civilization is something more. What they think should be added is what we perceive as the physical appearance of our world—the way we build our houses, how these are assembled in villages, towns and cities, the fact that we transport our bodies and our goods frequently and rapidly from place to place in trains and in automobiles and in the air. What difference that alone makes will be made dramatically plain on recalling Henry Adams's eloquent description of the state of communication in the United States in the year 1800. Other elements in the appearance, perhaps the surface appearances of our lives, must include electricity and the all but unimaginable uses to which that has been put by applied science and technology. In any modern mechanized farm, if two copper wires were to break, heat would cease to be generated in houses heated with oil-burning furnaces; food would not be cooked because of dependence on electric ranges; at night houses would remain in darkness; if water were pumped with a motor it would be necessary to do without it—without heat, light, cooking, water, ice—all dependent on two copper wires, the playthings of the elements. I need not recapitulate the innumerable ways in which discovery, invention, manufacture of foods, clothing, furniture, have transformed every aspect of our lives. Besides ideas, customs, and behavior, these contributions of pure science and applied science have shaped our existence. All together—food, shelter, clothing, beliefs, and conduct are inextricably interwoven. They fit each other as pebbles come to be faceted by constant intimacy, by friction, by wearing away, by mutual adaptation.

Now these are not the elements which every civilization exhibits. This scheme may have cohesion, may be consistent, and its elements may appear to be indissolubly assembled. But it is only one of the forms with which we are familiar even in our day. It is not an inalienable possession—this civilization of ours. We may lose it. Some say we should thereby recapture our own soul. But if we lose it, must we lose it in whole or can it be abandoned in part—can we decide to modify it by casting out spurious elements, by limiting the exercise of harmful mechanical or scientific processes, by modifying the law or the Constitution? What it is essential to comprehend is that our civilization has a shape, that no matter what the external, no matter what the environmental compulsions, we, consciously and unconsciously both, gave it that shape—and in its essence gave it that shape in our ancient history, in the 18th and again in the 19th Centuries, undoubtedly in certain of its elements from choice, after due reflection and extended debate. We made it, and so it can be unmade. If we are driven to undertake to unmake it, we assume a heavy responsibility. Being man made, in large measure it must be man secured. If eternal vigilance is the price of liberty, it is at least as relevant now, as ever it was, to utter this warning.

Civilizations can have, as is abundantly clear, many complexions. If a civilization is not quite a garment that can willfully be put off, corresponding more or less intimately to the genius of the Society that made it and having appropriateness to its time and place, the Society which has evolved it or which has adopted it and to which it is appropriate has, nevertheless, given to it something individual. In a general way, the English (and the French before Vichy), live under dispensations in many respects similar to our own and yet no one would regard the ways of life of these three communities (they may properly be termed Societies) as being identical. The difference is the measure of their individuality and represents the extent to which it is possible to employ the word "Society." The factors which are involved in establishing the differences depend without doubt on the influence of geography; but beside geography, history plays its own conspicuous role. In a sense, a society documents its individuality in the selection or the rejection of elements of contemporary novelty; it takes what suits it—it rejects the rest.

Now a society, being a collection of human beings, differs from a civilization in the assemblage of manners and customs which that society manifests. A society is that group, originating in a large variety of ways, which manifests those choices as to purpose, function, and law to which I have already referred. Our own Society has deliberately chosen and keeps on choosing as it leaders, Moses and Christ, Plato and Aristotle; Dante and Shakespeare, Shelley and Wordsworth; Galilei and Harvey; Copernicus and Lavoisier; Pasteur and Lister, Faraday and Maxwell and Gibbs; Volta and Edison, Morse and Marconi; Bach and Beethoven, Brahms and Wagner, Giotto, Rembrandt and Michelangelo; Samuel Adams and Patrick Henry; Washington and Jefferson; Madison and Lincoln. What these men thought and did is our civilization. Not so long ago, France, when it was offered a single choice, chose Pasteur. Each society does in this way choose its laws and its heroes. And by their choices are they known.

Our Society, while passing through the crucible of its birth, attained its form through mature deliberation and the sufferings of two wars. The debates before the War of the Revolution, before the adoption of the Constitution, before the Civil War are, as anyone familiar with them knows, as fine a flowering of the function of reason in exploring ways of corporate existence as is to be found in political literature. If ever reason was adopted as a guide to conduct, and if ever reason prevailed in the analysis of a complex social context, it did so here. Its great achievement is that the scheme has worked. From the results of that enterprise retreat is now unthinkable.

A few short years ago the question of retreat was scarcely raised in these United States. More recently on two fronts, on the front of political science and on the front of natural science, defeatist voices have been raised. The suggestion is made that in some manner, not clearly understood, the operations of reason have somehow mystically failed. Men begin to forget that in the 18th Century, when escape from the ancient regime was being planned, the fate of the common man was at least as much debated as it is now and that then, not for the first time, examination of his problems in the light first of sympathetic understanding and then of reason was successfully undertaken. Ever since, in these 150 years, life has been lived under the dispensation then formulated. All this seems in process of being too easily forgotten, of being too lightly brushed aside. We are told democracy is facing failure (1) partly because we cannot control the results of the operation of science, and (2) partly because in the march of economic organization we lack the insight and the power to master our destiny. Being man made in its building, no doubt we can unmake what has been so elaborately constructed.

But why? There is general agreement that what has been achieved has not been equaled either in the standard of general living, in the opportunity for further development, or in the degree, obviously not yet superlative, of satisfactoriness in our intellectual and spiritual lives. How if, in our democratic faith, the method of reason has had this measure of constructive achievement to its credit, can the conclusion be drawn that reason is bankrupt? Study, deep study is on the march. In the various offices of the League of Nations, in the explorations of the Independent Labour Office, in the Commissions of President Hoover, in the investigations of Committees of the Congress, in Great Britain through reports of Royal Commissions, as frank, as fearless, as intelligent efforts to solve social problems in an incredibly complex economic background, have been undertaken as ever in the rough adjustments of Western societies.

And in science, how is retreat possible? The progress onward of science can be likened to the movement of a train of freight cars. Articles of value have for centuries been accepted as cargo. The pressure pump, the magnetic compass, the telescope have all been regarded as articles of value. So have the telegraph, the telephone, the radio, the railways, genetics, bacteria and physiology; rayon, cellulose, electric light and the products of power engineering. Reason, the same reason, has been at work when the use of these agencies turns out to be beneficent as when it has been turned to uses hostile and deadly. When the attempt is made, as has recently been done, to find ways of deflecting discoveries and inventions away from evil uses, it becomes a social responsibility of the first order to gain correct insights into what doing this means. Otherwise there can be no correct decisions.

There is beyond doubt, the possibility of disaster through the misuse of discovery. Scientists, as has been pointed out, are integral parts of our Society. They carry the burden for getting on with the business of accumulating natural knowledge. They do so in large part as social agents, but in part also as citizens. In the interest of the national safety they may omit no act likely to serve the interests of their group. In the interest of national comfort they are not likely to do so. But political arrangement intra- or international is not their primary function. That function is the responsibility of politicians and statesmen. Scientists can go no further, I think, than to point out the consequences of their discoveries. How to use them humanely is not their concern further than it is that of other citizens. Is it not unreasonable to hold them responsible for accomplishing that which they are told off by the rest of Society, their ultimate employers, to devise—for good or evil? Power of decision, in the end, does not rest in their hands. Before interfering with the scientific process, before deciding which of its contributions is harmful, it behooves us to explore the workings of so complex a mechanism, remembering the assumption that we are somehow in control of our destiny. What do we stop, if we stop scientific research?

And by the same token what do we find, if we examine social behavior? It is a subject, the latter, which Shaw analyzed to good purpose in *Arms and the Man.* There is no way decently in which to justify man's inhumanity to man. To curb it, law, in the form of the *Decalogue,* has appeared among us; and persuasion in that of the *Sermon on the Mount,* their predecessors and successors through all time. The reign of conscious effort has, as time goes, been brief—not so brief but that we are already conscious of evil and are setting in motion the agencies of amelioration. To curb seems infinitely preferable to destroying; to correct and modify, as functions of reason, to dispensing with reason. The will to goodness is strong—stronger, I believe than is often recognized and stronger as I think than ever before. The view is general that the same degree of success in social control has not been attained that is so apparent in the control of nature—success of natural science as opposed to social and political science. That judgment is often accepted as self-apparent. But it must be clear that we do not control nature. What we control are a few forces of nature—not the tides, not the winds, not the movement of the crust of the earth. We are a little deceived by our words. In appraising the difference between natural and political science, is it captious to ask for the evidence? To be certain that it is correct, a yardstick is wanted. But where is that yardstick to be found? To be able to measure these two advancing fronts, social and scientific, would be desirable had we proper instruments. Obviously the better a yardstick is made to measure the one, the less likely is its success in measuring the other. Measuring is a function of the thing that is to be measured. Yardsticks are made to measure yards. The mind of man has been powerfully concerned with both fronts. It seems unwise to destroy one because we suspect, correctly or incorrectly, we cannot manage the other—unwise to restrain science until we learn how to restrain men. There is in point of fact social control—in large measure. There is the force of public opinion; orderliness without omnipresent police; control by means of a simple white line drawn down the middle of the road. And in a larger sphere has it not been justly observed that

Peace to the world from ports without a gun

has turned out to be a possibility?

Suppose we decide not to destroy science but to curb it. But how? The belief is widespread that there are two kinds of science, disinterested science and purposeful science. We should without doubt not oppose advance in the disinterested variety. How is this end to be achieved? How has science been made? Nothing affected the thought of the 17th and 18th Centuries like the discovery of the law of gravitation and the laws of motion. On no subject has Voltaire been more eloquent. Nothing seemed more innocent. But if the analysis of Hessen is correct, Galilei's interest, and Newton's, were derived in large part from concern with military affairs, with metals and forces. Science like that grows, as men would now say, out of sin—if war is sin. And to the extent that these laws are the operating cornerstones of all the science that has come afterward, these discoveries have issued again—in sin. All our crimes, all our mechanical civilization, have issued from these innocent calculations. On a lesser level, as much can no doubt be said of every other first-rate scientific speculation. The gas laws are not unrelated to explosion nor the perversion of anthropology to theories of race. Astronomy and explosives, aeronautics and bombing are not far apart.

It is conceivable that protection can be found against misuse. Do we not paint red the wagons that carry explosives? And yet such protection is directed not against the primary activity of research, applied to the analysis of natural phenomena, but to derivatives in positions at the 2nd or 3rd or 4th remove. In spite of such reflections I prefer not to take the defeatist position, not to restrain the urge to discovery. Better management will come, not with applying less reason but with the exercise of more, not with ignoring our problems but with an ever greater effort to solve them.

This Society, at all events, is dedicated to the notion that this civilization, deeply rooted in regard for the common man, developed by experience and achieved through reason operating as social and scientific thought, shall advance to the greater good of man and to the realization of a greater measure of human contentment.

# 3. SCIENCE: ITS MATERIALS, METHODS, ENDS

# THE PURPOSE OF SCIENCE

## *by* Arthur H. Compton

IN NO OTHER part of the world and at no previous time in history has life been so greatly influenced by science and technology as in the United States today. The need for technology is for us only emphasized by war. Our means of living, our amusement, our thinking, and our religion, all are molded by science.

American civilization includes great cities, which need for their existence mechanical transportation, steel rails and girders, electric elevators, refrigeration systems to preserve food, careful sanitation, and control of disease. It embraces great areas of thinly populated farm land which supply the nation with an unparalleled abundance and variety of food. With the help of rapid communication, the government co-ordinates the activities of a widely distributed people, and our continent becomes a national community.

The uniqueness of American technological society was impressed upon me when recently I was speaking on the human effects of science to a group of students in India. I was about to comment upon the applications of science in everyday life, such as the electric light, motor transportation, mechanically woven cloth, scientifically selected seed, inoculation against disease, pasteurized milk, and conversations over the telephone, when I realized that these things were no part of the experience of my listeners. Even in England I found my colleagues dreading the approach of the world of technology, which we have come to take as a part of life. East or west or north or south, the American sees a life less dependent upon technology than his own.

There is no doubt that science and its applications have·supplied real needs. Through their help our average life span has been nearly doubled. We enjoy better food, housing and clothing. We are freed from long hours of physical drudgery. New opportunities for education, amusement, and cultural development abound. "Yesterday my son was married," remarked the foreman of our shop. "With a wife, a car and a radio, what more does a man want?" Thus the American rates high the contributions of science.

Upon our social organization and our cultural life the effect of this technology has been revolutionary. The men and women who live in our cities and farms have become completely dependent upon each other. Each contributes his own share with the efficiency of a specialist, and receives from many others most of the things with which he lives. In prosperous days the resulting life in America is more abundant in material goods than has been the life of any large social group in history. Yet when times are hard, as in older less technical civilizations from time immemorial, unemployed laborers, dispossessed sharecroppers, and bankrupt business men live on the verge of starvation, and curse the technology that has built a world in which their own efforts cannot bring forth the necessities of life.

In factory and in home are those whose monotonous tasks make them feel as cogs in a great machine. Yet the average level of public education by our schools and colleges is rapidly rising. Through magazines, radio, moving pictures, and unprecedented travel by rich and poor, our contacts with the world are greatly multiplied. New professions arise that are based upon science. It becomes profitable as well as satisfying to search for new knowledge, and scientific research becomes our great intellectual quest.

Science thus gives to man three Promethean gifts. First, it supplies more adequate means of living, giving longer, healthier life, and a richer variety of experience. Second, by placing a high premium on expert knowledge and by rewarding more abundantly co-operative effort, it stimulates man's social development. Third, science serves as a vehicle for cultural expression and forces our further moral and religious growth.

The gift of fire was a mixed blessing to man. So also are the gifts of modern science. With new powers war becomes more fearful. Rapid social changes bring maladjustment and misery. Even the anchor of religion is found to drag as the storm of science blows. One is reminded of the legend in which the people complain to Daedalus that the steel sword he has given to King Minas will bring not happiness but strife. Daedalus replies, "I do not care to make man happy, but to make him great." For those who have courage, the new powers thus given by science present a challenge to shape life on a more heroic scale. Here is a vision of a new world which only the brave may enter.

## SCIENCE STIMULATES SOCIAL GROWTH

George Sarton, in his recent book, *Science and the New Humanism*, shows how through the ages man's increasing knowledge of the world has made him develop a distinctive life. Science and its applications, he points out, have made man human.

Note how technology in American society places an unprecedented emphasis upon the value of increased education. The use of steam and electric power has decreased the need for common labor, while growing specialization has increased the need for those who co-ordinate our activities. Thus the slave has been freed, and unskilled labor has been to a large extent unemployed. Skilled labor, however, remains vital to American society for building and operating our machines, and is rewarded with shortened hours and higher pay. Business requires middlemen to handle its varied commerce. Vastly increased numbers of professional men and women have been absorbed in occupations of responsibility which before the era of technology were hardly known. Here we find the engineer, the secretary, the economist, the patent lawyer, the research scientist, and many others. The citizens responsible for planning the work of society have never been so driven by ceaseless demands as in today's America. Reflections of this pressure are to be seen in the multiplication of governmental offices, in the rise of schools of business and public administration, and in the frequency of nervous breakdown among professional men strained beyond endurance. The masters of Society have indeed become the servants of all, in a driven labor that knows no rest. By emphasizing the need for intelligent direction, and reducing the need for unskilled labor, technology is thus spurring Americans of all levels toward an ever higher standard of training and education.

Our European contemporaries have presented cogent arguments to show that the American system of universally available higher education must lead to severe unrest as men and women trained for a life of the intellect find that they must live by their hands. About twenty per cent of our total population of college age are now attending college. Fifty years ago the figure was less than two per cent. It is amazing that these vastly increased numbers are finding the white-collar jobs they seek. In spite of our mass education, unemployment remains less frequent in the professions than in common labor. The European prophets of doom had not counted on the growth of the specialized society based on technology, which has demanded increasing numbers of highly trained men and women as rapidly as our universities have been able to supply them. The result instead of being tragic has been the happy one of giving our citizens an unparalleled opportunity for intellectual growth. Thanks to their more extended education, millions of our citizens are awakening to a new understanding of life's values. Such is the humanizing action of science.

To visualize how our gradually growing knowledge has from the beginning stimulated man's growth, let us imagine the last million years of human history to be compressed into the lifetime of a middle-aged man of fifty. Let us suppose that he is reading this essay on a Saturday evening. It was then as a child that he learned, perhaps from his parents, the use of certain odd-shaped sticks and stones as tools. The meaning of sounds became definite as he learned to talk, and as his vocabulary increased so likewise did the clarity of his thought. By the time he was forty, he had developed the art of skillfully shaping stones to fit his needs. Last year he became an artist, and a few months ago learned to use simplified pictures as symbolic writing. Less than two months ago the Phoenicians introduced to him the alphabet, and soon afterward came the brilliant art and science of ancient Greece. Five weeks ago was the dawn of Christianity and the beginning of the Roman empire. Our reader recalls how a week later Rome fell, hiding for some weeks the values of civilized life. Last Sunday morning, so the report has it, Galileo dropped the heavy and the light cannon balls from the Leaning Tower of Pisa, refuting a proposition of Aristotle and starting the period of modern science. By Wednesday afternoon this had led to building the first practical steam engine, and it was at about this time that the United States came into being. On Thursday the major laws of electromagnetism were being discovered which by last evening had given us the telegraph, the telephone and incandescent electric light. Only last night X-rays were discovered, followed quickly by radium and wireless telegraphy. It was this morning that automobiles came into general use. Air mail began to be carried only at noon today. Popular short wave broadcasts, practical color photography, and fluorescent lighting were unknown until this afternoon.

We were discussing recently the problems faced by the rising generation. My dinner partner remarked that she saw no need for worry on their behalf. "With the introduction of the automobile, the moving picture and the radio it has been during our generation that the great changes have occurred. The rising generation can now use our experience as a reliable guide."

This is comparable with the view of those economists who, noting that no further geographic frontiers exist, are basing their predictions on the hypothesis that our nation has reached a stable economic maturity.

A survey of present technical publications and patent office records shows on the contrary that the rate of growth of our scientific knowledge and of useful inventions is at an all-time high. It is these advances that are responsible for the accelerated social changes exhibited by our quick review of history. If our experience can reliably tell the rising generation anything, it is that they may anticipate an even greater development of technology and corresponding change of social customs.

The knowledge of nature, which from the beginning had been man's gradually but accidentally increasing heritage has now become the conscious objective of alert minds. In the time of Benjamin Franklin, science was the hobby of a few amateurs. Now there are in the United States nearly two thousand research laboratories, equipped with refined apparatus, where thirty thousand highly trained men are striving to enlarge our understanding of the world. It is their new-found knowledge which changes our lives.

## DOES SCIENCE THREATEN HUMAN VALUES?

It is not surprising that those who have known and loved the tradition of classic culture should dread the approach of a technology which threatens the values they have cherished. They see science replacing the human interests present in literature, art and music with technological developments in which the human factor becomes less and less significant. The most fundamental values of morality and religion are ruthlessly shaken, with the implication that their value is negligible. It is just because so many scientific men seem blind to these human difficulties that one feels the greater concern lest in following science mankind may lose its soul.

There is a passage in Plato's *Phaedo* in which Socrates describes his early interest in physics and how he had found that physics fails to account for the important things in life. Thus, he explains, Anaxagoras would say that Socrates sits on his cot waiting to drink the hemlock because of certain tensions of tendons acting on his bones. The true reason is rather because he has been condemned by the people of Athens, and as a man of honor he cannot creep stealthily away. Such moral forces as honor are not to be explained by science; yet these are the forces that shape men's acts. Since it did not meet their human needs, the followers of Socrates and Plato abandoned science, and the study of the truths of nature were forgotten for a thousand years.

For those who know science, its inhumanness is a fiction. We have noted how science is making man develop into a social being. We can now begin to see the cultural expression of this social growth. We look to science to satisfy the human hunger for a better understanding of the world. The civilization which is being built with the tools of science is one which requires man's moral growth. We must recognize with Plato that without a central objective life has lost its meaning. Yet in this age when men throughout the world are trying to formulate a philosophy by which they can live, it is to science that they are turning with confidence in its truth.

## CULTURAL LIFE IN A CHANGING WORLD

"Johnny, is that your 'cello?" Kenneth, who asked the question, was the first playmate our son had found on coming to the new city. "One of the 'cellists in our junior orchestra has graduated to senior high, and we need someone to take his place." Thus Johnny found that after all he wasn't going to miss playing with the school orchestra which he had so enjoyed at home.

Ten years ago we were noting with alarm the elimination of the professional musician by the radio. The musical public was, we were told, degenerating from players to listeners. Now we find millions of Americans for the first time aware of orchestral music. In the shops the demand for violins and flutes and cornets and drums has multiplied. Most of these instruments have gone to the tens of thousands of school orchestras and bands which are giving boys and girls the chance to share in producing harmony. Throughout the country the musical standard is rising. College glee clubs sing better songs. Sound movies and radio programs find they must continually improve their variety. A hundred professional symphony orchestras now play where there were a score.

The example of the school orchestras is typical of the way in which a broader base for the fine arts is being developed among millions in our country. It is not impossible that use of the radio may mark the birth of a new era in American music. In a similar way good color reproductions of the best (and perhaps the worst) paintings have recently become widely available. One might have feared that the opportunity thus afforded for the vicarious enjoyment of great pictures would discourage the amateur painter who sees that he cannot compete with the masters. The director of the Metropolitan Museum of Art tells me, however, that sixty thousand professional artists are now listed in New York City, and that the interest in amateur painting is rapidly increasing. Over the country are to be found likewise camera clubs and photographic exhibits where amateurs vie with each other in finding the most pleasing effects. Thus artistic America as well as musical America is finding its soul in individual expression.

The culture of our scientific era is, it is true, that of a rapidly changing society whose customs and ideas are only partly adapted to the new conditions. For example, I have been living recently in an apartment by which a street car clangs its noisy course. The installation of these cars gave the rapid transportation that made the city possible. Now, however, the demand is insistent that the street cars be replaced by quieter, streamlined buses that will permit conversation by day and sleep by night. Thus the first application of technology was to meet the primary need of transportation, but eventually the refinements come that add to life's enjoyment. As long as growing science brings such rapid changes in our life it is futile to hope to attain an adjustment of the art of living that can compare in refinement with the classic culture initiated by the Greeks and developed in Europe and England through centuries of slow social change. As our knowledge grows, however, we seek to build a greater culture upon a broader, firmer base.

## SCIENCE IN AMERICAN THOUGHT

It is but natural that in a society so profoundly affected by science our intellectual life should likewise be focused in that direction. At Oxford it remains doubtful whether science has yet earned a true place in education. At Chicago, on the other hand, three of the four main divisions of the University are called sciences. A part of this emphasis is indeed ascribable to the need for at least a passing knowledge of science in every profession; but it nevertheless represents truly our educators' judgment of the value of science in enriching life.

To the man of science himself, it is primarily as a method of developing the human spirit that he values his work. In this regard science is to him a truly cultural pursuit. His study affords exercise of imagination and broadening of perspective. Whereas to Plotinus it appeared that, "It is through intuition rather than through reason that we may approach our highest aspirations," the scientist finds that in the discipline of unprejudiced search for truth lies the beginning of wisdom. Thus, in the words of Thomas Huxley:

Science seems to me to teach in the highest and strongest manner the great truth which is embodied in the Christian conception of entire surrender to the will of God. Sit down before a fact as a little child, be prepared to give up every pre-conceived notion, follow humbly wherever and to whatever abysses nature leads, or you shall learn nothing.

To a certain degree this humanizing aspect of science is esoteric, since it can be fully appreciated only by those who have themselves submitted to the discipline required to share in the effort to widen the horizons of knowledge. Certain fields of science, notably astronomy, have, however, enabled amateurs to take part in their enterprise, and anyone can learn to practice a scientific approach to the everyday facts which shape his acts. It is hard to suggest any method more effective in bringing about a widely spread regard for impartial truth than by the growth of such participation in scientific endeavor. Herbert Hoover speaks for American science when he "would strengthen the national fiber by inculcating that veracity of thought which springs alone from the search for truth."

This direct encouragement toward reliance upon tested truth is but one of the moral implications of science. Perhaps more evident in historical perspective is its indirect consequence in the moral growth required by the socialization of man. Just as the automobile demands sobriety, or congested life makes necessary careful sanitation, so the mutual dependence of people in a technological civilization implies consideration of the rights of others. James Breasted has shown how the growth of community life along the Nile stimulated among the Egyptians the "dawn of conscience." Professor Cheney, in his retiring presidential address before the American Historical Association, lists prominently among his "laws" of history the trend toward a greater consideration of one's fellows as society grows more complex. In our American technological society, when each contributes his expert part, our needs are fully met; while hardship comes to all if any fails his share. Thus science and industry are emphasizing as never before the need of the will toward co-operation. This is simply the Christian doctrine of the love of our neighbors as expressed in service.

## SCIENCE DEMANDS RELIGIOUS GROWTH

Both directly and indirectly science also affects religious attitudes. The effect of the impact of modern science on Christian doctrine is an example of a long historical development of religion as influenced by man's growing understanding. Among the more thoughtful members of the American community there appears no longer any serious intellectual conflict between religion and science. Saint Paul has described the religious man as one who "is alive to all true values." By enabling men to see more clearly what these values are and to work for them more effectively, science has, as Dean Inge recently remarked, become an ally of religion. If our young men dream dreams of a greater world they would build, and our old men see visions of a better society, it is largely because of the new powers that science has given. As never before we can share with our Creator the great task of making our planet a fit place for life.

On the other hand, the world of science and technology is one in which an adequate religion is most urgently needed. We have noted above that the great demand of modern life is for adequate guidance in directing the mighty forces at our disposal. Such guidance implies knowledge of the road toward the best. Thus attention to the fundamental problem of ethics is the supreme demand of an age of science. Technology supplies the motive power. Organized industry and government constitute the control and steering mechanism. But who will tell us where to go? In America it is only our religious leaders who have seriously attempted to answer this question.

## THE TRENDS OF SOCIAL EVOLUTION

The changes in man's mode of life which we have been discussing are biologically speaking, an aspect of adaptation to environment. It is, in fact, social evolution. In a short thousand generations man has changed from an individualistic to a social animal, and that change is continuing at an increasing rate. It is thus important to consider what the directions may be along which this evolution will proceed.

We may expect those modifications in our way of life to survive which give strength to the social group. Prominent among these strengthening factors are knowledge and co-operation. Enough has been said regarding the strength that comes through science and technology. The continuous growth of scientific knowledge which Sarton observes throughout human history is thus to be expected from the fundamental principles of evolution. In a highly competitive, war-like world, that society cannot long survive which neglects the truths of science.

Co-ordination of effort is another great requirement of a technological society. We are a group of specialists, and when each man's effort is properly fitted to his neighbor's, our group is tremendously productive of the things we need. But if the co-ordination is broken and the gears of society become enmeshed, its state is chaotic. No longer can the individual support himself, as in a more primitive society, by his own efforts. To a wholly unprecedented degree, society based on technology thus requires co-operation among its members, and cannot tolerate disturbances to its smooth operation.

Here is the practical reason why wars and industrial revolutions are now considered as sins against society. In an earlier era men hailed Alexander or even Napoleon as the great conqueror. A Hitler receives no such world acclaim, for he has disorganized the world. Only within Germany, whose strength he has multiplied by its close unification, is he admired. Thus a more highly co-ordinated and co-operative society is likewise to be considered as an inevitable evolutionary trend.

It is noteworthy also that the conditions have now become such that the larger economic, social and political units are the stronger. Before the period of rapid communication and transportation large units became unstable. As a result of geographic exploration, steam and motor transportation, telegraph and telephone, press, the moving pictures and the radio, we already share each other's lives and obtain our needed supplies from far corners of the globe. Intellectually, science has already made man a citizen of the world. The present turmoil is at least in part ascribable to the need by a technological world for the development of larger economic and political units. We are rapidly moving toward the condition under which the only stable life is that in which the whole planet is a unified community. Probably that condition already exists, but the unification is delayed by traditional boundaries and adherence to the idea of national sovereignty. World government now seems inevitable, and in the not distant future.

Most significant of the factors that give strength to society is, however, a goal worthy of supreme effort. "Without vision the people perish." By inspiring his people with a great objective, Lenin rallied all the Russians to support a communistic world revolution. Hitler makes a sick Germany throb with vitality by the sacrificial call to every man to devote himself to the welfare of the state. Here are unifying religions in action. If there is a fatal weakness in American society it is in our lack of an objective. With our divided counsels, an efficient social evolution will not let us survive in competition with nations or social groups that know where they want to go. Our formal religious organizations offer just such divided counsels. As one who has been actively concerned with efforts to bring amity and understanding among Catholics, Protestants and Jews, I find it easy to become discouraged. There are those who know best that to glorify their God they must seek the welfare of all mankind. Yet among them are suspicions and jealousies, deeply based upon historical conflicts, which roughen the road of friendly co-operation. If the counsels of our spiritual leaders divide us, where is our hope? We must look to them for vision. "Art thou the Christ, or look we for another?" "To whom shall we go?"

Thus science presents to religion the greatest challenge of a millennium, that of presenting modern man with an objective adequate to his needs. We cannot be satisfied with the cold, godless nationalistic doctrines of Europe. Untold strength and comfort lie in the ancient teachings; but we find no life in much of the diluted, supine and self-interested dogma that is now being taught in the name of religion. Yet religion we must have. Never were men more eager to work for the best. Without the unifying religion that can show us that best, our lives are purposeless and our society cannot long endure.

Science itself is not that religion. Nevertheless, though the student of science may not feel qualified to choose for others that which gives life dignity and worth, he does supply the data from which that choice must be made. How can we correctly orient ourselves without learning the facts about the world and dispassionately considering their implications? Thus the Christian's great need is, as Paul says, "that your love may grow richer in knowledge and perfect insight, so that you may have a sense of what is vital." It is, I believe, in just this direction that science must ultimately make its greatest human contribution. Science must clarify the vision of the seers who would point out to us the goal of life.

Of the three Promethean gifts of science, it was the greater variety of life which Francis Bacon saw as he wrote in his *New Atlantis:*

The end of our society is the knowledge of causes, and the secret motions of things, and the enlarging of the bounds of human empire to the effecting of all things possible.

It was its responsibility for man's social evolution which led Sarton to describe the growth of science as the central thread along which may be traced the biography of mankind. To the scientist himself comes the satisfaction that with his new knowledge an addition has been made to man's heritage which not only is permanent but is a seed that will grow from more to more. With Democritus he can truly say:

I would rather learn the true cause of one fact than become king of the Persians.

Having eaten of the fruit of the tree of knowledge we have in a new sense become as gods, with greater power for good and evil. We have been cast once more from the paradise of a well-established, traditional life. Punishment for our errors is wrought by an angel with a keener sword as we live the hard life of new responsibilities. Thus we are forced to search for greater wisdom to govern our greater powers. If a brighter paradise is to be regained, it is that of the joy of the struggle toward greater humanity.

# SCIENCE, THE MACHINE
# AND DEMOCRACY

## by Waldemar Kaempffert

IT IS no accident that we dance rhumbas instead of min-
uets; for the dance is part of our culture. It is no accident
that we ride in automobiles, listen to music broadcast half
around the world, have our offices in fifty-story skyscrapers,
turn our wheels by electric energy; for these, too, are manifestations of a culture.

When we speak of a culture we conjure up a picture of group
behavior—of a community or a race influenced by common
instincts, passions, motives and interests. A social tension is
evident, a tension which compels men to act, dress and think
more or less alike. In the Middle Ages that social tension expresses itself so strongly in religion that there are 110 religious
holidays in the year (literally holy days), that a new architecture is evolved, that the whole of Europe rises to the spiritual
need of wresting Jerusalem from what is regarded as infidel
control. If today we rush in airplanes through the atmosphere
at 200 miles an hour, talk to one another across the Atlantic
Ocean, read two-cent newspapers, determine the chemical and
physical constitution of a star by light that left it when dinosaurs shook the ground, it is not because the human mind is
intrinsically any better than it was 10,000 years ago but because it has acquired different interests under social tensions.

Tension of any kind seeks relief. To a socially tense people
relief comes through art, philosophy, arms or science, depend-
ing on the crucial need of the epoch.

Anthropologists and social scientists no longer believe as a
class in the "great man" theory of culture—a theory expounded
by Carlyle in his *Heroes and Hero Worship*. Great men

do not of themselves produce cultures, nor do cultures necessarily produce great men. In every race there are leaders—strong, gifted personalities that respond sensitively to social tension. Hence Dante, Shakespeare, Voltaire, Bach, Newton, Watt, Morse, Bell, Edison, Marconi and Einstein must be regarded as devices that enable society to short-circuit itself by following the lines of least resistance. Generally neither society nor its leaders are aware of the process.

When we say that "the time is ripe" for the appearance of a work of art, a scientific discovery or any invention we say merely that social tension seeks relief. There was no technical reason why an ancient Greek should not have invented the hot-air balloon. All that he needed was a fairly dense fabric, a basket and a fire. The materials were available 10,000 years ago. A Greek simply did not think in this fashion, because "the time was not ripe," because the social circumstances were not of the kind that stimulate technical thinking. Experimenting and inventing held little interest for him.

On the other hand our instruments for measuring the velocity of light could not have been devised by an ancient Greek. He did not think of light as we do. In fact he did not know that it had a velocity.

There never was a time when men did not experiment to satisfy their curiosity and to contrive. We must never forget that as far back as we can go, even as far back as the Peking Man, which is at least 500,000 years, the use of fire was known, and crude tools of bone and stone were in use. Such inventions as the sail, the bow and arrow, the fire-drill were known to the most primitive savages of whom we have any record.

The accomplishments of ancient astronomers were by no means insignificant. And the inventiveness of the Romans is expressed in thousands of relics excavated on the site of Pompeii and other ruined cities. There were always scientific experiments, always machines.

It is not until we come to our own time that we begin to speak of "Science" with a capital "S" and of the "Machine" with a capital "M." George Washington, for example, undoubtedly spoke of "the church" and "the law" but he did not, like us, sweep into one all-embracing generalization the many mechanisms which were known even in his day.

Science and the machine, as we know them, evolved with democracy.

Democracy arose out of the needs of commerce, and out of the needs of commerce rose science. And most of the great discoveries in science were made either during or immediately after revolutions fomented by the liberal class. Who was it that overthrew feudalism? The merchant. He had to be a revolutionist to escape looting and oppression. No merchant can prosper if his caravans and his ships are waylaid by robber barons and pirates. No miner will forever pay outrageous tribute to a feudal ruler. No manufacturer will placidly accept the exactions of a nobility that sees only in conquest a means of enriching itself. Feudalism had to go. And when it went national and international trade flourished as never before.

It is a characteristic of trade that it deals with all men on the same basis. Whatever their traditional dislike of each other may be Asiatics and Europeans, communistic Russians and capitalistic Americans sell goods to one another, asking not about race, creed or nationality, but only about credit. At the teller's window of a bank, at the counter of a shop lords and laborers are equal. Business is essentially democratic. With the rise of a merchant class it was inevitable that there should also be a rise of democracy. And because the triumphant merchant, manufacturer and miner needed the scientists in furthering trade science arose out of democracy.

Nothing irritates the laboratory recluse more than to be told that when he blasts open an atom to find out how matter is put together or determines how cells reproduce or decides that the universe is finite and closed rather than infinite and open, he is engaged in work that has a hard, practical value, even a commercial value. He glories in what seems to him the utter uselessness of his findings to the market place. He cherishes the illusion that he is animated solely by a desire of adding to human knowledge. And yet he is but responding to the intellectual and practical needs of a democratic society of tradesmen, manufacturers, miners and farmers. ○

A physicist of our own day, who is not a student of the social sciences, would hotly deny that Sir Isaac Newton was in any way influenced by the practical needs of overseas trade when he first began to think of gravitation. No doubt Newton himself would have resented such an imputation. But what are the facts? B. Hessen has presented them in *Science at the Crossroads*, a compilation of papers prepared by Soviet delegates to the International Congress of the History of Science and Technology held in London in 1931.

After America was discovered and the trade routes to its riches and those of India were opened captains of ships had to know their positions. They could no longer follow the coasts or rely on dead reckoning. Latitudes they could determine with the aid of the stars, especially the north star. But longitudes? There were no accurate chronometers in the 15th century. There was also the problem of the tides to baffle the navigators. They rose and fell in accordance with the moon's position. Tides had to be observed. They could not be predicted on a strange coast.

There was no general outcry on the part of traders and their shipmasters to have the mysteries of longitude and the tides cleared up. But the need was there just as we recognize the need of finding out the cause of cancer. A mathematical physicist of Newton's imagination could not help thinking about the moon and the related subject of gravity. The subject was "in the air," so to speak, just as the horror of cancer is in the air now. Newton considered not the commercial need of the time, not the scientific problem presented by longitude and the tides, but just the moon and gravitation, much as a biologist in a university laboratory today considers not cancer as such but the problem of the living cell in general. So, quite oblivious to the practical value of what he was doing, Newton established certain relationships between any two bodies in the universe and hence between the moon and the earth. Out of these relationships came his laws. Astronomy at once emerged as an exact science; navigation was placed on a sound basis; engineering was born.

There is no doubt that the discovery of the laws of gravitation was also aided by the physicists who engaged in military research. Professor Robert K. Merton of Harvard University (*Scientific Monthly*, Vol. XLI, pp. 542-545), remarks that "the study of the free fall of bodies, which since Galileo occupied such a prominent place in physical research, is necessary, if the trajectory and velocity of a projectile are to be determined. The connection between these problems was made explicitly when an experiment was frequently performed before the Royal Society 'for finding the velocity of a bullet by means of the instrument for measuring the time of falling bodies.'"

The influence of war on the scientist has been similarly examined by Professor Merton. Nearly all the great scientists of the sixteenth, seventeenth and eighteenth Centuries were concerned with weapons, especially after the introduction of gunpowder. Leonardo designed a polygonal fortress, steam cannon, breech-loading cannon, rifled firearms; Niccolo Tartaglia studied gunnery scientifically; Galileo suggested that the trajectory of a projectile was a parabola; Leibniz wrote on military medicine, military mathematics and military mechanics and devised an air gun; Newton attempted to calculate the effect of air resistance on the trajectory of a projectile. There is no doubt that the problems themselves were intrinsically interesting. Whether or not rulers and captains wanted some efficient means of dealing death the scientist was bound to attack the mysteries of gases. He could not help but wonder about "the information, temperature and volume of the gases into which the powder charge is converted by combustion, and the work performed by the expansion of these gases upon the gun, carriage and projectile" in Professor Merton's words. The social circumstances, in this case the military circumstances, posed the problem. Since the waging of war has been a continuing activity the physicist's interest in explosives and guns persists down to our own day. Gay-Lussac, Chevreul, Graham, Piobert, Cavalli, Mayevski, Otto, Neumann, Nobel and Abel followed in the footsteps of Galileo and Newton. Chemistry and metallurgy both benefited by the researches of these men and so did industry and hence society as a whole.

Watt was a model-maker for the University of Glasgow

when his interest in the steam engine was aroused. He had to repair a model of a Newcomen engine for the University and noticed how wasteful it was because the steam had to be condensed within the cylinder by cold water that flowed over the exterior at regular intervals. So he invented the separate condenser and with it achieved an economy of fuel for which mine-owners, who used the Newcomen engine as a pump, had been longing. The next step was to save more fuel, because of economic competition in manufacturing. But this was impossible unless the conversion of heat into energy was understood. The physicist attacked the question not because he was conscious of any great need to save fuel but just because the problem interested him. In the end thermodynamics was established as a branch of physics and engineering with the result that steam engines and gas engines of unprecedented economy were evolved.

These examples show that scientists are not wholly free agents—that they think and act much as their fellowmen do. Democracy created a certain tension, a certain atmosphere, certain needs, obvious or implied. Science and invention proceeded to fill them, sometimes consciously, more often unconsciously.

It is clear that the genius, the great man, as Carlyle conceived him, is not the fashioner of a society but its tool. He may be rare, but he is not unique. In other words, if Newton had not given us the laws of gravitation someone else would have done so. Professor William F. Ogburn, with Dr. Dorothy Thomas, presents in *Social Change* a list of 148 major scientific discoveries and inventions which were made by different men independently and simultaneously. Thus Newton and Leibniz devised differential and integral calculus; Wallace and Darwin simultaneously hit upon natural selection and the survival of the fittest to explain the origin of species; Gray and Bell filed patent applications for the telephone within an hour of each other, and both were quite ignorant of the efforts that Reis, a German, was making to talk over a wire.

There are no "first" inventions—no "first" electric lamp, no "first" dynamo, no "first" telegraph. Every invention is rooted in old principles, and every inventor has a technical heritage without which he could not progress. Edison certainly could not have invented the carbon incandescent lamp had he been a Cro-Magnon man in southern France 50,000 years ago. Without Galvani, Volta, Faraday and Henry the telegraph of Morse would never have been conceived.

Just as trade is international so is science. We must not be deceived by the brilliant record that Germany has made in chemistry or we in mechanical invention. Science and invention respond to social tension. Germany must make the most of her natural resources. Hence the exploitation of coal tar and the rise of chemistry. America on the other hand was long deficient in labor but rich in natural resources. Hence America has been the great inventor of labor-saving devices. As our population grew the old differences between America and Europe disappeared. Now American achievements in chemistry equal those of the Germans. In other words, the kind of economic and social community in which we live determines the kind of scientific research and the kind of invention on which we embark. This does not endorse the old myth that necessity is the mother of invention. An inventor in the right environment can no more help inventing than an artist can help painting pictures. What is invented has its roots quite as much in what may be called "the soul of the environment," as in its material opportunities.

The great subject of practical science is energy. Until the coming of the steam engine it mattered little industrially whether a country possessed coal deposits. After James Watt coal was potential energy that could be released to produce goods. Nations were willing to fight for it. The regions where coal was abundant became the seats of industry. Those that had no coal sought salvation in water power both before and after the electric generator was developed.

At first the steam engine could be utilized only near the mine or near a navigable stream on which coal could be transported in bulk. Later the railroad made it possible to establish industries based on steam farther from the mine. But not too far. The distance to which power can be transmitted by a steam engine directly is limited to a few feet by a belt or a rope. As a result the engine had to be used individualistically. That is every factory generated and distributed its own energy. By 1930 some 270,000 individualistically operated steam engines were running in the United States. To these must be added some 50,000 individualistically operated steam locomotives which haul more coal by weight than they do wheat, corn, oats, hay, lumber, steel and iron combined—haul energy in the form of solid, black lumps, largely for their own consumption.

When Edison built the first central station in 1881 this picture was destined to change. Energy in the form of electricity became free. It can now be flashed hither and thither for about 250 miles. Not only this but central stations can be interconnected so that a few of colossal size can take the place of many. Thus regional power pools can be created which can be tapped wherever land is cheap, railways and waterways are at hand and labor is reasonably abundant. After James Watt workers flocked to the steam engine; after interconnection electricity could be flashed to the workers wherever they might be.

What we have, then, is a definite trend to the collectivistic use of energy generated in a few centers. There is nothing accidental about this. The engineers of the great utility companies have for years kept this goal in view. So has every important government.

If the introduction of the steam engine is one of the factors that brought about the Industrial Revolution then the advent of electric energy marks a second revolution destined to have far-reaching consequences. This does not mean merely electrified farms and households, with Muscle Shoals and Niagara Falls milking the cows and sucking out dirt from the carpet by way of a vacuum cleaner, but a profounder change which may affect the very nature of government and society, as we shall see. Electric energy has become like water or gas—something that steam energy could never become.

The introduction of the steam engine gave an enormous impetus to invention. Before Watt's day engines were used only to pump water out of mines. Watt made an engine of the old pump. After that any machine could be driven by steam. Machines were invented to build other machines, and thus a process of reproduction was inaugurated that seems appalling to some sociologists and romantically captivating to others. The countless machines that do the work of hauling, lifting, pressing, punching, boring, folding, twisting, cutting and bending are all highly specialized, artificial organisms. Industrial processes are carried out, for the most part, by tireless automata which are nothing but extensions of human muscles and human senses controlled by the human brain. What we have here is something much more important than the subdivision of labor. Skill and intelligence have in part been transferred to the machine.

With the invention and introduction of the steam engine we see a civilization rising, a new civilization based on coal, on energy. The thought that a steam-driven machine of some kind can do the work of muscles takes possession of manufacturing minds. Mass production is old, but mass production on the scale that became possible with automatic machines had never been conceived. Automata were devised for every purpose.

Mass production on this scale implies control—organization. The need of organization was recognized from the first. A man like Arkwright, inventor of important spinning machinery, organized his mills after a fashion that commands admiration even at this late day. In this transformation Bertrand Russell emphasizes the need of experts who plan the organization and control it. Without them there is only chaos.

When mass production finally reaches a point where pig iron is poured at the rate of thousands of tons a day and automobiles are produced by the million every year the need for more organization, more control arises. Out of this need came what is known as Taylorism in Europe and scientific management in America. Machines have already been arranged with an eye to their general relations to one another. But before Taylor there was no scientific co-ordination of machines and their tenders. He converted the factory itself into a colossal machine.

The machine stands for mass production. And mass production means regimentation on a vast scale—what the engineers more politely call standardization. It is the machine in the last analysis that makes us dress more or less alike, ride in automobiles that are more or less alike, see at night by lamps that are absolutely alike, live in houses that resemble one another and are even identical when they are built in rows for the occupancy of millhands, eat foods that come in cans and packages indistinguishable from one another. Fifteen million people a day see precisely the same films. Donald Duck is as familiar to western ranchers as to Rumanian shopkeepers on New York's East Side. By radio an entire continent listens to some popular comedian who is "sponsored" by an oil-refining company with gasoline to sell. Water comes from a common reservoir, gas from a common central station. Living has become a collectivistic activity. For life in Lima, Ohio, in its technological aspects is much like life in Chicago, San Francisco or New York.

Mass consumption, mass recreation, mass distribution of energy and the collectivistic utilization of identical things are impossible without control of mass production, without organization. If gunpowder, in Carlyle's famous phrase, "made all men the same height," the inventors have standardized behavior, pleasures, tastes. Because of invention there is less individual liberty than there was a century ago; there will be still less tomorrow. The patents speak eloquently enough on the point. In the first third of the twentieth Century 1,330,000 were granted in this country, with more than that number expected in the second third. Few are supremely important, but their increasing number indicates that technological thinking is more than ever directed toward utilizing energy for the production of goods.

Control. Organization. We come back to these. For without them mass production is impossible.

Who are the controllers, the organizers? Bertrand Russell's experts at the top of the pyramid—efficiency engineers who see to it that even the hugest steel mill operates as if it were a single organism with a super-machine-tender in charge called the "president." Hired designers or inventors of ever more complicated automatic labor-saving devices, technicians who do nothing but keep the machines in perfect condition constitute a new caste that owes its station not to birth or privilege but to sheer mentality and opportunity.

How many aristocrats of test tube, electromagnet, and gearwheel are there? No one knows. The total for the world cannot be more than a million, with perhaps two hundred thousand in the United States. Suppose they were to perish in a night—these million. Back we would slip to the 18th Century. People in cities would starve to death or die in two weeks of epidemic diseases. And yet with experts on top of the structure inventing and controlling the mechanism, and above these financiers who rule all, what is to become of us? We are brought face to face with the problem of government.

The whole trend of society for about 150 years is now clear. We see energy supplanting muscle in manufacturing; machine after machine appearing; mass production standardizing life; ships and railroads becoming mass carriers; the machine so far dominating industry that invention becomes a recognized profession, with group invention taking the place of the inspirational, individual, "heroic" inventor; the standardization of goods as a result of mass production; the gradual abandonment of thousands of individualistically operated steam engines for a few central stations that transmit electric energy over vast regions; electrical communication designed from the outset for mass utilization; mass production, for whatever purpose, demanding and receiving more and more organization; a handful of experts controlling the machinery of modern civilization.

It has been said that mechanical invention, or applied science, has outstripped our institutions—that we need social invention to save ourselves as well as to make the utmost use of the gifts of science and engineering. If we are willing to forget their follies and look deeply for the purpose that inspired their creators we must regard fascism, communism and socialism as social inventions designed to cope with the problems presented by science and the machine.

Whether democracy can survive the increasing strain to which it is being subjected by machine methods and scientific progress no one knows. If it does it will be vastly different from 18th Century egalitarianism. We have but to cast our eyes backward to note the trend. There is less personal liberty than there was a generation ago; there will be still less a generation hence. There will be more and more need of organization, more and more need of integration of workers and machines, more and more need of experts. Fraternity may remain, but conceptions of liberty and equality must change. Mass production and mass consumption—we shall have more rather than less of them. Hence there will be more uniformity rather than less. Even now western Europeans and Americans are indistinguishable so far as their clothes are concerned.

Russell sees danger in a standardized world, with one language, one radio system broadcasting standardized music and entertainment and information, one newspaper, one common way of thinking. There would be no excuse for traveling except for a change of scene. The social environment would always be the same. Such a world would be intolerably dull— would languish and perish of sheer inanition. The very nature of science is a safeguard against such stagnation. For if technical and social history has taught us anything it has taught us that human aspirations change as science reveals new depths and new sublimity in the universe—in the environment.

Democracy as we know it is a social and political conception of the 18th Century. There were no steam engines, no railway trains, no gas works, no central stations, no machines to turn out thousands of cigarettes a minute, seal thousands of cigarettes or cans of tomatoes an hour, or bend, twist, punch and squeeze steel for skyscrapers and ocean liners. There is no denying that as against a ruling military caste of hereditary aristocrats, invention has given us another ruling caste of technologists and financiers. And the new ruling class is far more powerful than the old. It has had to be curbed by such democratic devices as compensation laws, shorter working days, unions, interstate commerce and federal trade commissions, public service commissions. The curbs are the evidences of a deep conviction that the very existence of democracy is at stake. Social problems have become largely technological problems. On the one hand we have democracy trying to settle by popular vote highly intricate problems of finance, taxation and industrial control, all arising out of invention; on the other a colossal mechanism of production, designed and operated by highly competent experts who are guiding our lives. So we ask: Are the technical experts to run a whole nation because they happen to run its industrial machinery? Or is the government to run the experts, the inventors, the creators of this evolving culture? The totalitarian states have decided that the course of scientific research and of invention must be socially directed. The 260 research laboratories of Soviet Russia take their orders from the Academy of Sciences, and the Academy is an integral part of the government. Long before the Polish invasion of 1939 Germany was trying desperately to achieve what was possible in economic self-sufficiency by indicating to the university and industrial laboratories exactly what discoveries and inventions were wanted. Mussolini had a National Research Council, of which the late Marchese Marconi was the guiding spirit and which was primarily concerned with Italy's industrial problems. Every totalitarian state plans for the future and holds scientific research to the plan.

Planning is distasteful to a democracy. It clashes with individualism, with the egalitarian right of every voter to decide what he wants his government to be and to do. So instead of the clear-cut program of totalitarian states we have much floundering.

It is not that democracy is unaware of its danger, but that it does not quite know how it shall deal with the machine and the social problems that it has raised. In President Hoover's time, we had the report of a Committee on Social Trends, which discovered that social invention lagged behind technological invention, meaning that some social mechanism must be devised to soften the impact of scientific advance. President Roosevelt appointed the National Science Advisory Board, which insisted that we needed new industries to absorb the unemployed, and that inventions in the long run always create new industries. It went so far as to indicate what problems should be assigned to research physicists, chemists and engineers in a systematic effort thus to cope with the economic problems of the depression. More recently we have had the report on Technological Trends by the National Resources Committee, an attempt at predicting what H. G. Wells calls "the shape of things to come," on the theory that if we can foresee that shape we may be able to avert the disastrous consequences of carelessly introducing the formidable inventions that are even now in the making. The prophets who wrote that report argue that it takes from twenty to thirty years for industry to adopt a revolutionary invention—time enough to read the handwriting on the wall, time enough to foresee more obvious social effects, time enough to prepare for the inevitable by formulating adequate legislative and economic policies.

There are manifest impossibilities in thus attempting to predict the shape of things to come and preparing for them. Did Arkwright foresee the slum when he transferred the textile industry to the factory? Or Watt when he converted Newcomen's mine pump into a steam engine, capable of driving other machines? Did Daimler, Duryea and Ford imagine that the automobile would transform rural education, reduce many railway dividends to zero and inspire 500,000 Americans to lead a gypsy life in trailers? Did Whitney know that his cotton gin would revive a dying slavery and that a Civil War would have to be fought to settle some of the issues raised? Or did Otis and his backers realize that his elevator would give us the skyscraper and with it a rise in real estate values and a problem in transportation whenever a single building discharges on the sidewalk some 50,000 people between five and six o'clock?

Yet democracy is not utterly helpless because it dislikes prediction and planning or because it is bewildered by what the scientists and inventors are doing to change modes of life. We have an example of what it can do in the case of the railroad.

At first the steam locomotive was simply an iron horse that competed with the living horse. Then steam became a powerful factor in opening up new land in the Middlewest, in spanning the continent, and in developing new industrial centers. In England, the country developed the railroads; here they developed the country. The full significance of the railroad burst upon us during the World War, when it was recognized by the masses for what it was—a colossal carrying machine sprawling over a continent, linking thousands of towns together. We talked of transportation with a capital "T."

When the war ended the question arose whether or not the roads should be returned to private ownership and management. Their subsequent history is probably the eventual history of all public utilities, possibly of all major industries based on great inventions. In other words, transportation, the generation of gas and electricity, the supplying of water to a community, the production of foods, clothing and shelter can no more be left wholly to private capital than the exploitation of the atmosphere for breathing. We behold the railroads transformed by democracy into real servants of the public. The conditions under which their managers employ labor, the issuance of securities, the rates to be charged for carrying goods and passengers—all are subject to governmental scrutiny and approval. The railway companies are reduced to the status of administrators. They may not even give up an unprofitable branch line without the government's consent, and, against their will, they must apply the profits earned in crowded communities to provide transportation in regions where traffic is thin. We have here about the most striking example to be found of democracy's ability to direct an invention to good social purpose and to appraise the social importance of a scientific discovery or invention.

It happens that science stands for something more than coal-tar dyes, electric lamps, X-rays, radioactivity and monstrous fruit-flies bred by experimental geneticists. It is an attitude of mind, an objective, dispassionate approach to the outer world—what Professor Whitehead calls "the most intimate change in outlook that the human race has yet encountered." This attitude, this objectivity is inconceivable without freedom of expression.

All this being so—and the case has been convincingly presented by historians of science and political philosophers—the advocates of a society planned from on high, with the necessary suppression of free thought, face a dilemma. They need the scientist. Yet they must deny him the liberty of mind that is the very essence of his objective attitude. If his researches relentlessly expose the fallacy of a fundamental principle dinned into the populace by the government, either he must be hanged as a meddler or the high social plan must be scrapped. In totalitarian Germany, Italy and Russia there may be no hanging, but there is exile or a concentration camp for the dissenter, and not a sign of scrapping.

Moreover the votaries of science constitute an international brotherhood the like of which this world has never seen before. It is impossible to say of a discovery or an invention: "This was the work of a German—or a Finn—or a Scot." Nor does it matter much to a real scientist or engineer what the nationality of a discoverer or inventor may be. It is enough for him that the man did his work and described it in a readily accessible publication as an addition to the general stock of knowledge. As a force in achieving true internationalism even religion pales in comparison with this subjugation of self and country. In spite of the uses for hate and destruction to which invention may be turned, science itself furnishes the most striking evidence we have that men are able to sink passion for the good of the race.

Our hope, then, lies in science. If democracy is to save itself the scientific outlook, the scientific method of detached appraisal of facts and situations must become part and parcel of the electorate mind. This is a problem in education. Or as Wells puts it the choice is between "chaos and education."

There are signs that, even without adequate education and the general inculcation of the scientific attitude, the masses in democracy are beginning to turn instinctively to the scientist and the engineer for guidance. There has been much scoffing at "brain trusts," but the fact must not be overlooked that, inept as they have been on occasion, they have emerged from the orderly process of democratic government. Their British counterparts are found in Royal Commissions that patiently examine proposals and decide whether or not they meet the social needs of the hour. It is much that two great self-governing peoples have thus drawn the scientific expert into administration, even though his recommendations may be brushed aside. For all its emotionalism, it is hard to escape the conclusion that the electorate does somehow sense that science and democracy owe much to each other.

# MECHANISM AND CULTURE

## *by* James T. Shotwell

SOCRATES, according to Plato, lamented the passing of that time in Greece when the only known facts about the past were those treasured in the memory of the tribal bard, and the coming of that degenerate age when people no longer would bother remembering things they could read in books. He deprecated the invention of writing. Yet it was by the written page of his pupil Plato that the conversations in the cool gardens on the outskirts of Athens have survived, to secure his own immortality.

This objection of Socrates to the invention of an alphabet was something more than the proposition of a philosopher in need of an argument. It was a protest against mechanism. Making black marks on Egyptian papyri or skins from Asia—those skins the merchants of Pergamum later made into parchments (pergamenta)—compares with reciting an epic as the use of machinery compares with hand labor. Socrates, we suppose, would have preferred telling the time by a guess at the lengthening shadow on the square rather than by the use of such an instrument as a watch. By ignoring inventions one kept "close to nature."

This is an attitude to be found throughout the whole history of culture. Its most earnest advocates have been the artists, impatient of anything interposed between nature and the individual. But idealists generally have joined in the denunciation or shared the contempt for mechanism, no matter what their field. Literature has held aloof, except in patronizing, romantic moods, until the present. History has ignored the very implements of progress—the tools of work, the mechanism of effort—even while recording the results. There has, therefore, developed a gulf between "culture" and achievement which has widened with each new invention.

There have been, in recent years, some signs of a revolt against the conspiracy of the poetically-minded to ignore the creations of the practically-minded, but unless the revolt becomes a revolution we shall never square ourselves with reality. If we are to make anything intelligent out of the world we live in, we must free ourselves from this romantic sentimentality, which goes back to Socrates and beyond. Idealism, left to itself, is futility. There is no sadder fact in the tragic circumstances of the present than that idealism failed to avert the desolation of Europe. It will always fail, so long as it holds itself aloof from the grimy facts of daily life.

Like the forces of nature, ideas must be harnessed and set to work, or things will remain exactly as they were before. One cannot weave cloth with an idea, but embody the idea in wood and iron and it will replace all the hand-loom workers in the world. Wherever a locomotive sends its puff of steam through the smoke-stack, the idea of George Stephenson is at work—an idea that a forced draught on the fire would give the engine enough power to pull its load. There are spindle whorls in the Grimaldi caves along the slopes of Menton, used by the fingers of spinning women of the late stone age, over 10,000 years ago. How often in all that stretch of years have spinners dreamed of something to carry on the motion of the whorl besides the arm and hand! Out of such longings came—no one knows from where—the simple spinning wheels of the late Middle Ages. Yet it was only in the 18th Century that a tinkering watch-maker helped Arkwright to get his roller-frame to work, and the work of spinning passed forever from the fireside to the mill. New cities arose by the marshy waste of Lancashire, and the shipping of Britain carrying its goods overseas, made possible a world-empire—not created in a fit of absent-mindedness, as an idealist historian declared, but through the might of the Industrial Revolution.

Few students of literature stop to think that its existence depends upon paper and ink as well as thought! The records of history depend upon the cutting of the chisel in the stone, the sharp impress of the scratching stick, on clay or on wax tablet, the scrawl of charcoal or ink on leaves of trees, papyri wrappings or leather. Before these devices were used lie the unnumbered centuries of that period we call the prehistoric; this side of it, is the world of history. History begins with writing; the prehistoric, as we use the term, is a synonym for the preliterate. History depends upon that mechanism which transfers thought from brains to material substances, and so enables thought to endure while the thinkers come and go.

It is strange that the extent to which thought depends upon mechanism for its preservation seldom occurs to us except when the mechanism fails. We know that the burning of the library at Alexandria blotted out for all time much of the culture of the distant antiquity which it had gathered in the papyri on its shelves. We know as well that the last classics of Greece and Rome perished in the moldy rolls of papyri which could not last in the climate of the northern Mediterranean as it does in Egypt. The book trade of the ancients was careless of the future—as ours is today. But had it not been for papyri rolls dealt in by those astute traders who brought their goods to the wharves of Athens and Ostia, it is doubtful if the literature of classic Greece and Rome would have been produced at all. Had there been nothing better than clay tablets to scratch, how would the Augustan Age have achieved what it did? Imagine Dante in his exile, accumulating the mud cylinders necessary for the *Divine Comedy*. Or, to bring the matter down to our own time, what would our modern literature and journalism amount to if the Arabs had not invented paper? A printing press without paper is unthinkable; and literature cannot exist without them both. We need a *Sartor Resartus* in the history of literature to show us how naked and helplessly limited is thought except when provided with mechanism.

There have been two great creative epochs in the history of our civilization; that of ancient Greece and that of today. The one produced critical thought; the other applied it to produce machines. Beside these two contributions to secular society, all others rank as minor. The one stirred into activity that critical intelligence, upon which rests our whole apparatus of knowledge; the other made nature our ally not merely by applying its power to do our work, but also by supplying the means for extending knowledge itself, almost to the infinite. Seen in this light the protest of our modern humanists against mechanism has little of that insight into reality which was the characteristic note of Socrates.

What is needed in both humanists and scientists is the Hellenic sense of just proportion, so that neither thought nor machines shall become master of life. For thought turned upon itself, divorced from the setting in a real world, becomes as idle as the speculations of the schoolmen; and machines become, not instruments for human liberation, but the dominant element in society. Education in a modern world must respond to both these demands. It cannot be purely literary or idealistic without losing touch with the spirit of the age in which we live; it cannot be purely technical and remain education.

How many of us realize that a steam engine is as genuinely a historic product, as fittingly the symbol of an age as the feudal castle or the medieval cathedral; that a modern factory is as much the center of historical forces as the ancient city?

We shall never see the true perspective of history so long as we accept unquestioned the mediocre outlook of what we call common-sense people. We need imagination and insight even more than judgment for, otherwise, our judgments simply circumscribe and limit our activities. If there were only one factory in the world, if the power that Watt released from the coal mines were so concentrated that instead of invading every hamlet of the civilized world it was confined to the single valley of the Clyde and drew to it there the work of the world, we should have some feeling for the importance in history of one of the great inventions. But instead, its effects penetrate the environment of common life everywhere; and so we miss its meaning.

Invention is an art. It is the projection into matter itself of the conscious will. It makes matter a part of the agency of control, and also a part of intelligence. Loose grains of muddy ore, lying in the bosom of the hills, become iron axes. They have nothing in themselves to indicate axes. They might, if placed too close to a fire, under certain circumstances become hardened into a mass. But while the ore is merely matter, the ax is matter plus mind. It bears the impress of intelligence, and that to so great a degree that the anthropologists passing before the rows of axes in the cases at a museum can reconstruct from their form and composition the state of culture of the makers, like a pianist whose symphonies arise from the keys of his piano. The ax implies both consciousness and purpose; it means cutting. The same is even true of a forked stick which the savage uses as a spade, though here the injection of the human element into the material is less obvious, because the object has not been refashioned. The fork was a result of its nature as a branch; that is, a part of a vegetable mechanism for catching air in leaves and conveying nitrogen to the trunk. It was not produced by nature to dig potatoes. Nature leaves the branch in the air and the potato in the ground. But in the hands of man the fibers of wood, like the particles of iron are turned into something else, they become part of conscious action, a continuation of muscle and an agency of mind. The potentialities of the tool are those of the brain that conceived it and controlled the fashioning hand, as much as they are those of matter. Invention is a projection of consciousness into the unconscious; a creation.

If this can be said at the dawn of invention, and of a tool like a digging stick, which itself embodies no thought, which is not a tool except when so regarded or used, the utility of which is accidental, it is abundantly evident when invention produces not a tool but a machine. The difference between a tool and a machine is that the tool helps a man to do his work, but the machine does the work itself. The man changes his position entirely with reference to it. His business with the machine is simply to make it work. The factory operative does no spinning; he mends threads and makes the spindles spin, forces the steam to move the iron and the iron to transmit its energy to the whirling spools, and they in turn to gather up that energy and imprison it in the spirals of thread or yarn, where our fingers later may find it stored up—a source of strength against strains and pulls. The factory spinner merely assists at this transformation like the impresario at a theater. Steam and iron and fiber dance before him into new combinations, like a dream from the *Arabian Nights*.

The machines that do these things are the perpetuation of the initial energy of their inventors. In the steam engine, for instance, Papin, Newcomen and Watt have found an immortality larger than we have yet realized. In its gliding rods and noiseless wheels the brain of the inventor lives as that of Virgil in the *Aeneid*. But while the art of the one is cast cathedral-like, in static mold, to resist the forces of time by its perfection and its strength, that of the other—the invention—is thrown, as it were, into the crucible of change, and creates itself the forces that reveal its imperfections and weakness. The engine develops the speed that breaks it down. Yet the immortality of the invention is perhaps the surer of the two, for it enlists its destroyer as its ally. It becomes part of change itself, and so gains some control over it. It sets going the irrecoverable march of events, which make up what we call time, and becomes an integral part of the ever-fleeting present. For its immortality lies in its use. By the work it does it disturbs the poise of phenomena so that once started it creates the demand for its own continuance. It contains its own stimulation, for its imperfections call as much for further invention as its successes encourage new ones. So it is a social phenomenon of the most complex nature. If it immortalizes the Watts and Arkwrights, it is only by merging their creations into that of a vast composite whole. The original engine of Watts and spinning frame of Arkwright are in museums; but both machines are also preserved wherever engines are at work or cotton is being spun. The original inventors have become contributors to a more august creation than they guessed. The brain of the individual scientist or mechanic fuses its creation (steam valve or automatic brake) into those of all society and all future time. It will live only so long as it can be adjusted to the changing machine. Each bolt and bar, each wheel or crank is the crystallized thought of some nameless engineer. When they fit and go, the structure lives, and each part is instinct with life. Apart or unfitted they die. The cylinder that might hold the power to drive ocean-liners is good only for the scrapheap unless the pistons fit and the gearings work. And so, if one could imagine the whole dynamic force of the Industrial Revolution gathered together and concentrated in a single cylinder, with a power compared to which that of Niagara would be like that of a rivulet, it would be as useless as the energy of ocean tides today, unless there were the nicest adjustment in the parts of the machine. Machinery is a social creation and is itself a sort of society!

Thus, in the social preservation of inventive thought, by a strange paradox, this individualistic age is the annihilation of the individual. Its greatest art-creation, machinery, it maintains and treasures only so long as the individual contributions are in tune with the whole.

There are two kinds of immortality: the immortality of monuments,—of things to look at and recall; and the immortality of use,—of things which surrender their identity but continue to live, things forgotten but treasured, and incorporated in the vital forces of society. Thought can achieve both kinds. It embodies itself in forms,—like epics, cathedrals and even engines, —where the endurance depends upon the nature of the stuff used, the perfection of the workmanship and the fortunes of time. But it also embodies itself in use; that is, it can continue to work, enter into other thought and continue to emit its energy even when its original mold is broken up.

It is the first kind of immortality—the monumental kind— which has mainly drawn our attention, for it is clearer, if not larger, in our consciousness. Use, on the other hand, obliterates outlines so that the things used most are often least seen. So in keeping with our natural tendency to visualize our thought even in the things of use, as if to make up for this indistinctness, we encourage the perpetuation of form,—in institutions and traditions,—and enshrine it in art.

Let us be clear about this monumental side. Poems live in themselves and not simply as stimulations to deeds or other thoughts. Form imposes itself on thought and preserves by means of its external beauty, even though it is often only a successful distortion of the thought with which it started.

Cathedrals stand before us out of the Middle Ages which created them, defying time in their own right, by the double strength of poise and beauty in stately columns and towering walls. These formal perpetuations of thought in its own expression are the most appreciated, as they are the most obvious. They require no penetrating analysis to detect; they are matters of pure observation. Thought grips materials without effort, but hesitates to tackle thought; so the concrete world lodges in the memory while the abstractions slip by unnoticed.

So important is this formal apprehension of things, that it has been taken at its face value by society,—as society takes things at their face value (which includes of course the value of the face not simply its looks),—and made synonymous with art; as if there were not a greater art in the mastery of those intangible, elusive forces which have escaped from their mold and penetrate wherever thought can go,—the art of mathematics, science, and invention. Indeed the same tendency which makes us see the obvious first and prize it most, carries us still farther. It tends to become a sort of sacramental attitude, consecrating not only the form in which the thought is cast, but the material embodied in it and the environment which molded it. The tongue of Dante, of Luther and of the King James' Bible, are monuments of such consecration. We even carry this sacramentalism to its primitive conclusion. Although we know better, a strain of fetish worship runs through us all. The bones of men receive our reverence, as if in them resided—or resides —the efficacy of their thought and action. Placards are posted where thinkers have lived and died, as if their thought belonged like some haunting spirit to walls and garden walks.

Now all of this is legitimate enough so long as much of our thought *is* sacramental and our feelings stir with fetishistic suggestions at historic sites or relics. But it obscures the larger life and the truer immortality of thought,—the immortality of use. Dante's vision has entered into many a scheme of the world besides that into which he wove the picture of the Florence of his day. In fact for centuries it molded the cosmology of all Christendom and it still colors the common dream of immortality. It is this larger vision, built of the universal hope and fear, that is the real *Divina Commedia*, not the epic locked in its stubborn Tuscan rhymes. No form of art, however perfect, can imprison or contain all of a living thought. If thought is alive it is more than its form. It will escape and live. Often it carries with it in its new use broken fragments of its form, and so may still be recognized at sight, as the architecture which produced the medieval cathedral breaks up into the buttressed piles of a modern city,—a dome here, a flying arch there, walls soaring for the light, towers that carry forever the memories of Italy,—but all disparate and merged into a new creation. This new creation, however, is no massive, self-contained whole, it is instinct with life and change. It is not static like the old, but eternally re-creating itself, replacing arches and domes by girders, and leaving the old architecture behind with the problems it faced and the material it faced them with. The one imperishable thing is the science of which these are the fleeting traces.

It is the same with history as with art. At first glance what one sees in it is the formal event, the embodied institution, the externals of things. But when we look deeper we find that what happens in a given time and place is only a part of the real event. The cause and results are also parts of it. The result is merely the prolongation of the event in other circumstances, the releasing or the destruction of its potentialities. Battles are more than charging cavalry and riddled squares; they are not over when the firing ceases. They still continue in the hatreds and enthusiasms they arouse, in policies of state, in armaments, in nations themselves. The German Empire was Sedan crystallized—Sedan and other things. The battle itself is only the most concentrated form of an event, just as a poem is the most perfect expression of an idea. But the real significance, the essence of both is something larger than the form, however concentrated or complete it seems.

Now, it is in the same way that the cylinder syringe and separate condensers of Watt's first engine are curiosities for the historian, but the idea, the creative power, of that invention is moving on with all the forces of the Industrial Revolution. It was born of an application of Scottish ingenuity to Scottish thrift for all that Watt had in mind when he set to work was to save coal by making an engine that did not have to heat a cool cylinder at every stroke. But the engine that was invented to save coal, in its generation of power has eaten into the heart of every coal deposit of Britain, while the power it releases has not merely changed the material environment of civilization, but actually brought millions of human beings into existence— each with his and her own world of thought and work—in the stimulation of population through the production of wealth.

Indeed in a sense one may say that machines—the product and embodiment of invention—attain a sort of life of their own. They enter the field of industry to play their own role, always incalculable, often achieving what their creators never dreamed of and the opposite of what they intended. They are not simply aids to labor, doing more things than the hand-worker, producing more and more things of the same kind, in an endless addition to the stock of goods. They are changing the mental and moral outlook of society as well as its physical basis. To what extent they do this must be left to a consideration of the economic interpretation of history. But when even philosophy (in the metaphysics of Bergson) recognizes that the machine steps, as it were, into the main problem of life, adjustment and adaptation—and so becomes an element, and the largest element—in this present phase of our biological evolution, it is time for history to wake up to this tremendous fact. It is not a fact for economists or philosophers alone. Not only is it, in itself, an *event* of keen human interest, clear definition and notable prominence, but it underlies every other event of large importance in the political history of the last half-century. The Industrial Revolution and the machine will inevitably furnish the central text of those histories of the future which deal with our era, as Bergson says. It is our privilege even now to see how magnificent the text will be.

Compare the transport of the 18th Century with that under the control of the engineers of the 20th. The overland trade in the goods of the world was carried or drawn by horse. Now there is more horsepower dragging the freight trains of this country than all the horsepower of all the ages put together. Go down to the great power-house where the force is generated to drive these trains and see what degree of control over nature has been reached with reference to the needs of civilization. There the power is generated from the coals. The heat stored in from suns of geologic ages is released once more under the exacting control of an engineer and adjusted by automatic devices to correspond with the weight upon the floors of the cars, so that it is hardly a figure of speech to say that as you step upon the train a few more leaves of prehistoric forests crackle away in the energy of heat, and that energy becomes a substitute for the human energy of the traveler. Talk of miracles, with such an annihilation of time and control of power!

No writer that I know has ever expressed so well the full significance of the inventive art as the man who protested most against the changes which it wrought in the society of the 19th Century. Let me close by quoting this extract tucked away in a hidden corner of the works of John Ruskin:

"What may be the real dignity of the mechanical art itself? I cannot express the amazed awe, the crushed humility, with which I sometimes watch a locomotive take its breath at a railway station, and think what work there is in its bars and wheels, and what manner of men they must be who dig brown ironstone out of the ground and forge it into that. What assemblage of accurate and mighty faculties in them, more than fleshly power over melting crag and coiling fire, fettered and finessed at last into the precision of watchmaking; Titanian hammerstrokes beating out of lava these glittering cylinders and timely respondent valves, and fine ribbed rods, which touch each other as a serpent writhes in noiseless gliding, and omnipotence of grasp, infinite complex anatomy of active steel, compared with which the skeleton of a living creature would seem, to the careless observer, clumsy and vile. What would be the men who thought out this, who beat it out, who touched it with its polished calm of power, and who set it to its appointed task, and triumphantly saw it fulfill the task to the utmost of their will, feel or think about this weak hand of mine, timidly leading a little stain of water color which I cannot manage, into the imperfect shadow of something else . . . mere failure in every motion and endless disappointment; what I repeat would these iron-dominant genii think of me? and what ought I to think of them?"

# THE POSITION OF SCIENCE
# IN MODERN INDUSTRY

## *by* Harold C. Urey

TO EVALUATE any activity, it is necessary first to state and to agree upon an objective. My statement of the objective of all of us who strive for more than our own personal desires and wants is almost commonplace. This is stated so often in terms of money values that we often forget that money is not an object at all, but only a medium of exchange for the real objectives. The real purpose of our endeavors is to contribute something somewhere and at sometime to the sum of human satisfaction, as man lives for a brief span of time on this small planet. This statement includes the primary objective of those who devote their lives to literature, art, the sciences, the social sciences, industry, and religion. The spiritual and intellectual satisfactions are usually regarded as being on a higher plane than the physical, because they distinguish us so markedly from the other animals, but a certain minimum of physical needs and comforts is necessary for the appreciation and enjoyment of these more distinctive human wants. In spite of the many imperfections of our present civilization which are emphasized by many discourses and more by much discomfort and disappointment, it is probably true that people live better today, in both an intellectual and spiritual as well as a physical sense, than they ever have before in all history.

One perhaps should say that this desirable state has been due to the application of the sciences to industry, but this would not give a proper appreciation of our true position. No one group can claim a wholly unique position. The applied sciences owe much to pure sciences in which knowledge is pursued for its own sake, just as pure science owes a great debt to the applied sciences. Moreover, both owe much to the social order in which they exist. Perhaps we should note that the great development of the scientific method has taken place parallel with the growth of humanism. This development has occurred largely in democratic or partially democratic countries, and I predict that the center of gravity of the sciences in the future will move with the center of gravity of liberal government. In recent years the movement has been toward North America.

Recognizing our dependence on all other cultural groups of our community, I believe we can maintain that the technical applications of science have contributed a most important part to the well being of the world that recognizes Europe as the mother of its civilization. The 19th Century witnessed the development of most of our forms of power in the hands of our various branches of engineering. This development has been greatly extended during the years of this Century and, in addition, such developments as the radio, the motor car, and airplane have become possible luxuries and now necessities. During the 19th Century, chemistry contributed only a few outstanding technical advances in addition to age-old processes in general use. Among these, the use of petroleum, coal tar, and dyes may be mentioned. During this century, in addition to aid in the development of the motor car and airplane (fuel, lubrication, and finish), chemistry has contributed so many far-reaching processes that their number bewilders us. If there were not so many, they would be known more widely than they are. Nearly everything we use today has been improved or created by the chemist. The golden age of applied chemistry comes in this century. We supply an effective method, but the successful outcome of the project requires the co-operation toward a common objective of capital and labor and a sympathetic understanding of all groups of the community.

It is impossible for me to mention more than a few of the more important chemical processes developed here and abroad during this time, and to discuss more than a fraction of these. Such a list cannot be credited to any particular men, laboratories, or countries, for science is highly co-operative and international. Moreover, though these important advances in technology are essentially chemical, they cannot be regarded as the product of that science alone, but as the product of all pertinent knowledge from all sources.

Some of these important technical processes developed in the closing years of the 19th and the beginning years of this century are:

1. The utilization of coal tar.
2. The development of the petroleum industry.
3. The fixation of atmospheric nitrogen.
4. The development of plastics and rubber.
5. Artificial textiles and fabrics.
6. Improvements of ceramics and glass.
7. Hydrogenation of coal.
8. Synthetic or derived foods.
9. Protective coatings.

Convention requires that such a list contain the magic number ten. I reserve this number for the multitude of individually small processes which together constitute the most important of these groups. One's imagination is not stirred by tetraethyl-lead as compared to the petroleum industry, or by such things as the lowly and privately used soap or sulfur and its products which are the servant of so much of technical industry and others.

I wish to mention more particularly two of these ten technical developments because of their fundamental importance— the fixation of atmospheric nitrogen and the hydrogenation of coal. The credit for these two must be given largely to German scientists. That this is true is not the result of chance, for Germany was the first great nation to realize fully the important connection between science and industry. The United States has grasped this connection only since the World War. It has been recognized in the Scandinavian countries, but their limited natural resources have not permitted its full development. It is apparently appreciated by the new Russian Government and by England, and almost not at all by other countries.

The fixation of atmospheric nitrogen is accomplished today

by a chemical reaction between nitrogen and hydrogen to form ammonia and is known as the Haber process. Simple chemical processes convert this into substances suitable for use as plant food, or for use in the manufacture of dyes and explosives. This development illustrates the close co-operation of the sciences, pure and applied, in a problem of this kind. Thermodynamics, which was developed by physicists of the 19th Century, was first used to show that the process was possible. This study shows that, under high pressures, this reaction is possible and that it is favored by low temperatures. However, it does not show how fast the reaction takes place. Studies by physical chemists showed that a catalyst is necessary and that the reaction proceeds more rapidly at higher temperatures. A compromise is necessary, and maximum yield favored by low temperatures must be balanced against the time required, which is less for high temperatures. The production of nitrogen from the air for use in the process is accomplished by the distillation of liquid air produced by physical methods. The hydrogen needed is secured by chemical methods from water and coke. Special alloys are necessary, since hydrogen gas passes through ordinary steel at high temperatures and pressures almost as readily as water through cloth. These many factors require the co-operation of chemists, physicists, and metallurgists for their successful solution. And, in fact, the successful process is built on careful scientific work of nearly the entire century preceding the actual commercial production of ammonia in this way. At the beginning of this Century, no method of removing nitrogen from the air was available. Without this element, the fertility of soils could not be maintained in order to produce the food supply for the present large populations of the earth. Today the problem has been completely solved, and the fertility of our agricultural areas, so far as nitrogen is concerned, can be maintained. The ammonia produced is also essential for the production of many dyes used so widely that Solomon, in all his glory, would look rather shabby today. It is also essential for explosives, which are used far more for peaceful than for military purposes. Somewhere in industry, about five pounds of ammonia produced by this means are used yearly for every man, woman, and child in the United States and Europe.

Our petroleum supply is limited, though few attempt to guess how long our natural supply will last. Because of the discovery of new fields, we always appear to have an adequate supply for the next ten or twenty years in spite of an increasing rate of consumption. But we all agree on one point at least. The rate of consumption of oil deposits is considerably greater than the rate of geological deposition of oil, so that sometime consumption will overtake deposition. Liquid fuel is a necessity in our minds at the present time. The development of the hydrogenation of coal by Bergius as a means of producing liquid fuels and lubricants, if not immediately useful in competition with natural petroleum, is a comforting backlog against the day of ultimate exhaustion of this liquid. The method of development follows much the same general outline as the development of the fixation of nitrogen. The magnitude of the development illustrates the faith that must be put into modern scientific developments. I have been told that the I. G. Farbenindustrie expended 150,000,000 gold marks in the development of this process. I cannot guarantee the exact accuracy of this figure, but its order of magnitude is probably correct. The time is past when a few test tubes, a piece of string, or a wire is sufficient apparatus for scientific discovery. Our problems today are more difficult than those of a century ago. Yet each new problem can be attacked with confidence, because the theoretical knowledge and technical facilities, developed in the past, are available for the new problems.

These two problems were undertaken from the standpoint of national defense: the first during the World War in order to supply explosives when Germany was cut off from the Chilean supply of nitrates; and the second during recent years with the object of giving that country an internal supply of liquid fuel in preparation for another war. However, the other eight developments listed above have been carried forward with peaceful objects in view, so that the picture is not entirely discouraging.

It is of interest to mention briefly another development

which is taking place. We are all aware of the importance of artificial silk at present, and the rapid growth in its use and production in recent years. The silk worm, sheep, and cotton plant are evidently not the most efficient producers of textile fibers. Cellulose, the woody material of plants, is suspended in caustic soda solution giving a viscous material which is then shot through fine holes into an acid solution. The acid neutralizes the alkali, regenerating the cellulose in the form of a fine thread. This can be spun into fabrics resembling in physical properties the product of the silk cocoon, but it is very different in chemical composition from this natural silk. It can be made at such costs that it is an important competitor, not only of silk but also of cotton. But other synthetic textiles are coming. Two regiments of the Italian Army are wearing imitation wool uniforms made from the casein from skimmed milk; furthermore, such textiles can be made from meat scraps. In the future the less tender cuts of meat will appear as a lady's smart spring suit or a man's trim dress suit. This year wool textiles for women's suits are on the market containing some 70 per cent artificial silk. They have the desirable quality that they do not crease. Artificial textiles and fabrics are in this interesting stage of being created in our chemical laboratories so that various desirable qualities can be controlled at will.

This development brings before us some disturbing by-products of the applications of science to industry. In times past, industries were born, lived, and died at leisurely rates so slowly that society adjusted itself to the change without more than grumbling complaints. Today industries are often born, grow to maturity in a year or so, and are then often murdered. The change is so rapid that people cannot adjust themselves to it, and even though the end result is beneficial, the intermediate situation may result in actual want and privation for many people. The fixation of atmospheric nitrogen ruined the Chilean nitrate industry; artificial silk has caused difficulties in Japan, and also has contributed in all probability to the difficulties of cotton farmers in the South. Will artificial wools ruin our sheep farmers in the West? To change the type of crop grown in a section of the farming area of this country requires approximately the time of one generation. People, especially older people, change the habits of a lifetime slowly. These are real difficulties which have been considered too little or not at all. After all, each of us has but one life to live and that life is our most valuable possession. We should not overlook and excuse the sentence of poverty, privation, and disappointment on an innocent fraction of the population on the grounds that the result is good for the greatest number, nor should we excuse our responsibility in the matter because of the indirectness of the method. Some thought on these problems might make us more co-operative in solving them; and, who knows, if we gave the matter some thought, we might even supply a good idea from time to time.

The future cannot be estimated as the past can be evaluated. However, those of us most closely in touch with present scientific developments are certain that the present technical applications of science are only a substantial beginning. We have found that we have not been able to foresee developments of a few years ahead. The results of our work completely outdistance our dreams. We only can state that many fields have hardly been touched with careful and logical scientific methods. So far as we can see, the only limitation to the future developments lies in a limitation of the number of capable men for this work. Certainly the expenditures for research pay such handsome dividends in new articles of commerce that we cannot afford to economize in this direction. But find the men! That is the problem. Farmers' and ministers' sons often make good scientists, and perhaps even the sales force might contain a good brain or two. The scientific group is sure that such proselyting is justified.

So far we have largely been using our natural capital, the naturally occurring and readily available resources of the earth's crust. This age is often referred to as the age of steam, the age of electricity, the scientific age, etc. None of these is sufficiently broad to describe an age of the length of the Old Stone Age, or the New Stone Age. I think this age may be referred to 5,000 years from now as the age of dissipation. It will be the age during which man completely scattered in fine dust over the face of the earth and the oceans all the natural resources of the earth's crust. It may be thus regarded if enough remains of our metals and sources of energy to support a civilization such as ours at that date. Man may be back in the Stone Age and on the way to extinction at that time.

In the not too distant future, man must live on his income, consisting of energy arriving from the sun. This source does not appear to be disappearing as rapidly as petroleum and coal and may last a billion years yet. But how make use of it? Perhaps the physicist and his technical children may solve this problem by sun engines. I have more hope for the success of the biologist and chemist. The new knowledge of heredity has been applied to agricultural problems in only an empirical hit-and-miss fashion up to the present, and chemical research on agricultural products is still in its infancy. In the future, we probably will grow our fuel supply by plants especially developed for the purpose. Our supply of metals appears more discouraging. Will our descendants drudgingly mine our waste dumps for those precious metals, iron, aluminum, tin, lead, and others? Our income of metals from space in the form of meteorites is wholly inadequate. The probability of conquest of Mars and Venus is rather remote. This beautiful and delightful spending of capital will go on for a while yet but eventually must stop. These readily available resources have enabled us to get a powerful knowledge of nature, which is the heritage of those who follow. Perhaps they will be as clever as we and, we can only hope, far wiser. The human organism has a remarkable adaptability and the necessary scientific discoveries and industrial developments will come. In the list of recent developments given above more than half apply to products derived from materials which are renewed as we use them. Our research will move in this direction in the future.

Scientific men on an occasion of this kind, the purpose of which is to relate science to man, must refer, as I have done, to the social importance of their work and justify it on those grounds. We do this because we believe sincerely that this is true. We are satisfied with modest salaries because of our own personal satisfaction in work well done. This work has a permanence and lasting stability that the work of few other professions has. I believe I speak for the vast majority of all scientific men in industrial laboratories and in our universities. Our object is not to make jobs and dividends. These are the means to an end, mere incidentals. We wish to abolish drudgery, discomfort, and want from the lives of men, and bring them pleasure, comfort, leisure, and beauty. Often we are thwarted and our efforts perverted to other purposes, but in the end we will succeed. You may bury our bodies where you will, our epitaphs are written in our scientific journals, our monuments are the industries which we build, which without our magic touch would never be. This is our statement of our pride in our work. We hope that those who work with us, capital and labor, will carve their names on these monuments with the same pride in their work that we take in ours.

# THE PSYCHOLOGIST AMONG
# THE SCIENTISTS

## *by* K. Koffka

IN WHICH FIELD and by virtue of which methods psychology has won recognition as a member of the family of sciences, it is not the purpose of this essay to discuss. And yet, the very fact that this question can be raised is relevant to our topic, for, consciously or unconsciously, psychologists have, since the beginning of the experimental era, been influenced in the choice of their topics and the philosophy of their methodology by their desire to be accepted as scientists. Today this tendency finds its most pointed expression in Behaviorism, that group of tenets which rejects all "subjective introspection" in favor of "objective observation" and therefore prefers animals to human subjects because while the latter may wish to report their own private, and therefore unscientific experiences, the former simply allow themselves to be objectively observed.

If psychology could do nothing better than follow this precept, then, however important and valuable its contributions to the total sum of our knowledge might be, it would have no characteristic that would give it a unique position in the family of sciences. It would, as a branch of the biological sciences, be closely related to physiology, and the task of delimiting the various biological sciences would have comparatively little general or philosophical interest. If this were the opinion of the author of this essay, he would not have attempted to write it. And thus the thesis which the following pages are intended to prove is that psychology has a function which no other science can fulfill, a function, moreover, which brings the psychologist near to, if not within, the confines of the philosopher's realm.

This function derives from a task which the psychologist shares with no other scientist and which, at the same time makes him, in principle, though certainly not in fact, indispensable to all scientists. The physicist has the task of explaining inorganic nature, but he does not consider the working of the physicist as a part of his science, nor does the biologist treat of the biologist, even though the species of homo sapiens belongs to his field. But the psychologist cannot in any sense build a system of his science that has not a place for the psychologist, or, for that matter, for the scientist in general. And this simple assertion entails the unique position that will be claimed for the psychologist.

Two lines of argument lead to this assertion. In the first place psychology is the science of behavior in general and of human behavior in particular. Scientific work is human behavior, and therefore belongs ipso facto to the domain of the psychologist. Thus formulated this argument seems obvious and does not, for this very reason, reveal all the implications of its conclusion. For it might seem possible that psychology, after having developed certain explanatory principles, could simply apply them to that form of behavior that is called science. But such an interpretation overlooks an essential characteristic of scientific behavior which distinguishes it, if not in kind at least in degree, from many other kinds of behavior: the results of scientific behavior, the discoveries, deductions, generalizations, are more or less permanent, and, what is even more important, they are not merely in actual fact, contingently, connected with the preceding behavior, but stand in an intrinsic, necessary, relation to it. If, therefore, one chose as the prototype of all behavior a concept that lacks this characteristic, then one could not explain scientific behavior, because one would be unable to deal with its most significant aspect. Concepts of this kind are the reflex, the conditioned response, the association, all three representing prototypes of purely contingent relations.

Let me demonstrate the truth of this statement by the example of the conditioned response. In its purest form, today hardly accepted by anybody, it establishes a purely external connection between a stimulus and a response, based on mere coincidental repetition. To repeat the classic example of Pavlov's dog: a dog when stimulated by the sight or smell of food begins to salivate, but does not do so when a bell is rung. If, however, for a number of times a bell is rung each time before the dog is presented with food, then the mere ringing of the bell, unreinforced by presentation of food, will produce increased salivation, an effect which will gradually disappear when the "conditioned stimulus" of the bell has gone unreinforced a number of times. On this well established fact, and many others of the same kind, the conception of the conditioned reflex is based, a conception which in the opinion of many psychologists is a, if not the, fundamental explanatory concept of psychology. The facts, to summarize, are these: it is possible by suitable experimental procedures, to connect almost any response with any stimulus, proof that the connection thus established is purely external. It is a long cry from the statement of this fact to the theoretical position that holds such external connections as typical of *all* behavior. Another view would be that the conditioned response is the extreme case of a much more general form of connection, and that the externality of its connection is due to the very special conditions under which this behavior is elicited. But this is not the place to give a theory of the conditioned response. What we wanted to demonstrate was that scientific behavior cannot be explained by the concept of the conditioned response, because the response, being coupled with its cause, the stimulus, in an entirely external fashion, cannot be called either true or false, whereas these predicates dominate the pursuit of science. True and false imply internal relations, and these play no part in our concept.

Therefore, the fact that the psychologist has to include himself, and every other scientist, in his subject matter has far-reaching consequences for psychology itself: it determines the choice of its fundamental explanatory concepts; for these concepts must be such that they explain internal relations characteristic of the results of scientific behavior.

The other line of argument which we are to follow starts in the realm of physics. Physics is based on observation and deduction. Observation of nature requires natural events to be observed and observers who observe them. Thus every physical observation depends upon two kinds of factors, those outside and those within the observing organism. The physicist aims at establishing laws of nature that are free from the observer, and every great progress in physics up to the general theory of relativity has been a step in this direction. A history of physics written from this point of view would be highly significant, because it would reveal the different devices which the physicists have developed in order to reduce the influence of the observer to a minimum. One of the most eminent astronomer-physicists of our time has clearly discerned the fundamental importance of our problem. Sir Arthur Eddington believes that the solution consists in eliminating more and more sense organs from physical observation, until no more than one eye is used and, since Einstein, no more than the central part of its retina, because most observations in modern physics are reduced to pointer readings, i.e., the perception of coincidences of a pointer and a mark on a scale.[1]

The principle underlying Eddington's solution is the assumption that the fewer nerve fibers of the organism are excited for a single observation, the less will this observation depend upon the organism, and the more will it be determined by the natural object itself.

That this assumption is incompatible with several facts will be pointed out presently. But first we should ponder upon the fact that pointer readings of some sort or other have gained such importance; for clearly, the reason cannot lie in the phenomena observed by pointer readings; it must lie in the observer, and therefore this choice can find its final justification only through the study of the observer, i.e., through psychology.

If through the use of pointer readings the physicist expects to eliminate, or reduce to a minimum, the subjective component of observation, a theory of pointer reading as a particular form of behavior would seem desirable. Such a theory presupposes a detailed and accurate description of the act. Roughly this would run somewhat as follows: an observer who makes a pointer

[1] Sir Arthur Eddington, *New Pathways in Science*, New York, The Macmillan Company, 1935, p. 13.

reading sees two larger units, a pointer and a scale, the latter being subdivided into smaller units of the marks of the scale; the simple unit, the pointer, moves across the scale until it stops in the neighborhood of one of the marks. This mark then has to be distinguished from all others, has to be given a name, say 10.5, and recorded.

This cursory description shows that, considered as a piece of behavior, the reading of a pointer on a scale is by no means a particularly simple performance. As a matter of fact it is less simple than many a procedure that has been abandoned in favor of it. To test a substance with one's tongue in order to find out whether it is sweet or salty, to observe litmus paper turning red or blue, these are behavior forms a good deal less complex than that of reading a pointer.

Let us analyze its complexity: it presupposes knowledge of a value series on which each individual mark has its place; it entails the perception of motion, the existence within the visual field of separate units, and the apprehension of the relation between two or three such units—the position of the pointer with regard to one or two marks; and most generally, it requires the establishment of space and objects within it.

If of all these achievements required of the organism of the observer who wants to take a pointer reading we single out the simplest, the segregation of individual units for further analysis, we find that the formation of such units demands that the field comprise more than these units; for unit formation requires inhomogeneities in the field. And for this very reason it is impossible to do what Eddington claims to be Einstein's contribution, viz., to cut down the functioning part of the sense surface to a small minimum. Much more than that is required in order to produce space and objects within it; as a matter of fact patients with retinitis who have left as much intact retina as Eddington accords to the physicist are, for all practical purposes, blind, and certainly unable to take pointer readings. Eddington is, in a way, aware of this, for he mentions that the Einsteinian limitation of the observer to a small central part of one of his eyes makes it impossible for him to recognize form or extension in the external world. But he overlooks the fact that then the achievement which he still deems possible, viz., the apparent coincidence of two things, is also abolished. Thus the attempt to reduce the influence of the observer on his observations by reducing the number of fibers of the optic nerve breaks down at the very place where it seemed to have been demonstrated: such reduction would make pointer readings impossible.

This attempt must, however, appear absurd when one remembers that Köhler [2] has pointed out that it is not true that all physical observation is limited to pointer readings. The physicist must know what his pointer indicates, volt or ampere or temperature or velocity or what not. In order to do that he must observe the entire set-up, the way in which his measuring instruments are connected with the system whose properties he wants to measure; all this is surely very much more than pointer readings, although like those it entails the existence of segregated units in the field and the apprehension of a definite network of relations between them. Thus the organism of the observer, which seemed to have been so nicely eliminated by the device of pointer readings, remains in the observation situation as an integral part. The physicist cannot get rid of it, and therefore, in order to evaluate its influence on observation, he needs the psychologist to study the organism.

Physics, as we said before, is not based on observation alone but implies deductive reasoning. For far from being a mere collection of facts it is a rational system in which all available facts can be logically derived from a minimum of factual relations. Such a system requires concepts and ways in which concepts are interlocked, inferences, deductions, proofs. It is obvious that concept formation, inferring, deducing, are all forms of behavior; they occur within the organism, and yet without them no knowledge of the world outside the organism is possible. And thus it seems that the whole attempt of the physicist to free his data from subjective factors is futile. The problem of an objective science dependent on subjective activities was recognized in its full scope by Kant, and his solution has

[2] W. Köhler, *The Place of Value in a World of Facts*, New York, Horace Liveright, 1939.

influenced philosophers to the present day. The rational factors of knowledge, so it says, are *a priori*, i.e., independent of experience. They express the essential forms of the mind, and scientific knowledge is developed by catching within these forms the irrational, contingent, *a posteriori* elements. Scientific knowledge thus is "objective" because within the compass of our experience it is necessary. But apart from our experience it can claim no validity whatever. Nature follows the laws of thought because only what can be grasped by our forms of intuition and reason can become nature for us. And thus the rationality of nature, far from being the rationality of a universe independent of us, is the rationality of our own spiritual essence. It seems strange that Eddington who tries so hard to eliminate the subjective element in observation, adopts a view very similar to this.

For our purpose it is not even necessary to show why the Kantian solution is inadequate; for a consideration of the *a priori* itself, quite apart from its connection with *a posteriori* material will confront us with our particular problem. Mathematics has a truth of its own, independent of all experience, and quite apart from its application to problems of physics. How is such mathematical truth found, how is it known to be truth? As soon as one begins to answer these questions one has to leave the realm of timeless "subsistences" and is faced with concrete events occurring in specific places and at particular times; for discovery and recognition of truths are parts of human behavior. And therefore, quite apart from the Kantian problem, the question arises how behavior, an empirical occurrence, can lead to truth, a timeless *a priori* state of affairs. How can anyone know that proposition A is true, proposition B false, unless proposition A were, either by itself or within a larger context, different from proposition B, different, that is, in such a way that its truth stands out against the other's falseness? But this is only saying that at the bottom of the logical difference of true and false there lies again a psychological problem: what characteristics must thought processes have in order to carry the "tone" of true or false?

Thus the psychologist is needed by the physicist not only

when he observes but also when he systematizes his observations. And yet this is not the whole story; for the argument bends back on its origin like a snake that eats its tail. Thought processes are impossible without simultaneous brain activity. But can we ask the same question about this brain activity, this physical event, which we have just asked about the thought process? Can we demand that the brain processes corresponding to the true thought of proposition A are in the same sense different from the brain processes corresponding to the false thought of proposition B, in which the thought processes themselves are different?

Perhaps the same problem will appear less speculative when it is given a slightly different twist. Thought processes usually issue in some kind of action that involves innervation of muscles and movement of limbs. Now these latter are palpably and incontestably events in the world of the physicist, and therefore their occurrence should be explained by him. But the dilemma with which the physicist finds himself confronted when such muscular activity is the direct expression of a thought process has been most lucidly formulated by Eddington: "Suppose that I have hit on a piece of mathematical research which promises interesting results. The assurance that I most desire is that the result which I write down at the end shall be the work of a mind which respects truth and logic, not the work of a hand which respects Maxwell's equations and the conservation of energy. . . . If the mathematical argument in my mind is compelled to reach the conclusion which a deterministic system of physical law has preordained that my hands shall write down, then reasoning must be explained away as a process quite other than that which I feel it to be. But my whole respect for reasoning is based on the hypothesis that it *is* what I feel it to be." [3] To this statement I have only one objection: it sounds as though the physicist Eddington abandoned the solution of a problem in physics to the philosopher Eddington; and I cannot admit that a physicist has a right to delegate the solution of his problems to anybody else. If the physicist assumes that every physical event must be connected with

[3] *Loc. cit.* pp. 90-91.

preceding and simultaneous other physical events in such a way
that if the latter are given, the former must occur,[4] while if
they are absent, the former will also fail to appear, then the
writing down of the solution must be in this way connected
with other physical events. And then Eddington's dilemma
can be expressed as a type of overdetermination: the writing
down of the correct solution is on the one hand completely
determined by antecedent physical events—in the nervous system of the scientist—and on the other, equally completely in
all essentials,[5] by his preceding thoughts.

But philosophically we cannot tolerate such overdetermination. We should be apt to abandon either determination for
the other, and thus either accept physical determination and
then consider the mental and logical determination as a purely
illusory epiphenomenon, or believe in the power of the mind
to discover truth and then abandon the previously formulated
fundamental axiom of the physicist and instead admit cases
in which events outside of and different from the realm of
physical nature break into this realm and impose upon events
that occur within it laws that are alien to them.

Eddington sees very clearly that the first alternative is impossible; and so he accepts the second. But, as I said before,
that seems equally inadmissible to me.

True enough, the second alternative is not absurd, it is free
from internal inconsistencies or contradictions, which the first
is not. But if we accept it, we thereby relinquish once and for
all the idea of a unitary system of science and put in its place
an ultimate dualism, if not pluralism, of modes of being and
acting, without any possibility of understanding the relationship between these different spheres. For if mind is utterly
different from nature, how can it have knowledge of nature?
The view under consideration can produce no answer to this

---

[4] It makes no difference for this argument whether one substitutes for the
word "must" the expression "is very probable to occur"; for the probability
of such global actions is always as great as to be practically indistinguishable
from certainty.

[5] There are aspects of the transcription that are not so determined; the
size of the letters, is one such; another would be whether they are written
in long hand or on the typewriter.

question other than accepting such knowledge as a fundamental irreducible fact, for which it does not even claim to have an explanation. And in practice, what does it mean to accept two kinds of entities and laws? Where will the physicist be justified in stopping short in his tracks and ascribing the rest of the observed effects to a non-physical factor? Has anyone yet demonstrated a criterion for such a decision? But as long as this has not been done, the physicist, so it seems to me, has no right whatever to stop anywhere; instead he has, as a physicist, the moral duty imposed upon him to persevere to the bitter end.

It seems that this argument leads back to that overdetermination which, I said, was philosophically intolerable. But there is one assumption—and I believe only one—which makes it possible to retain both sides of the dilemma and yet avoid the blight of overdetermination. This assumption is the opposite to that which made Eddington's statement so incisive, his dilemma so real, the ordinary assumption, namely, that physical events and those characteristics of mental events which have to do with truth and logical necessity are fundamentally different from each other. One can formulate the difference by saying: that nature is a realm of facts, whereas mind is a realm also of "requiredness" to use this general term coined for this purpose by Köhler.[6] But to those who like the classical physicists are not shaken by Humean skepticism and post-Humean positivism and believe in a true causal necessity in nature, the difference is one between two kinds of requiredness. Blind necessity, factual necessity as it were, in nature, intelligible necessity in mind. The corresponding categories would be cause—effect on the one side, reason—consequence on the other. Or one may say it again in Eddington's words. " 'Ought' takes us outside chemistry and physics."[7]

The new assumption which would, as I said, do away with the overdetermination of certain events, is simply that this sep-

[6] W. Köhler, *The Place of Value in a World of Facts*, New York, Horace Liveright, 1939.

[7] Eddington, *The Nature of the Physical World*, New York, The Macmillan Company, 1928, p. 345.

aration of mind and matter is grossly exaggerated, that instead both fact and requiredness are denizens in either realm, and that again, both in nature and in mind, requiredness may vary as to the internality of its relation. Under this new assumption Eddington's dilemma would disappear, for the antecedents of the final act of writing down the solution, whether in the realm of thought or physical events would have the *same* character which made first the solution itself and then its recording required. According to this assumption, then, something of "ought" is inherent even in physics and chemistry.

The name of this assumption is psychophysical isomorphism. It is a hypothesis which it is the psychologist's task to confirm or refute. How this can be done, and what steps have already been taken on this road, that cannot be reported in this essay. But isomorphism as a psychological problem does indeed give an unique position to the psychologist among the scientists. For, whatever his present achievements are, he alone can ultimately give scientific justification to all science, just because science is part of his subject matter.

We shall summarize the different aspects of his contribution which we discussed in the course of our argument by repeating and developing the main points.

All science is based on observation, and observation is dependent upon the observer. The attempt to minimize the subjective element of experience by reducing the functional sense surface of the observer and therewith the type of observed data has been shown to be a failure. All observation remains subjective in the sense that it depends upon the organism of the observer, and no trick employed by a physicist can modify this fact. It loses its menace for the objectivity of observation if one treats the study of the subjective observation as a science no less objective than physics. For the observation of any physical event, the motion of a pointer across a scale, or what not, is as much a natural event as that physical event itself. It takes place in an organism, whereas the physical event takes place outside an organism, e.g., on a scale. The naive person knows nothing of this duality, he believes that the event as observation and as a physical fact are identical. But as soon as this naive realism has been abandoned, it is clear that the knowledge of the physical event is possible only through the mediation of the observed event. Many observed events, however, are not simple and direct guides to physical events: the earth looks flat, and yet we know that the ancients who believed that the earth was really flat were mistaken. This example teaches us not much more than that singly observed events are only part of the requirements for knowledge of real events, other parts being the systematization through reasoning of many observed events. Another example will add a new insight: we all experience ourselves as active at some times, and passive at others; i.e., we make things and we are moved about by forces stronger than ourselves. Such experiences are more dominant in other cultures than our own, cultures which we call animistic or magical. Now science had to fight magic in order to come into its own, and so it banished all concepts that smacked of activity and passivity. Some extremists, and they are not few in numbers nor lacking in authority and appeal, wish to banish all concepts like force or causality from true science and replace them by the concepts of regular sequences and concomitant variations. But magic, whatever its value for our knowledge of the physical world may be, is first of all a psychological datum, and as such also an event in nature which cannot be discarded in a system of knowledge. The psychologist should understand why magical connections are experienced as well as why so-called natural ones are. And then he must examine why those observed facts did mislead as signposts into the realm of physical nature. In such an examination he might well discover certain aspects which a zealous science has too radically rejected, for in magic the relationships are internal, and this very fact may be the reason for the general skepticism against all internal relationships in nature.

In short, on the level of observation the psychologist encounters the problem of describing observed facts as observed and scrutinizing their value for our knowledge of the external world. And such scrutiny will reveal that the purification of science has gone too far, and that the scientist who philosophizes about physics may temper his criticism of the scientist who creates physics and in so doing uses concepts which seem illegitimate to him in his critical hours.

In the realm of the other source of science, in the realm of reason, the psychologist has the same problems before him: to describe rational thought as an occurrence and to establish its value as an indicator of events beyond thought. And here the significance of his work is even greater; for not only has he to deal with requiredness, with internal relationships, with values, than which no more philosophically important objects exist, but he has to convince the physicist that his own fundamental conceptions must be so changed or re-interpreted as to allow the explanation of requiredness as events in nature. Thus the psychologist studying science as part of behavior makes the same kind of contribution whether he studies observation or ratiocination. He alone can, as I see it, overcome the otherwise irreconcilable difference between naturalism and spiritualism, relativism and absolutism, fact and value.

# FACT, VALUE, AND SCIENCE

## *by* Brand Blanshard

THE THESIS of this essay is that values are sometimes causes. They dip into the stream of our experience and behavior, blocking it, diverting it, or hurrying it along. Since they are thus determinants of mental events, any science of human nature must take account of them. But to take account of them it must pay a price. It must be prepared to break sharply with an old and immensely powerful tradition, the tradition of natural science itself.

That this tradition has proved its right to power is of course not questioned here. Since we shall have some critical things to say of natural science later, let us make clear at once that these spring from a background, not of enmity to such science, but of immense respect and admiration. Modern science has made modern civilization possible. We depend upon it in a thousand ways for food, for health, for comfort, for transportation, even for amusement. More than that, in its disinterestedness, its clearness, its system, the irresistible weight of its proofs, it is probably the greatest single achievement of the human spirit. Its history for three centuries has been one of such continual and mounting triumph that it has gained a reputation in the general mind for invincibility. To be sure, there are knots that it has failed to untie. It is still groping about for the causes of cancer, and has suffered some loss of dignity over the common cold. It does not know how life comes into being, nor what it is that makes old age and death inevitable. There are mental phenomena such as the functional diseases by which it has been puzzled into giving confused and conflicting explanations. But in the light of the past, can we say that these failures are more than temporary? Science has been repeatedly confronted with problems that seemed as insoluble, and after a little well-directed research has quietly produced the key. Even when it has said incredible things, things that flagrantly flouted common sense and the plainest observation, such as that the sun never really rises and that a rock is mostly empty space, it has turned out right. Men who opposed or questioned it have been so uniformly put in the wrong that of the great army of doubters, embracing once the majority of mankind, none now are left except a few fundamentalist sects and a scattering of forlorn guerillas.

Science is in the saddle. It is so firmly in the saddle that those who respect and admire it are free to ask questions about it without the least fear of unseating it. One such question, a very large and important one, we are going to raise in this essay. Is there any limit to what we may expect from natural science? More specifically, what is the prospect that natural science can continue its triumphant march from the physical region, which it has already so largely conquered, right through the inviting but relatively misty and uncharted regions of the mind?

The answer to this question depends on the answers to two others: What is it essentially that natural science is trying to do? and, can this sort of thing, in the nature of the case, be done with mental process? The latter is the main problem of this essay and our answer to it will appear only gradually. The former question may be dealt with at once.

What natural science attempts to do is to explain. Physics attempts to explain why rainbows appear, why spoons in glasses of water look bent, why the earth goes round the sun. Geology attempts to explain why volcanoes break into eruption, how canyons are formed, how rocks come to be stratified. And so with the other physical sciences. But what is meant here by explaining? Explanation means various things. Sometimes it is teleological. We may ask why Shakespeare chose to introduce into the midst of the terrible storm in *Lear* the chattering of an idiot? The natural answer would be that he chose to do it *in order to* produce a certain effect, to deepen, let us say, the impression of human helplessness. This is an explanation, but it is clearly not the kind of explanation that is sought in natural science. Sometimes the method is logical. One may ask why a triangle inscribed in a semi-circle should be a right angle. The explanation would consist in demonstrating that if you start with certain axioms, the proposition about the triangle follows with logical necessity. This again is not the sort of explanation that natural science uses; the physicist may state the action of the sun on the earth in an arithmetical formula, but if challenged about it, he would defend himself by comparing it with fact, not by demonstrating *a priori*. He knows that he could not do that if he tried. His explanation is neither teleological like the literary critic's, nor logical like the geometer's; it belongs to a type of its own.

What kind is it? It is *causal* explanation. From the point of view of natural science, to explain a rainbow or a volcanic eruption, a disease or a rising tide, is to state the cause of it. And by stating the cause of it we mean stating the *law* of its causation. The physician, as a practitioner, may be interested in the cause and cure of a particular disease in a particular patient, but as a scientist, his interest is in what causes the disease as such or in general. He wants to know the *sort* of cause that produces this *sort* of effect. Can something further be added about what qualifies anything to serve as cause or effect? Yes, whatever stands in either place seems always a physical state or a physical change. A physical state—for example, a stratification of rock—is an arrangement of physical objects, ultimately perhaps such things as protons, electrons, and photons, in certain spatial relations to each other. A physical change always consists of motion, that is, an alteration of position of physical objects with reference to each other. And when the scientist speaks of a causal connection between such states or such changes, what does he mean? Not, certainly, a connection between means and end; he would not dream of saying that floods deposited sediment *in order to* produce stratified rock. Nor yet a connection between ground and consequent; he would not say that from the activity of a certain bacillus the recurrence of a certain disease could be logically deduced. What he means by "A causes B" is that the physical state or change A does in fact always precede the physical state or change B. For him a causal law is neither more nor less than a ruie of succession connecting two physical states or changes. And if the rule is to be precise, it must be quantitative; it must correlate a certain amount of A with a certain amount of B, and state how changes in the one amount vary with changes in the other. Thus the ideal physical law is one that can be put in a differential equation.

When we speak of the program of natural science, we mean a program that would bring everything it deals with into a web of such correlations. It is true that this program is not all there is to science. Mathematics, for example, is not concerned with these correlations, however useful it may be in formulating them; but then mathematics is not a natural science, and we are here speaking of natural sciences only. The botanical description of a daisy is scientific work, but it is rather preliminary to the program than a part of it, and we are here confining ourselves to the business of explanation. Again, many generalizations have been made in anthropology, sociology and biology that are very useful indeed, but are quite lacking in the precision demanded. However, most workers in these fields would say that their sciences, so far as they do fall short in this way, are failing to qualify as full-fledged natural sciences. If they were sure that there was something in the subject-matter of their science that made such correlations impossible, they would no longer claim for it the position of a natural science. But they will not abandon that claim before they have to. If their science has not achieved the exact correlations desired, what this proves, they would say, is not that their enterprise is no natural science at all, but only that some sciences are more advanced than others. The most advanced of all is physics, since here the widest and most precise generalizations have been achieved. It is the ambition of the other sciences to bring themselves into a like position; and while this may be a long business, and much longer in some cases than in others, the difficulty is one of practice, not of principle.

Now it is the not wholly pleasant purpose of this paper to show that such optimism is unfounded. There *are* difficulties in principle, difficulties so deep as to confront natural science with the alternative of abandoning either part of its field or its program. If it clings to its present program of explanation, it must abandon part of its field, since in that part its program cannot be carried through. On the other hand, if it keeps the whole field as its own, then it must abandon its program as clearly inadequate to that field. Both points may be made clear by showing one thing, namely, that in the subject-matter of some of these would-be sciences there is that which resists the application of the program we have described. By resisting such application we do not mean merely the offering of problems that natural science has not yet solved. Even in physics there are countless problems that are not as yet nearly solved, but no one suggests that because they are not solved yet, they never will be. Our argument is of a more serious kind. We are suggesting that in some of the regions which natural science would like to take over, and more specifically in the field of mental process, there is something in the character of the subject-matter which puts it intrinsically and therefore forever beyond the reach of such science.

Let us begin with the obvious. What is natural science to do with consciousness? Its program is the correlation of a cause, consisting of a physical state or change, with an effect, consisting of another such state or change. But no species of consciousness can stand in either place, for it is not a physical state or change at all. A headache is not an arrangement or rearrangement of particles in one's cranium. Young ideas do not literally shoot, in the sense of dashing up a dendrite and down an axone. When we look at a violet, the end-organs in our retina are being stimulated by a series of waves whose length can be measured; they are about 397 mm. long; and it is probable that a change precisely corresponding to that wave-length is set up in the optic nerve. But of course our sensation of violet *is* not this change in the nerve, and is no more like it than it is like Aladdin's lamp or the Sphinx; it is without size or shape or weight or density or movement. With the faintest and simplest element of consciousness, natural science meets something for which it has no pigeon-hole anywhere in its system.

Confronted by these unassimilable elements, the natural scientist may take one of three courses. He may deny that such elements exist. This is the course of the behaviorists. Or he may admit that they exist, but say that they belong to a region in which natural science has no interest, the region of the supernatural. This is the course of those psychologists who have been won over by the method of behaviorism, but are unconvinced by its implicit philosophy. Or, admitting that conscious elements exist, he may say that science should try to deal with them, and should revise its program in any way which that end makes necessary. It is this last view that I think is the right one; and I shall suggest presently some of the revisions that such an adjustment would seem to call for. But let us look first at the other alternatives.

First as to the proposal of the behaviorists. They are clearly right that their psychology is the only one that will fit into the traditional picture of natural science. Whatever is to fit into that picture must be a state or movement of a physical object, must be more or less exactly measurable, and must be accessible to public inspection. The behaviorists insist that consciousness, even if it existed, would not meet any of these requirements. Consciousness, writes Dr. Watson, "has never been seen, touched, smelled, tasted, or moved." [1] "The behaviorist cannot find consciousness in the test-tube of his science." [2] The reason why he does not find it is, of course, that such means of search as touching, moving, and examining in test-tubes apply to physical objects only, and consciousness is not such an object. Nor is it quite obvious that it can be measured. We sometimes speak of measuring the loudness of a sound, but usually that means measuring the amplitude of atmospheric waves, which is an entirely different thing. And even granting that sensory intensities can in a way be measured, is there any meaning in comparing the intensity or volume or velocity of my thought of democracy with those of my thought of monarchy? Quantitative measurement is here inapplicable. So is the other requirement, publicity. If quantitative relations are to be guaranteed, they must be freed from subjective dis-

[1] *The Battle of Behaviorism*, p. 15.
[2] *Ibid.*, p. 27.

tortion, and they can be so freed only if the observations of one reporter can be checked and verified by another. Now my observations on my own consciousness can never be checked by anyone else. An observer may make more or less probable inferences as to what is going on in my mind from my words or gestures or reactions to a test. But the evidence is circumstantial only. We do not know each other's thoughts, and cannot hope to know them as we know our own.

The behaviorist, then, is right that consciousness is beyond the province of traditional science. Is he also right about the inference he draws from this? Using the implicit major premise that what is not scientifically observable does not exist, and fresh from his demonstration that consciousness is not thus observable, he goes on to conclude that therefore consciousness is a myth. Now I do not propose to discuss this position seriously; I have attempted to do that elsewhere.[3]

Here I can only say that there is something so grotesque in solemnly denying that one ever feels an ache or a pain, in solemnly doubting whether one now can be really doubting, in solemnly judging that neither oneself nor anyone else has ever judged or inferred or had any sort of idea, that if scientific men say these things, then so much the worse for their common sense and their science; there is a limit to what we can accept even from the most respected authorities. But of course scientific men do not say these things, except as one or other of them becomes the victim of speculative midsummer madness. Normally scientists hug experience; they believe, as Huxley put it, that an ugly fact will slay the most beautiful theory. They have been trained to take facts seriously, and they consider it axiomatic that they must never deny a fact because it is inconvenient, or because it fails to fit some *a priori* definition. Now behaviorism sins against this elementary principle. It provides a conspicuous example of the practice it most loudly protests against, namely, the distortion by metaphysics of factual observation. Thus in the delimiting of its province it is scientific in the sense in which Christian Science is scientific.

[3] *The Nature of Thought*, New York, The Macmillan Company, 1941, Vol. I, Chap. 9.

Just as the Christian Scientists insist, on *a priori* grounds, that there is no such thing as matter, so the behaviorists insist, on *a priori* grounds, that there is no such thing as mind. This may be a gallant act in both cases, as Nelson's was a gallant act when, told that his admiral was flying the signal for retreat, he put his blind eye to the telescope and swore that he saw nothing. But gallantry is not science.

This naive and dogmatic metaphysics, however, with its "logical necessity of affecting anaesthesia," is peculiarly difficult to get at. If you try dialectics on it, after the manner of Descartes, and show that thought *must* exist because to doubt it is to do the very thing that is being doubted, the behaviorist, commonly untrained in philosophy and suspicious of all that passes under that name, complains that he is being tricked. If you appeal to experience and insist that when people talk of pleasures and pains they actually mean pleasures and pains, and not electro-chemical transformations in their cerebra, indeed that they had been talking of pleasures and pains for a hundred centuries at least before they heard of nervous systems or cerebra, the behaviorist merely blinks at you and declares that he has not the slightest idea to what either they or you refer. And in a sense he has scored a stale-mate. If he insists that all he means by pleasures and pains is nervous changes, you do not refute him by showing that other people mean something else. Absurdity, Paulsen once said, has this in common with truth, that it cannot be refuted. One is faced by the difficult task of making the behaviorist see what a previous partisan commitment inhibits him from seeing. His "party line" has laid down what shall be recognized as fact and what not, and he is faithful unto the death of all humor and common sense. We shall not argue with him. We shall only indulge the hope that he may some day reacquire these humble but serviceable faculties.

Those who hold the second alternative mentioned above are more formidable. They are the persons who, while too sophisticated to be victimized by behaviorist metaphysics, still believe that the behaviorist method is the only scientific method of studying mind. They admit the existence of consciousness and the breadth of the abyss that separates it from matter in motion, but precisely because of that breadth think it foolish for science to hazard a crossing. Let it keep to the field where its methods are clearly applicable and where they have so brilliantly succeeded, and let it surrender consciousness to those less disciplined disciplines that are willing to dabble in intangibles and imponderables—esthetics and literary psychology, ethics and religion. Psychology as a natural science is the science of behavior, and behavior means physical response. We fully grant, they would say, that associated with this response in some obscure way there are processes of affection, recall, perception, desire, and so on. These are by-products of physical change, but they have no return effects upon it; and since the physical series thus takes its course uninterrupted from without, its by-products may be disregarded and it may be studied by itself. This was the program of natural science as conceived by the school of Huxley, and it is implicitly adopted by many recent writers who would hesitate to avow it explicitly. To be sure, the theory is not as clean-cut as at first appears. At the very moment of announcing that between the two sides there is a tremendous fixed abyss, it is engaged in throwing a precarious rope bridge from one side to the other and encouraging quiet trespassing. Since mental processes vary with physical according to law, it is tempting to make psychology include psycho-physics, even though the correlates on the mental side do not strictly belong to nature. Current psychology largely consists of such psycho-physics. It preserves its self-respect as a natural science by saying that if it does talk about conscious states, at least it recognizes them for what they are—impotencies, shadows, *undinge;* they make no difference to the executive order of things, the order of matter in motion; they make no difference even to the psychical states that inconsequently succeed them.

Even those psychologists who have not accepted this epiphenomenalist theory are often deeply affected by it. Titchener, for example, repudiated it; he was a psycho-physical parallelist; yet it is easy to feel in Titchener's thought the powerful drag of a natural science that was bent on depriving mind of much of its distinctiveness and autonomy. That part of a mental state which makes its organization most irreducibly different from that of any physical state, namely meaning, Titchener excluded from his psychology altogether. He analyzed what was left much as he would analyze a mosaic, by breaking it down into its components, of which he recognized three sorts only—sensation, image, and affection. These, combined in various patterns, exhausted the realm of mind. And since no connections could exist among these elements that were not strictly paralleled among their physical correlates, Titchener's strained and meager explanations of the higher thought processes were those of a man weighed down with self-imposed chains.

Now there are two prime difficulties with the epiphenomenalist program and both are difficulties about causality. First, if it is admitted that body acts on mind, how can it be plausibly denied that mind acts on body? The evidence for a causal movement in one direction is of precisely the same kind as the evidence for a movement in the other. If causality means correlation, then we must say with the epiphenomenalist that a prick causes a pain, that veronal causes stupor, and that santonin makes things look yellow; the mental changes are clearly correlated with preceding physical changes. But if the epiphenomenalist says this, he must say, on precisely the same sort of grounds, that the perception of a bear makes him run away, that he reads detective stories because he likes them, and that his decision to stand up has something to do with the standing up that follows; here the physical changes can be correlated with preceding mental changes. If the causal escalator moves up, why should it not also move down? The epiphenomenalist cannot protest that moving down would mean an intrusion into the physical series from a non-physical realm and therefore a creation of energy out of that which, physically speaking, is nothing; for he has already admitted a process which on that score is equally objectionable, namely, the discharge of motion and energy into the inane. Between the abolition of energy and its creation there is, physically speaking, nothing to choose.

Secondly, epiphenomenalism, holding that the only causes

are physical, is committed to an intolerable consequence, namely, that there are no causal connections among mental events. My hearing that an old friend is dead has nothing to do with my grief. The anger a man feels when insulted makes not the slightest difference to his desire to "tell off" the offender. Now even if we were to admit that the direct insight we seem to have here into mental causation is illusory, the facts of correlation give ample basis for accepting the linkage as causal. If mental events are causal at all, and causality reduces to correlation, then causality among purely mental events must be conceded, since fixed conjunctions may be clearly shown between them. To admit the premises and reject the conclusion is unscientific and worse; it is a violation at once of logic and of common sense.

We have now seen that of the three alternatives confronting the natural scientist when he comes to deal with consciousness, two are far from plausible. It will not do to deny outright that consciousness exists; it will not do to admit it and then deny to it every manner of influence. If it is admitted to the domain of science at all, the admission should be an ungrudging one; there should be none of the old studied looking in the other direction, but a frank and full recognition that the new object of inquiry has a nature of its own, that this nature is radically different from material change, and that a science formulated to deal with such change must be prepared for large revisions if it is to cope with its object satisfactorily.

What are the revisions required? The question is too large to be handled here in detail. But the *sort* of revision called for may be made clear if we fix attention for a moment on a mental process that everyone will agree to be of the first importance and interest. Let us consider what is required if one is to deal with the mental events called *judgments*.

We begin with a distinction. It is an all-important distinction, a very watershed of reflection about the science of mind. The failure to see it is at the root of most over-sanguine expectations as to what science can achieve in the mental domain. If it is clearly seen and its force conceded, one will begin to understand why a long succession of first-rate thinkers, running from Hegel through Green and Bradley to Mr. Joseph, have distrusted "scientific" psychology as a means of illuminating the higher processes, and why some great foreign institutions of learning, such as Oxford, have taken toward it an attitude that to the outsider—and particularly the American outsider, whose confidence in psychology is unbounded—seems so churlish and inexplicable. The distinction I mean is the distinction between judgment as an event and judgment as a cognition.

On the one side a judgment is just as truly an event as any occurrence in physical nature, as the splash of a raindrop or the stubbing of a toe. It has a date and occupies a certain time; it is normally preceded by certain events of a physical kind as well as of its own kind, and followed by others; and if it cannot intelligibly be said to occur at a certain place, it is at any rate associated in a very intimate way with events that occur in someone's head. It would thus seem to be well suited to scientific treatment, that is, to admit perfectly well of being explained, after the fashion of purely physical events, by causal correlation. What possible reason is there for treating it in any other way? The reason is that it has another side, which reveals it as a vastly different kind of thing from stubbed toes or falling drops. The judgment that is on one side an event in a series of events is on the other side an apprehension of something as true. Besides being an incident in my history, it is the presence in my experience of a content or object—the attractiveness of that picture, the high cost of living, the death of Caesar in 44 B.C. This presence to thought of an object is not something adventitious to the thought; it is the very essence of it, that which makes it what it is; one can identify it only by saying what it is of.

Now just as the thought, considered as an event, has a context of other events in terms of which science explains it, so, considered as the presentation of an object, it has a context of other objects to which it is logically related with varying degrees of intimacy; no judgment springs into the mind like Melchizidek, without genealogy or relations. Even when at first it does seem to appear in this way, a closer scrutiny will always reveal some logical filaments. When the thought arose about Caesar's death, for example, I may have been thinking about Hitler and the chances of his survival, or about how likely it is that men of prominence should arouse jealousy, or the moral desert of tyrants; or perhaps the line was running through my head: "the paths of glory lead but to the grave." What is contained in the setting matters less than the fact that the setting is there. This context of objects, or to speak more accurately, of relevant propositions, may be called the ideal context. And the question now is: When we attempt to explain this remarkable event called a thought, is it enough to consider its relations merely as an event, that is, its *de facto* conjunctions or correlations with other events, or must we also take into account its relations as a content to its ideal context?

Let us take an illustration in which we may look at the matter more closely. Let us suppose a philosopher meditating in the twilight on the problem of evil, and let us put him through some typical paces. Since we must start him somewhere, let us have him begin with the thought of a loving and benevolent Deity. Now if God loves His creatures, he philosophizes, He would not inflict upon them, particularly perhaps upon animals, which are so little able to profit from it, continual and excruciating pain. It follows that if such pain is inflicted, as in fact it appears to be, this must be because God, though willing to prevent it, is unable to prevent it. But that means that He is not all-powerful. This comes as an unwelcome conclusion; so our philosopher starts again, this time from the position that he has just been unwilling to surrender. God is unlimited in power. Well, the philosopher reasons, if God's power is unlimited, He could prevent this gratuitous suffering. But the fact is that He does not prevent it. Now if, while able to prevent it, He declines to prevent it, He cannot be perfectly loving. In sum, if God is all-powerful, He is not all-loving, and if all-loving, He is not all-powerful. He cannot, the philosopher concludes, have both these attributes at once.

Here is a fairly typical example of what is called a higher mental process. Suppose that when the philosopher comes to the end of it we ask him why he arrived at that particular conclusion. If he is a behaviorist, he will launch upon a protracted account of how his vocal processes were "conditioned." Unfortunately we shall have to leave his account unchallenged, for long before he has completed it, we shall inconsiderately have fallen asleep. If the philosopher is an epiphenomenalist, he will tell us that what really went on was a series of discharges across synapses, and that if we are to account for the course of the reasoning, we must do so in these terms. It is true that the first set of discharges figured in his mind as a set of premises and the final set of discharges as a conclusion, but we must not allow ourselves to suppose that the conscious grasp of these premises had anything to do with the appearance of that conclusion. That would be a bad mistake, just as it would be to suppose that the thought of that conclusion had anything to do with the speech in which it was ·uttered. Once again, if our philosopher draws his psychology from Mill or Bain or Titchener, he will reduce the reasoning to a train of images which follow as they do because (though till now he never knew it) he has had a marvelous past in which he has filled his mind with millions of firm associations by taking them in enormous habit-forming doses.

Now I submit that this is rubbish, all of it. The attempt to be scientific has ended by running itself into the ground and producing a set of accounts that nobody can really believe. The reason for the incredibility lies on the surface. It is that all these programs are trying to explain reasoning from the outside. They ostentatiously turn their backs upon the clues supplied by content and ideal context, clues that fairly cry out for recognition. They try to explain the development of my thought on the assumption that *what* I am thinking about makes no difference, that reasoning in geometry and the recall of nonsense syllables are the same sort of process. They refuse to recognize that contained in the content itself there are impulsions and necessities that tend to keep the current in its channel. The upshot is a strange spectacle. We see science holding the fort of a sterile and grim fundamentalism against the joint attack of metaphysics and common sense.

We are arguing that the higher mental processes have a large measure of autonomy. What positive reasons are there for believing this? We shall offer two arguments, a direct and an indirect. The first is based on inspection. If our philosopher were to state faithfully what went on in his mind, he would probably begin about as follows: My thought of God as kind and loving led on naturally to the thought that such a being would seek to make His creatures happy. If you ask me why this thought should follow, part of the answer, no doubt, is that at the time I was trying to think, that is, to develop what was implied by the matter before me. But of course it was not my interest in thinking that determined what I should find; that was determined by the character of the object. If the thought that God would seek to make His creatures happy cropped up in my mind rather than any of a million other things, it was because my first thought implied it; the line of logical implication was the line of natural development for any mind that was really thinking. To think is to infer; to infer is not to fabricate conclusions arbitrarily, but to allow one's eye to follow the structure of the subject-matter. One reasons soundly just so far as one succeeds, not in taking the lead one-self, but in doing precisely the opposite, surrendering oneself to the object and following the argument wherever *it* leads. And where my thought is at its best, I know directly that this is what is happening.

It is the same with the remaining steps of the argument. The hypothesis that a benevolent God exists implies not only that His creatures would be happy, but that they are happy; so the logical impulse carries one on to an inspection of the facts. The logic of the case directs the movement of attention. Of course what it brings to light when attention falls upon the facts is not determined by this logic; facts make their independent contribution. But it is instructive to see that the mind does not come to rest upon the fact. The fact holds interest because of its context, and thought takes note of it only to leave it instantly and leap on along the line of implication: given all this gratuitous pain, God must lack power to prevent it. The fact is a springboard for inference; thought is carried beyond it at once by the immanent logic of the situation. And so of the later steps, which would have to be dealt with in the same way.

It will be observed that this account is not a speculative one, like the so-called scientific accounts. It does not try to theorize thoughts away into images, or to explain familiar processes by reference to synaptic exchanges whose nature is conjectural and whose very existence is inferential. The evidence it appeals to is the direct evidence of inspection. We know from countless experiences that when we sit down to write a letter, our thoughts are under the control—which may of course be wavering in any degree—of a particular ideal context, and that under the influence of that context suggestions press themselves upon us that are wholly different from those arising when we try to add a column of figures or write a sonnet. To be sure, while we are writing the letter, we are not also watching to see how it manages to get written; but if at any moment we catch ourselves, or if we look back and ask ourselves why this idea offered itself rather than another, the pressure of the ideal context is usually so clear and sufficient that it is named at once as the self-evident cause. Perhaps I begin a letter to my best friend, "You faithless rascal!" What could have led me to do that? Anyone who knew him and me, and the long history that is implicitly operative in my mind, and my present feeling and purpose about him, would have no difficulty in understanding it. Anyone who did not know that would be quite in the dark about it, even though he knew more about my cerebrum than we are ever likely to know.

There are persons, however, for whom this sort of argument is inconclusive. They are ready to accept perceptual evidence that seems to some of us very dubious, but they will reject at once any evidence that comes from introspection, no matter what it may be. We cannot think this a wholly reasonable attitude. Nevertheless we should like to have these persons on our side, so we add to the above direct argument an indirect one. It is called indirect because it first draws some consequences of the "scientific" view, and then argues back from these consequences to the unsoundness of the theory that implies them. The argument seems to us a powerful one, since the consequences are nothing short of disastrous.

Among these consequences is this, that scientific thought is

itself discredited from beginning to end. Scientific thought, like
all thought, is inference. It involves isolating the relevant factors, leaping to the hypothesis which those factors require, and
developing this hypothesis into its implications. If the scientist
succeeds, it is because the suggestion that arose in his mind *was*
governed by the relevant factors, and because that hypothesis
*did* develop in his mind what it really implied. If he reached
his mark without such aid, it could only be by chance. Yet by
chance it must have been, if the scientific account is true. For
that account refuses to recognize that any constraint whatever
has been exercised by the subject-matter. The only agencies at
work, whether one takes the behaviorist view or the epiphenomenalist, are totally external to this, and consist in physical
changes in the brain. Even between these changes, it insists,
the only relation known is one of concomitance; with *necessary* connections it will have no dealings. Now what we want
to know is this: If we start with a hypothesis A, and our
thought succeeds in keeping to the groove of its implications,
developing what is involved in the character of A, and we are
then told that this character made no difference whatever to
the course of the thought, that B's being entailed by A was in
no way a favoring circumstance in B's appearance, then how in
the world does any reasoning ever get done? Scientists succeed
daily in solving problems that involve intricate and elaborate
reasoning, but no suggestion that ever arises in their minds is
affected by the requirements of the problem; the agencies that
bring success operate wholly from the outside. There is only
one conclusion possible. Their success is luck.

Fumbling attempts have been made at times to avert this
conclusion—fumbling, because the problem has not, as a rule,
been clearly seen. Many philosophers and psychologists, for
example, have held that logical necessity is only firm association, and hence that associative laws are all that is needed to
account for inference. If no answer to this is suggested here,
it is because the answer has so often been given.[4] It may be re-
plied, again, that logical necessity is not confined to the realm

[4] See, e.g., Cook Wilson, *Statement and Inference*, II, 618 ff. And cf. the
writer's *Nature of Thought*, II, Chap. 28.

of consciousness, that it exists also in the physical world, and that if the cerebral change corresponding to the premises itself necessitates in a logical sense the change corresponding to the conclusion, the scientific account will still stand. There are three comments to make on this view. First, it probably involves a confusion between physical and logical necessity. We must remember that the physical changes referred to are all ultimately motions. Now it is often said that one motion necessitates another, that the blow of the hammer, for example, necessitates the sinking of the nail. But what is commonly intended by this is that the blow *forced* the nail to sink in, whatever that means, not that the blow *implied* the sinking. And it is not quite clear that the phrase "motion A implies motion B" has any meaning. Secondly, whether it does or not, one cannot assume that it does without breaking sharply with the established program of physical science. We have seen that causal explanation consists for such science in correlation solely; not only does science abjure the search for logical necessities in the world of matter; it abjures even physical necessities, and restricts itself to regular conjunction. Thirdly, even if the scientist were to break with tradition and admit that the motions of his electrons were somehow linked by logical necessity, that still would not take him far enough. For there are many further relations that have a part in the control of ideas, relations that no sort of ingenuity can reduce to components of the physical world. There are such things as dramatic necessities which act in the mind of the dramatist when he is trying to conclude a play. There are necessities in painting, which may require that in the interest of harmony a certain color be introduced or removed. There are necessities in music which require that a piece begun in a certain key shall be continued in that key. Such necessities, to be sure, may have some sort of parallel in the physical realm, but these necessities themselves, the ones that exist and act in the process of creation, cannot possibly exist there. They cannot exist there for the reason that, by universal admission of scientists, the feelings and tones and colors among which they have their being do not themselves exist there.

We began by saying that values are sometimes causes. It will now perhaps be clear what we meant by this. We meant that mind at its best is autonomous. Granting that it is connected mysteriously and intimately with physical processes that natural science claims as its own, it cannot be reduced to those processes, nor can it be explained by the laws of those processes. The laws that govern it must be seen from within, not from without; to discover them, one must plant oneself at the point of view of the artist, the moral agent, the thinker, and note the kind of demand that his special subject-matter makes upon him.

If the natural scientist protests that that would strain his method to the breaking point, he has every right to be heard. He has no obligation to break the molds of his great tradition. By remaining within a severely limited field and employing his admirably definite standards of explanation, he has achieved results that are beyond gratitude. But if he chooses the limited field, he must be content with limited results. He cannot stay there and *also* offer a science of man. For whether scientists like it or not, man is a creature moving fitfully in a world of values, a world that is laying continual demands upon his reason, conscience, and sensibility. And these demands do make a difference—indeed they make all the difference—to his experience and his behavior. To admit the operation of these values among the determinants of science would undoubtedly muddy its waters; it would make science continuous with philosophy, and would include within its bounds a vast uncharted area of indefinite extent and shifting content, whose government would require profound and repeated revisions of traditional method. Such a science could not keep as its own the simple and clear ideal of traditional physics; and its old tidiness, alas, would be gone forever. But for all that it would be a science of man.

# 4. SCIENCE AND SOCIETY

# THE SCIENTIFIC APPROACH
# TO THE STUDY OF MAN

## *by* Bronislaw Malinowski

### I. THE SCIENCE OF CULTURE

THE SCIENTIFIC basis of anthropology must be established, for anthropology as the theory of culture provides in many ways the scientific basis of all studies concerned with man, his behavior, and his achievements. Culture is clearly the fullest context of all human activities. It is the vast instrumentality through which man achieves his ends, both as an animal who must eat, rest, and reproduce; and as the spiritual being who desires to extend his mental horizons, produce works of art, and develop systems of faith. Thus, culture is at the same time the minimum mechanism for the satisfaction of the most elementary needs of man's animal nature, and also an ever-developing, ever-increasing system of new ends, new values, and new creative possibilities.

An understanding of what this reality is, how it works, how it is constituted and determined, is indispensable for all humanists. The archaeologist and the historian, who have to reconstruct the past cultural reality from partial data, monumental or documentary, must base their reconstruction on the laws determining the relations between a part and the whole, between economic and juridical phenomena, and between the structure of a society and its creative output. They must be in possession of a scientific theory of culture, or else indulge in more or less inspired, sound, but always intuitive guesswork. In economics and the science of law it is increasingly recognized that the processes of production, exchange, and consumption do not happen in a vacuum, but within a cultural context; while legislation, the behavior of judges and juries, and the effective sanction of legal rules depend upon such factors as public opinion, economic necessities, the level of education, and the type of religion and ethics prevalent in a society. It seems hardly even necessary to stress the fact that the student of contemporary social phenomena and also the psychologist must attack their problems within the real context in which these occur, that is, the context of culture.

Science—to give an unpretentious yet clear definition or reminder—is the translation of experience into general laws which have predictive value. We have to inquire, then, whether it is possible to establish general rules and principles concerning cultural process and product. Such rules, to be scientific, must be inferred from observation and be subject to experimental test. They must be generalizations of universal validity. It is essential to have statements of principle which remain true whether applied to primitive or to highly developed cultures, to an arctic community or a tropical island-tribe in the Pacific. We have to establish clearly determined relations between cultural variables embodied into formulae of general applicability.

From a slightly different point of view, we can say that science establishes order into its particular subject matter by isolating the relevant factors and forces. It will then be necessary to prove that such relevant factors of structure and forces controlling the process do exist in the domain of culture. Such systems of relevant concatenation would give us the clue for the observation of a new culture and the means of describing it adquately. They would also provide the common measure for the comparative, that is, theoretical treatment of all phenomena of organized behavior.

The legitimate subject matter of anthropology, as well as of other social sciences, is culture. The experimental approach to this subject matter must be based on direct observation of collective, organized behavior through field-work. By field-work we mean the study of living communities and their material culture, whether at a low level of development or within our own civilizations. Such study must be guided by the general theory of culture, while observation has to be stated in terms of general principle. As in all sciences, so also here we shall have to inquire whether the final test of applicability through planned social engineering is possible in the case of social studies.

I am omitting on purpose from my definition of the scientific method the test of quantitative approach, and the feasibility of mathematical or semi-mathematical formulation. It is clear that wherever we have phenomena amenable to counting and measuring, the scientific approach would demand this type of operation. Also, in the rare cases where statistics yield sufficient data for curves or equations, these instrumentalities must be used. The general complexity of a subject matter makes it, as a rule, less amenable to quantitative treatment. In all such treatment, grave errors are introduced and increased in any algebraic manipulations whenever we count or compute entities which are not really identical. The problem, therefore, of identity or of isolation of relevant factors and of their relations is one which must be solved first, and then only can we debate whether mathematical formulations are likely to introduce more clarity or more presumptuous error into our arguments. It goes without saying that in vital statistics, in the statement of certain economic transactions, and in the description of technical processes, especially at higher levels, the quantitative, as well as the mathematical procedures have been already employed and cannot be left out of consideration.

As regards the primary character of science, that is, the cross-fertilization of observed fact and theoretical argument, the anthropologist has certain initial advantages and can claim certain achievements. Engaged as he is in the study of primitive cultures for which we have no historical records and very little archaeological documentation, the anthropologist, by the very nature of his material, was driven into the field. He had to become his own chronicler in methodical ethnographic researches in the field and to establish perhaps the first laboratory of social science. Since observation always implies theory, we find in modern anthropological studies that exchange of inspiration which comes from the contact with facts and the simultaneous striving to subsume them under general principles.

The wide range of cultural diversities was another motive which inspired the scientific trend in modern anthropology. Sound generalization must be derived from comparison and the use of the inductive method, and here again, unless we have some theoretical common measure of comparison, our induction fails.

As regards applications, anthropology has not as yet many achievements to its credit. Nevertheless, it may be said that social engineering presents certain facilities and a degree of viability when it comes to colonial affairs, lacking under our own modern conditions. The colonial power has a control, legislative and administrative, over a primitive tribe, far greater than that admissible in a democratic commonwealth. Totalitarian experimentation, again, is not based in its sociological aspect on a scientific policy. In democratic countries, the typical politician is a disturbing link when it comes to the scientific guidance of public events. He is, as a rule, more keen to become a lawgiver than to be amenable to law in the scientific sense.

Obviously anthropology has no claims whatsoever to deal with the scientific problem of culture single-handed. It had certain initial advantages. To use them fully it must first and foremost disclaim some spurious pretences. The savages are not the only representatives of man. We know full well that modern savagery is as illuminating as its primitive version. Thus, sociology, as soon as it becomes fully infected with the field-work habits of the anthropologist, will have at least as much to contribute to the scientific theory of culture as its humbler collaborator. Indeed, in the science of culture we would fail completely as anthropologists unless we establish full co-operation between the study of the human mind, of modern societies and cultures, and of such well-established specialties as jurisprudence and economics.

## II. THE NATURE OF CULTURAL PROCESS

Considering culture as a whole, that is, at all levels and in any environment, we have to recognize first its instrumental character. We might survey the organization of an arctic community, a tribe living in the tropical jungle, a horde of lowest primitives, such as the Australian aborigines, and anywhere and everywhere we would find them wielding a body of implements, following rules of behavior, cherishing ideas and beliefs, engaging through all this in activities which integrate into a vast and complex instrumental apparatus. At higher levels of development, in the New World civilizations of Mexico or Peru, in ancient Egypt or in modern Europe, the apparatus and the activities are more highly developed, but the total effect is instrumental and so is every one of the differential phases. Man everywhere is maintained by his culture, allowed to reproduce, as well as instructed and assisted in this, supplied with techniques, knowledge, recreation, art, and religion.

Were we to look more closely at any particular culture, we would find every activity related to some organization or other. In each we would find a group co-operating, linked by common interests and a purpose. Members of such a group or institution own conjointly a portion of the environment, some implements or machines, and dispose of a quota of national wealth. They obey prescribed norms of conduct and are trained in particular skills. Through their activities thus normed and implemented, they achieve their purpose or intentions, known to each member and socially recognized. They also produce an impression on the environment, social and physical; they achieve results which can be revealed through sociological analysis.

We would find such organizations in the homes of the people as family groups and domestic institutions. We would find that the food supply and the production of goods and implements are the result of such organized co-operative work. The temples and the courts of law are maintained and run by groups of people organized for the purpose, moved by definite motives or values, and playing this special part in public life.

This surface impression, dictated by sound common sense, might lead the observer to the statement of a few generalizations. Culture as a whole is an extensive instrumental system of organized activities. It is exercised by a system of related institutions, that is, groups of people united by common interest, endowed with material equipment, following rules of their tradition or agreement, and contributing toward the work of the culture as a whole. The interests which supply the motive power and dictate the tasks of the group are at times physiological, as in food-production, domestic life, and defense mechanisms. There are, however, other interests, values, and motives connected with science or with art which transcend any biological determinism. We are thus led to the fuller analysis as to what the drives or motives of human beings are, and also as to the principles and forces of human organization.

As regards the drives, man is obviously an animal; hence his organic needs will always give rise to a permanent biological determinism in all behavior. Men have to eat, sleep, reproduce, and protect their bodies from excessive temperature, as well as from physical destruction. There is a minimum of elementary conditions which have to be fulfilled so that the individual organism survives and the group retains its numbers. Even a slight but progressive deterioration of the healthy organic state would inevitably lead to cultural extinction.

It is equally important to realize that human beings live not by biological drives alone, but by physiological drives molded and modified by culture. As regards nutrition, food and its intake are not a mere exchange between man and environment. In a primitive tribe or a civilized community, there is an organized system of production, distribution, storing, preparing, which provides each member with his meals. Here again, consumption, that is, the intake of food, is fashioned by the taste, taboos and hygienic rules, which partly limit and partly redirect the normal appetite. Propagation is determined, in its very impulse, by the ideals of beauty and desirability in which the sex impulse integrates with esthetic, economic, and social considerations. The rules of specific taboo, such as incest and exogamy, as well as of preferential mating, dictate the type of courtship, while the production of children is universally defined by the law of marriage. Nor are the results of propagation merely biological. The extensive systems of kinship ties and grouping into clans, so prevalent in primitive communities, are the translation into sociological norms of the results of biological propagation. Bodily exercise is determined by economic labor and by systems of sports, recreational pursuits, or even artistic activities. Thus, man everywhere acts under culturally determined incentives, he submits to the norms prescribed by tradition, he co-operates and pools or re-distributes the produce of his labor.

There are certain phases in human behavior even more removed from biological fact than those here described. In a primitive tribe we find objects of magical virtue or religious sanctity or economic value: the famous bull-roarers of Central Australia, the totem poles of the North Western American tribes, or the millstones known from Micronesia. In order to understand the values attached to such objects and the activities which surround them, we would have to enter a world of mythological antecedents or social and economic conventions. We would have to learn the meaning of the dogmatic principles and see how they are expressed in ritual, ethics, or economic transaction. To understand why certain people indulge in head-hunting and others practice cannibalism, why in certain cultures valuable objects are produced only in order to be destroyed, we obviously would have to consider the formation of cultural value, of legal principle, as well as the native conception of wealth, social ranking, and the realities of magical or religious belief.

Man thus is not merely impelled by hunger and thirst, by love and the desire to sleep. There are other motives connected with ambition, rank, doctrine, and mythology which establish as powerful incentives to conduct as those of an innate drive. Instrumentality obtains throughout. In other words, we always find that a human being is impelled to a specific activity in order to attain a desired end. Culture, however, obviously not merely solves the simple organic problems, but creates new problems, inspires new desires, and establishes a new universe in which man moves, never completely free from his organic needs but also following new ends and receiving new satisfactions.

All this does not imply that cultural determinism introduces a mere chaos of relativity in which we would have to resort to the arbitrary biddings of some *deus ex machina*, of some specific tribal or cultural genius. We shall be able to give a clear definition and catalogue of biological needs which are the prime movers of human behavior. We shall also clearly establish what we mean by derived needs or instrumental imperatives. Finally, we shall show that the integrative values, such as ideas, beliefs, moral rules, are also determined and significant through their relation to culture as a whole. The needs of the organism and the raw materials supplied by the environment are the elements of the primary or biological determinism. The indirect cultural situation, however, in which the raw materials are obtained and elaborated and the human organism adjusted, imposes new cultural, that is instrumental and integrative imperatives, which are subject to determinism, hence also to scientific analysis.

The ability to establish and to maintain the cultural apparatus confers enormous advantages on mankind, advantages which consist, on the one hand, in a safer and fuller satisfaction of organic needs; and, on the other hand, in the gift of new necessities and new satisfactions. Culture thus satisfies first the minimum standard of living, that of organic survival. It also adds an increased artificial standard of enjoyment, in which man reaches what usually is described as intellectual, artistic, and ethical pleasures and satisfactions.

For all this there is a price to be paid in terms of obedience to tradition. Man has to submit to a number of rules and determinants which do not come from his organism but from submission to his own artifact and machinery, to co-operation, and to the tyranny of words and other symbols. The oft-repeated opposition as between man and machine, in which man is often described as the slave of his self-produced mechanism, his Frankenstein monster, contains an essential truth. Even when man is not enslaved beyond the limits of real necessity, he becomes permanently dependent on his artifacts once he has started to use them. Co-operation, the social give and take, implies a determined quota of contribution for which man receives, generally, a larger return, but has to remain bound to his cultural contract. As regards symbolic tradition, it does not always enslave, but it invariably redirects, limits and determines human behavior.

## III. THE BIOLOGICAL DETERMINISM OF CULTURE

We have stated that the biological determinants appear in every culture. We have also stated that they are invariably refashioned and intertwined with other motives. The problem arises, in what sense can we isolate and define biological determinism? And further, in what way is it related to more complex cultural phenomena? The answer is contained in the adjoining figure, in which the main types of biological determinism have been summed up severally and concretely. We see there listed a set of vital sequences which, it is maintained, are always incorporated into every culture. The concept of vital sequence means that the central activity or biological act, listed in column B, must be performed regularly and permanently in every culture. This part of the performance is integrally incorporated into culture, with modifications to be discussed later, as regards certain prerequisites and the conditions under which it is allowed to happen. The drive listed in column A invariably receives a profound modification, different from one culture to another. But although modified, the drive can be determined partly in its physiological character, partly in that it is always connected with the biological act. The items listed in column C are again definable in terms of biological fact: satiation, detumescence, the freeing of the organism of waste matter, the restoration of muscular energy, and the using up of biochemical tensions through muscular exercise and breathing.

The three phases can be defined by the bio-chemist, the physicist, and the ecologist. The actual intake of air or food; the act of conjugation; sleep, rest, nutrition, or excretion, are clearly defined activities, in which several branches of natural science are interested. Thus, the concept of vital sequence is neither vague nor devoid of substance. It refers to happenings within the human organism as related to physical and cultural environment. However much the drive or satisfaction might be refashioned by culture, both drive and satisfaction must be of such a nature as to lead to the performance of each physiological act, adequate in terms of biology. We see here that the

PERMANENT VITAL SEQUENCES INCORPORATED
IN ALL CULTURES

| A. *Impulse* | B. *Act* | C. *Satisfaction* |
|---|---|---|
| drive to breathe gasping for air | intake of oxygen | elimination of $CO_2$ in tissues |
| hunger | ingestion of food | satiation |
| thirst | absorption of liquid | quenching |
| sex appetite | conjugation | detumescence |
| fatigue | rest | restoration of muscular and nervous energy |
| restlessness | activity | satisfaction of fatigue |
| somnolence | sleep | awakening with restored energy |
| bladder pressure | micturition | removal of tension |
| colon pressure | defecation | abdominal relaxation |
| fright | escape from danger | relaxation |
| pain | avoidance by effective act | return to normal state |

*Figure 1*

concepts of form and function of human behavior are included, since each can be defined in terms of natural science.

The vital sequence is thus the projection of a complex cultural reality onto the physiological plane. We can now also define the concept of basic need over and above that of drive. In each culture there must be systems of standardized arrangements which allow of a full, regular, and general satisfaction of all the individual drives. We can, then, define the basic need in its several varieties as including all individual drives which have to be satisfied so as to keep the organisms of a community in a normal state of healthy metabolism. The non-satisfaction of any or every basic need would imply the gradual biological deterioration of the group, which, if cumulative, would lead to extinction. As regards procreation, the basic need here requires that a sufficient incidence of effective reproduction should occur to maintain the numerical strength of a community. In any culture where celibacy, chastity vows, abstinences, or ritual castration would exceed restricted numerical limits, we would have a process of gradual extinction. The concept of basic need differs from that of drive, in that it refers to the collective exercise of individual drives, integrated with reference to the community as a whole. The satisfaction of basic needs is predicated with reference to all the organisms, to environmental conditions and to the cultural setting of the community. It need not, perhaps, be stressed that in the study of cultural realities, whether through field-work or in theoretical analysis, we do not resort any more to our analysis in terms of individual drive, but have to rely on the concept of basic need. The drive—activity—satisfaction analysis contains an abstraction of great importance for the foundations of a sound theory of culture. In actual research on cultures, however, we do not meet this abstraction, but we are faced always with culturally organized satisfactions of integral basic needs.

Figure 2 summarizes concretely and in a highly condensed and simplified manner the basic needs and the cultural responses

---

BASIC NEEDS AND CULTURAL RESPONSES

A. *Basic Needs:* 1. metabolism; 2. reproduction; 3. bodily comforts; 4. safety; 5. movement; 6. growth; 7. health.

B. *Cultural Responses:* 1. commissariat; 2. kinship; 3. shelter; 4. protection; 5. activities; 6. training; 7. hygiene.

---

*Figure 2*

to them. Its meaning will become clearer in detail as our argument advances. For the present, it is clear that it corresponds to a large extent to our list of drives. Several of them, however, have been compressed into one entry here, as for instance the need of solid foods, liquids and intake of oxygen. All these are parts of the process of metabolism. Another important point is that each entry has to be considered as integrally related with reference to need and its linked responses. For, as we already know, in the human species biological motive never occurs in a pure and isolated form. Human beings breathe in closed rooms or caves; they have to combine breathing with rules of politeness or taboo, since human breath is, in some cultures, regarded as sacred and in others as dangerous. Nutrition, propagation, or bodily comforts occur as formed habits. Human beings eat according to a definite daily sequence. They conjugate in accordance with rules of law and morals, or else against them, and thus under cultural conflict. The need for bodily comforts does not arise in an environmental vacuum and then send off the organism in search of a satisfaction. Savages and more sophisticated beings alike wear clothes, carry out a routine of cleanliness, live in habitations, and warm themselves at some permanent sources of warmth. Thus we can say that the stream of necessities or motives arising out of each need flows, as it were, parallel to the stream of culturally obtainable satisfactions. In the daily round of life, as well as in the seasonal cycle, the human being normally passes through a routine of instrumental effort and of prepared satisfaction in which biological stimulus and organic effort are not hooked up by ad hoc, into direct,—short-circuited links of desire and satisfaction, but are interwoven into two long chains: one of large-scale organized work on culture and for culture; the other, a systematic drawing upon or consuming of already prepared cultural benefits and goods.

## IV. THE INSTRUMENTAL PHASE OF HUMAN BEHAVIOR

To make the last argument more concrete and precise, let us again embody it into a diagrammatic presentation:

INSTRUMENTALLY IMPLEMENTED VITAL SEQUENCE

$Drive(_1)$—Instrumental Performance—Culturally defined situation—$Drive(_2)$—Consummatory act—Satisfaction (meta-physiological).

*Figure 3*

This is obviously a much more accurate and less abstract representation than the vital sequence previously diagrammatized. Certain similarities between the two obtain. We are here still dealing with the vital sequence, one which includes a biological activity. There are in culture, as we shall see, sequences which do not include such a link. In this table there is a definite linkage in which all the phases are determined by the relationship between a biological drive and its satisfaction.

There are however differences. To be true to the reality of typical cultural concatenations, we had to split the drive into two. Drive($_1$) is the instrumental motive, the impulse to take the round-about way which man follows when he produces or purchases his food, prepares it, and places it on his table. In this he acts to a certain extent like the learning animal in a maze, who has to discover and to use the devices which supply it with food. Sex leads the human animal not to conjugation directly, but to courtship and in many cases to marriage. In short, the whole training of the human organism teaches the individual to obtain biological ends through the recognition, appreciation, and the handling of the appropriate means.

Drive($_2$) represents the culturally determined appetite. Man very often does not eat by hunger, hardly ever by hunger alone. He eats at the right time, the right place, and in the right company. His tastes and values are highly shaped, and even when hungry, he will not touch food defined in his own culture as disgusting, unpalatable, or morally repugnant. One man's meat is another man's poison: my cannibal friends in New Guinea would have developed a healthy appetite if confronted with missionary steak, but turn away in disgust from my tinned Camembert cheese, sauerkraut, or frankfurters, which latter they regarded as gigantic worms. Again, the impulse of sex, which in animal societies occurs between any two healthy organisms, is culturally inhibited by such taboos as those of incest, of caste prejudice, and to a lesser extent, by the appreciation of rank, class, and professional or racial discrimination. What is a comfortable means of sleeping to an African or a South Sea native would be torture to a pampered Parisian or New Yorker. Nor would our beds, bathtubs, and sanitary arrangements be convenient or even usable to a native from the jungle. Thus we have here a two-fold re-determination of physiological drives. Cultural drive occurs in two forms, and each of them is determined by the tradition in which an organism is trained.

Satisfaction in this series has been modified by an adjective. It appears invariably not as the satisfaction of a pure physiological drive, but of a cultural appetite. Breathing, as carried on by certain European communities within the non-ventilated and heavily modified atmosphere of enclosed rooms, would not satisfy an Englishman accustomed to a superabundance of fresh air. The satisfaction of appetite by food discovered to be unclean ritually, magically, or in terms of what is disgusting in a culture, does not lead to a normal state of satiety but to a violent reaction, often including sickness. The satisfaction of the sex impulse in an illicit or socially dangerous manner produces detumescence, but also conflict which may lead, in the long run, to functional disease.

Thus culture determines the situation, the place, and the time for the physiological act. It delimits it by general conditions as to what is licit or illicit, attractive or repulsive, decent or opprobrious. Although the act itself, as defined in terms of anatomy, physiology, and interaction with the environment, is constant, its prerequisites as well as its consequences change profoundly.

The greatest modification, however, in this new diagram consists in the insertion of the two terms: Instrumental phase— Culturally definitive situation. The instrumental phase, as we shall see in a closer analysis is always an integral part of a largely organized system of activities. The instrumentalities of food production would have tô be connected with agriculture or hunting or fishing. The storing, preparing, and consuming of food happen in a home or a club or a restaurant. The instrumental phase is also the open door through which such elements of culture as artifacts, norms, and co-operative habits enter as essential constituents of human behavior.

Let us consider any instrumental phase. Primitive fire-making subserves the needs of cooking, warmth, and light. It implies the element of artifact, the knowledge and the techniques of friction, and also the appreciation of the value of these objects and activities. In any food-producing instrumental phase we would discover the use of the digging-stick, the hoe, the plow; weapons, nets or traps; and also the whole system of technique and knowledge, of co-operation and distribution with its legal and customary basis. In every instrumental phase of preparatory activities we thus discover the following factors: (1) artifacts; (2) normed behavior; (3) organized co-operation; (4) symbolic communication by means of language or other signs. These four cardinal constituents of culture are present in each phase at any level of civilization.

One simple inference occurs immediately. The existence of culture depends upon the mechanisms and activities through which every one of these four constituents is produced and maintained, as well as generally distributed. First therefore there must exist in every culture forms of organization through which the material substratum of culture, that is, the body of artifacts, are produced, distributed, and consumed. The economic aspect of a culture is omnipresent.

The norms of behavior have to be known and they have to be enforced. Hence again we can postulate that some mechanisms for the statement, the interpretation, and the sanction of law and order must exist in every community. We know that at higher levels there exist everywhere legislative bodies, courts of law, and posses of police. In primitive communities such special institutions may be absent or rudimentary. Nevertheless, the equivalents of codification, of adjudication, and enforcement are never absent. The essence of custom or norm is that it co-ordinates behavior; hence it has to be known by all those who co-operate. Many norms curb innate tendencies, define privileges and duties, limit ambition, and circumscribe the use of wealth. There is invariably a tendency to circumvent them. Hence mechanisms of jurisdiction and sanction are indispensable.

Social organization implies authority and distribution of function. Together with the need of force implied in the imperative of social order, we have in authority a principle which implies the existence of force socially determined and physically implemented. We find everywhere therefore the political principle, that is, the socially or culturally determined distribution of force and the right to use it.

Finally, we found that communication, through language and other symbolic means, and the transmission of culture are essential parts of our extended instrumental sequence. Both can be subsumed under the concept of training, in so far as all the skills, technical and social rules of conduct have to be implanted

TABLE OF INSTRUMENTAL IMPERATIVES

| 1. The cultural apparatus of implements and consumers' goods must be produced, used, maintained, and replaced by new production. | 2. Human behavior, as regards its technical, customary, legal, or moral prescription must be codified, regulated in action, and sanctioned. | 3. The human material by which every institution is maintained must be renewed, formed, drilled, and provided with full knowledge of tribal tradition. | 4. Authority within each institution must be defined, equipped with powers, and endowed with means of forceful execution of its orders. |
|---|---|---|---|
| 1. Economics | 2. Social control | 3. Education | 4. Political organization |

*Figure 4*

in the growing organism and maintained through precept and exhortation. Education, at all levels, can be differentiated into schooling and adult education. Thus the derived need of training or fashioning of the organism for its cultural tasks is one which we can list as the fourth derived imperative of culture.

Figure 4 gives a condensed presentation of the instrumental needs of culture and of the organized responses to them. We have only to add that the instrumental imperatives have the same degree of cogency as those derived directly from biological needs. We have shown that all vital sequences occur in culture through instrumental implementation. Hence no biological need, that is, no need of the community as a whole, can be normally and regularly satisfied without the full and adequate working of the instrumental responses. These latter constitute together the integral mechanism through which the whole set of basic needs receives its regular flow of satisfaction in every culture. Since even the simplest culture raises the level of the quantitative and qualitative standards of living and thus alienates any human group from the direct hand-to-mouth satisfaction by contact with environment, the break-down of the cultural machinery would imply at least gradual extinction.

For this we have confirmation when we look at the evidence of historical facts. A serious break-down in the economic, political, or legal order which usually also implies deterioration in the systems of knowledge and ethics, leads human groups to disorganization and to the sinking of the cultural level. The break-down of many simpler cultures under the impact of Western civilization and the extinction of many racial groups supply one example. The ever-recurrent decay of once flourishing cultures which are then either replaced by others or enter a period of Dark Ages, is another case in point. Even today we are faced with a serious threat to culture, that of total war, which is waged not merely in terms of destruction and physical aggression, but also as economic war against the systems of production and, above all, nutritive maintenance. As propaganda, it aims at the breaking down of moral and social resistances through the sapping of the constitutional principles of organization, both as regards defense and the normal working of institutions.

## V. THE EMERGENCE OF CULTURE

We still lack a clear definition of the symbolic process. Its existence was implied throughout, especially in our statements concerning the codes of human behavior, the rules of conduct, the educational processes which largely consist in verbal instruction, and the inculcation of systems of value.

We may turn once more to very simple cultural conditions, which verge on the distinction between the pre-cultural behavior of man, the animal, and the emergence of truly cultural conduct. From the well-known facts of animal training, which have been now raised to a system of principles embodied in the psychology of stimulus and response, we know that apes and lower animals can acquire habits and be taught to use artifacts.

It is a fair assumption that pre-cultural man, living under conditions of nature, was led frequently to the instrumental use of material objects. Whenever he was placed, with a fair degree of regularity, under conditions resembling those of an experimental maze in which the rat or the guinea-pig is being trained, he probably developed individual habits. An individual habit implies at least the development of a skill, the appreciation of the instrumental value of an object, and finally, the retention of both skill and appreciation. This integral retention diagrammatically embodied in our presentation of instrumentally implemented series, corresponds to the concept of reinforcement, so fruitfully used by Clark Hull and other contemporary psychologists, as the pivotal principle of animal learning. It is not difficult to see that reinforcement, which means the integral retention by an animal organism of a definite sequence in instrumental activities, contains two concepts of great importance to the student of culture, the concept of symbol and that of value.

Reinforcement, however, accounts only for the formation of habits, that is, of individually acquired types of behavior. As long as habit is not infectious or public, it is not a real unit of culture. Culture begins when the transition between habit and custom is made. We can define custom as a habit made public by communication from one individual to others, and transferable, that is, capable of being ingrained by one generation on to the next.

We have to introduce two more factors as indispensable prerequisites for the transformation of habits into customs. We have, first, to assume the existence of a group in permanent contact and related on the genealogical principle. We have further to assume the existence of means of communication which would make possible discourse and symbolic training. The means of communication, moreover, have to be linked and standardized into traditional statements which can be transmitted from the elder generation to the younger. Thus we have to add two more factors to those previously listed.

And once more we come upon the same list of the cardinal constituents of culture: artifacts; skills and customs, that is, norms of behavior; organized groups; and means of communication, that is, symbols and theoretical systems of precept and value.

The raw materials of both sociability and symbolism can also be assumed as pre-existent to the actual emergence of culture. The long infancy of the human species and the formation of families and family groups were undoubtedly pre-cultural. These are mere assumptions of which proof need not be given, but which are essentially plausible.

The same refers to the raw materials of symbolism. If pre-cultural man was occasionally driven into developing habits, his behavior was determined by what the modern psychologist calls conditioned stimuli. Finding himself regularly within a context of situation and under the urge of a biological drive with no direct satisfaction, he would resort to instrumental behavior. In this the instrument, a piece of wood or stone and the association of previous effective activity with this object would provide the cue or the conditioned stimulus to action. The fact that an environmental sign directs the organism to action, is essentially symbolic.

Thus we can say that the artifact itself, the typical context of circumstance, the habitual technique, all these functioned symbolically, as well as instrumentally. We could also assume that the example of a performance was an act instilled with demonstrative symbolism. When we add to this such symbolic raw material as the bodily or facial expression of emotions, the deictic or otherwise significant gesture, and the natural sound symbols characteristic of many animal performances, we see that symbolism, as significant direction of activity between one organism and another, may, indeed, must have been, pre-cultural.

This allows us to define our idea of cultural emergence by relating a number of empirically substantiated facts. The birth of culture probably occurred as a gradual, perhaps age-long process. It was not the miraculous occurrence of sudden speech or intelligence or invention or social organization. It consisted instead of the all-round systematic and effective integration of the partial increments of cultural behavior. As soon as the use of artifacts, the employment of skills gradually tended to be-

come co-operative; in the measure that co-operation led to the
development of significant signs and sounds, entering into concerted work as an integral system of links; and these systems
of behavior became fixed in tradition—culture was born. The
pervading principle of cultural behavior might perhaps be subsumed under the concept of value.

Value means a deep change in the whole organism, especially,
no doubt, in the nervous system. It refers to all those attitudes which make for the retention of habits, the submission
to traditional rules, the appreciation of, and permanent grip
upon, material objects, and the adequate action and reaction in
terms of an articulate sound or formally determined symbol.
This latter aspect became, from the very outset, embodied in
systems of theoretical knowledge, of belief, and of mythological or historical tradition.

## VI. THE NATURE OF SYMBOLIC INTERACTION

Symbolism, as a type of human activity, as a means of communication, and as the basic substratum of tradition, still needs
some further consideration. It is necessary, first, to make clear
the relation between the instrumental use of a device and its
symbolic function. In so far as an activity is performed as a
means to an end, objects handled, devices constructed and
used, we can say that the organism is engaged in the instrumental use of the apparatus. Even when a certain material
device is used in a co-operative manner and there occurs an
exchange of services in the concerted performance of the task,
we can say that the co-operating organisms are instrumentally
related. But the same artifacts, devices, and habits may act as
signals or cues. We need only think of direct signaling at a
distance, or else of one member of a hunting or fishing team
following the lead of another when he sees him perform an
activity or is made aware of it by a symbol. In this case the act,
the object, or the sound performs a symbolic role within the
context of concerted action.

Even when we approach co-operative processes fully learned
and well-practiced, the distinction between the symbolic and the

instrumental function of any partial performance can be shown as relevant. We have only to remember that no co-operative situation, no concerted human action is so fully a matter of routine that the need for re-orientation or re-direction would not enter. This need is always subserved by the occurrence of a symbolic gesture or a sound which thus is an essential element in all the improvised, re-oriented, re-adjusted phases of human co-operation. The distinction between the symbolic and instrumental function is even clearer in the process of learning. The relevant cues or conditioned stimuli which lead the pre-cultural animal or the learning human individual through the maze of a new situation, stand out as the constant or unvarying sign-posts regularly encountered on the path to achievement. They are the symbolic elements which, together with the drive, the intrinsic instrumentality within the material setting, and the final reinforcement, lead to the acquisition of the habit.

The clear appreciation of the exact nature of symbolism in terms of learning, of co-operation, and of environmental factors will allow us rapidly to indicate the lines on which typical symbolic systems, of which language is the most important, gradually develop. Here, again, the misconception that a sound or a gesture "is made to stand for something else" must be corrected into the adequate assumption that the symbolic object or act is invariably a stimulus to action. The raw material for this can be found once more in the pre-articulate sounds of infants. The cry of an infant is symbolic in that within the social context of domesticity, it summons another person, the mother, father, or nurse, and commands attention and help. In so far as such sounds can often be discriminated by those in charge as cries for food, for cleansing, or as symptoms of pain or anger, they are significant. Significance always depends on the context of situation, including the principal actors, on the requirements of one organism and on the readiness of adequate response by others.

Exactly how articulate sounds developed from pre-articulate grunts, exclamations, cries, or calls can be left to the consideration of linguists, especially to those who prefer to hunt for unverifiable hypotheses rather than to study the general determinism of language. The fact is that articulation has occurred and that it probably occurred very early in the development of human culture.

The assumption of the emergence of articulate words, however, does not imply the slightest divergence from our concept of symbolism. The articulate word, exactly as a material object, a gesture, or a pre-articulate grunt, is invariably the signal to action. On the prototype of infantile cries we can assume the development of significant names for members of a co-operative group, and by name we simply mean here an unequivocal means of attracting, mobilizing, selecting. Again, on the pattern of significant gestures, of the pointing out of an object, we can assume that articulate names for important factors of the environment gradually came into being. The distinction between stone and wood, between wood and earth, between food and non-edible objects, became implemented into the human vocabulary. Such nominal elements in language function pragmatically in the concerted action of all primitives. Both for rapid instruction and effective co-operation they are indispensable. We can see here also how grammatical categories are embodied, not by the logic of reflection, but by distinctions inherent in the pragmatism of concerted action on a sociological basis. The category of nouns; the various typical relations of ownership, dependence, physical position in space, were naturally implemented by the grammatical instrumentalities of accidence and of prepositional modification.

Certain conditions of material to be used, such as "cold" or "warm," "dry" or "wet," "hard" or "soft," had to be verbally implemented, since the definition of state or quality or utility as raw materials for an artifact must have early become part of instruction in training, in co-operation, and in planning.

Another type of influencing by signals must have been the imperative call to action, increasingly diversified and differentiated. Here also it is quite easy to see how articulate words became only more viable and effective substitutes for gesture and pre-articulate sound. Verbs referring to forms of movement, the various modifications in the behavior of the human hand or leg, may have been first to appear. And here also grammatical categories, in order to be effective in instruction, had to express temporal, as well as modal, modifications. The grammatical forms of conjugation have to be related to commands and instructions concerning action in the pragmatic use of language as between elders and children and co-workers in concerted activity. The sociological basis of language obviously implies pro-nominal elements, inherent both in the modifications of verbs, in so far as the action is either that of *self* or of *thou* or of *the other*, and in the determination of nouns in possessive relations. Thus, vocabulary and grammar alike, can be related to the categories of socially organized, traditionally defined, and co-ordinated systems of cultural activity.

The main source of scientific insight into the nature of language as an ingredient of all human activities is to be found in the study of linguistic learning by children and in the observation of how words are used pragmatically, that is how they function in human work.

Language in proleptic instructions always refers to a future situation of action, in that its understanding is always based on a past experience of words used within a similar context. The narrative, in its almost indefinite range of varieties, is comprehensible only through the fact that it refers to a past context partially known but linguistically supplemented by certain variables also familiar from previous experiences. One type of narrative, the one couched in the most general terms, is neither more nor less than scientific theory. For scientific theory is, as we know, the most general statement of a type-situation empirically formulated with the proleptic intent of future guidance. Historical or traditional narratives very often refer to important events from the past, which have established a precedent in the legal, moral, or religious sense. The religious narrative or the sacred story or mythology of a tribe very often is an account of revelation, that is, of direct contact between man and the supernatural universe.

## VII. THE INTEGRATIVE IMPERATIVES OF HUMAN BEHAVIOR: KNOWLEDGE AND BELIEF

We have just seen that the understanding of symbolic function of language and other standardized signs leads us directly to the existence of systems of knowledge and belief. Any system of signs, gestures, or sounds which, through instrumental behavior, supplies the means of defining an object, of reconstructing a process, of standardizing a technique, can be regarded as a primitive form of scientific theory. Indeed, such a symbolic system, in its very simplest form, had to be precise in the sense that it provided a correct formula for the permanent incorporation and transmission of the technical achievement to which it refers. The system was effective because the drive of the physiological need was transferred and permanently linked to the objects and habits which, although indirectly, yet adequately subserved the satisfaction of the drive.

Such systems could be neither pre-logical nor mystical. Principles of human knowledge based on true experience and on logical reasoning and embodied partly in verbal statements, partly in the context of situation to which these refer, exist even among the lowest primitives. They must have existed from the very beginning of cultural tradition. Had this at any moment lapsed into mysticism or false interpretation of fact; or had it sinned against logic, that is, against the principle of identity, human actions, techniques, and economic routine would have become false and useless, and the culture would have been destroyed in its very foundations. Knowledge then, as a symbolic system organizing all the phases of reasonable human behavior, that is, behavior in which experience is logically integrated, is a permanent and essential imperative of human culture.

Knowledge, however, introduces certain new elements into the organic diathesis of man. Knowledge implies foresight, calculation, and systematic planning. In this it not only reveals to man how to achieve certain ends, but also lays bare the fundamental uncertainties and limitations of human planning, of his calculations, and, indeed, of his very existence. The very fact that man, however primitive, becomes accustomed to thinking clearly, to looking ahead, and also to remembering the past, makes him also aware of failures and potential dangers.

We have constantly emphasized that the birth and development of symbolism always occur under the control of organic drives. Man becomes reasonable because his instrumental actions contain a strong dynamic, that is emotional, tone. The principles of knowledge are always controlled by desire, by anticipation, and by hope. Their counterpart, the apprehension of failure, is equally strongly charged with emotions of fear, anxiety, or potential frustration. Man, even as his knowledge increases, becomes more and more aware of the fact that his desire is often thwarted, his expectations subject to chance—that there are always grave, incalculable potential dangers lurking ahead.

Man experiences ill-health and physical disability in his own life. He sees his kinsmen, friends and neighbors removed by death or disabled by disease. He often finds that the best laid plans are crossed and disorganized by the unexpected intervention of chance and fate. Calamity and misfortune affect the individual and disorganize the group.

What new integrative imperative could we assume to arise under such circumstances? The need arises from the conflict between hope, that is, positive expectation, and anxiety, that is, anticipation of possible failure. Any positive affirmations of success, stability, and continuity would satisfy the need. Here again we can indicate the psychological foundations for the occurrence of such hopeful signs. A chance association which might act as prognostic or be interpreted as good augury could be described as the secondary symbolism of good omen. The normal reliance of the individual, especially of the infant, on the protection of the group, might provide the prototype of the assumption of supernatural powers in those who are older, stronger, and more familiar with tradition. As regards death, the assumption of its being but an imaginary event while reality consists in the survival of the soul is brought near not only by the natural strength of the general impulses of "self-preservation," but also by collateral evidence of dreams, visions, and strong emotional memories.

Thus the dogmatic affirmations of religion and magic are brought near to us simply as standardized natural reactions of the human organism under conditions of conflict. The essence of much religious belief is the affirmation of man's dependence on Providence, that is, on some powerful, partly benevolent, partly dangerous principle pervading the universe. The other equally important source of religious attitudes is the affirmation of human immortality. Magic is, in its substance, the re-interpretation of the secondary causation in terms of good as against bad omens. It is thus the ritual production of favorable antecedents of luck and success.

Clearly, neither religion nor magic are mere dogmatic affirmations. Man believes in order to act with greater confidence. He also has to enact his belief. Thus, to understand any magicoreligious system, we have to study ritual as the enactment of dogmatic reality, and ethics as the moral consequences of man's dependence upon supernatural powers.

This is not the place to enter into the details of the various religious systems from Totemism to Christianity, or to study minutely the varieties of magic, sorcery and witchcraft.[1]

We are here interested primarily in the definition of knowledge, religion, and magic as integrative systems in culturally regulated behavior. Let me briefly sum up the place of integrative imperatives within the theory of the hierarchy of needs here developed. The biological need was defined as the conditions imposed by the interaction of the human organism and environment upon behavior. These conditions determine the permanent incorporation of refashioned vital sequences into every particular culture. These needs are definable in terms of biology, and we have to put them on the map of anthropological studies in so far as they are all invariably incorporated and also in so far as they impose definite limits upon human conduct. The concept of instrumental need corresponds to the regu-

---

[1] The principles here developed will be found more fully documented in my little book entitled *The Foundations of Faith and Morals*. Oxford University Press, 1936.

lar occurrence in every culture, and the permanent incorporation, of those types of activity which we have defined as economic, educational, legal and political.

The concept of integrative need declares that in every culture we find coherent systems of a symbolical nature. There exist fixed and standardized texts, verbal or written. These texts are closely related with recurrent, organized performances. These texts also appear in the processes of training the young and adolescent members, that is, the processes of their incorporation into organized groups or institutions. The continuity of culture, its transmission, and its maintenance depend upon the existence of those residues of action, crystallized into symbolic texts, diagrams, or inscriptions. The real functional identity of such symbolic systems is due to their having been developed as the by-product of experience and action. It may be the experience of training or the gradual adjustment of symbolic instrumentality and activity in co-operation. Once formed, symbols can and have to be used, both within the context of the pragmatic situation and outside it.

We can see that what is usually described as tradition closely corresponds to our concept of integrative imperatives. We have here linked this concept with the other determinants of human behavior, and assigned it a definite place and function within the hierarchy of needs. The integrative imperatives are clearly as stringent as the instrumental ones. A lapse in knowledge and deterioration thereof would undermine the techniques of production, as well as the organization of all productive enterprise. The deterioration of belief and of ethics derived from it would mean the gradual disorganization of groups, as well as the occurrence of conflicts and disruptive forces. If knowledge, belief, and ethics were progressively lowered in any culture, then individual initiative and responsibility, the social loyalties, and the organization of the institutions would perforce disappear, and thus leave the organism exposed to starvation, discomfort, and dangers. We see clearly that all three classes of imperatives—basic, instrumental, and integrative—are linked, supplementary, and equally stringent.

It may be profitable to supplement our previous two diagrams of vital sequence, plain and instrumentally implemented, by diagrammatic representations of cultural sequence in which there is no physiological link, and the act itself is of a purely cultural nature. This obviously does not mean that such cultural sequences are not related to basic needs. Such a relationship invariably does exist. Yet, if we were to envisage a culture in which specialization has reached the point where a large number of people live exclusively by instrumental contributions, we would see that a great many sequences of activities start with a motive and move through an instrumental phase to a performance which has only a derived or instrumental value. The individual satisfaction, and the drive as well, in such a case, are determined by the fact that achievements and contributions of this type receive an economic reward from their realization, by which the individual can satisfy all his basic necessities. If we think of the professional activities of a doctor or a lawyer or a clergyman, or of the type of work done in a factory by the business members, overseers, and workers, we would find that it fits directly into our diagram of culturally instrumental sequence.

---

CULTURALLY INSTRUMENTAL SEQUENCE

Motive (economic interest)—Cultural setting of instrumental institution—Act (professional service or contribution of labor)—Satisfaction (economic and social reward).

---

*Figure 5*

In this series we obviously have simplified matters. The motive often includes elements of ambition, advancement, constructive interest. The satisfaction is invariably in terms of economic reward, since no man can work without maintenance. But it includes also the satisfaction of self-regard, the admiration enjoyed by a good worker, a constructive engineer, or creative scientist or artist. The middle links of our series mean that in order to satisfy the motive for employment, the workman, the professional, or the businessman has to find some organized place of work. They can perform their act of professional or labor service only in a consulting room, a business office, a laboratory, a workshop, or a factory—in short, an Institution. All such series of purely instrumental contributions obviously fit into our concept of vital, instrumentally implemented sequence. They are really part of the extremely complex instrumental phase, which, as already noted, becomes in highly differentiated cultures a long chain of linked instrumental co-operation.

We could have slightly modified our present diagram in order to apply it to certain acts, mostly found in religion and art, in which the act itself is not instrumental, but rather a direct satisfaction of spiritual needs corresponding to the integrative type of interest. When a believer repairs to a temple in order to participate in a sacramental act, a slight re-interpretation of the sequence is necessary. The sacrament of communion or of confession, like the enjoyment of a symphony or of a theatrical performance, is to the believer or the artistically hungry man of culture an end in itself. To a certain extent, the concept of function breaks down in its instrumental character when we come to some of the most highly derived spiritual needs of human beings. The satisfaction felt by the mystic in a complete union with Divinity, as also the satisfaction experienced by the composer or by the musical fanatic when he listens to a symphony, may be related in some ways to the general integration of culture. They have certain indirect influences on cohesion, solidarity, and unity of the group. The other aspect, however, their self-contained character of an end in itself, has to be put on record as well. We can embody this argument once more in a diagram.

---

CULTURAL SEQUENCE OF DIRECT SPIRITUAL SATISFACTION

Motive (religious or artistic)—Cultural setting—Act (communion with the Supernatural; artistic experience)—Satisfaction (mystical ecstasy or artistic pleasure).

---

*Figure 6*

VIII. THE ORGANIZED SYSTEMS OF HUMAN
BEHAVIOR

In our analysis we certainly have not thrown overboard considerations of individual psychology or organic physiology. At
the same time we were constantly faced by the fact of human
organization. The cultural fact starts when an individual interest becomes transformed into public, common, and transferable
systems of organized endeavor. We shall have to define the
nature of such systems.

In the principle of prepared opportunities previously discussed, we saw that man never has to seek for the satisfactions
of any of his needs, bodily, instrumental, or spiritual: they are
awaiting him, stored and prepared. We spoke of the two
streams of requirement and satisfaction flowing parallel. Man
finds his food, his shelter, the remedies for ill-health, the re-
dress of injuries, and spiritual comforts in definite places and
within organized groups. Those are the home, the workshop,
the hostelry, the school, the hospital, or the church. We shall
describe such standardized systems of co-operation, as well as
their material embodiment and the groups running them, by
the term "institution."

We encountered this reality in our analysis of the instrumental phase of a sequence. We stated that such a phase was
always the integral part of a larger unit of organization. Fire-
making, as an instrumental phase, can happen at home and for
the household, or during an organized enterprise, or else ritually in a temple. Stone implements are produced to build a
house or to pound the raw material of food or to engage in
some organized agricultural work.

At a much higher level, we can see that no individual initiative is ever culturally relevant unless incorporated into an institution. The man who conceives a new scientific idea has to present it before an academy, publish it, teach it at a school, and
compel its recognition by the organized profession, before it
becomes an accepted part of science. The inventor has to take
out a patent, and thus obtain a charter. He has to organize the

group of engineers and workmen, to finance them, and thus to implement the production of his practical device. He then has to find the market of consumers by creating new wants or re-directing old ones, and make the productive activity of his organization perform a function in satisfying a need.

In our analysis of the concrete structure of the instrumental phase of behavior, we have seen that it always consists in the concurrence of artifacts, organization of the personnel, norms of conduct, and a symbolic factor which functions in the establishment of that phase and in its co-ordination. From this we can proceed to a fuller definition of the concept of organized activities, that is, institutions.

It is clear that the essence of organization implies prima facie three factors: a group of people engaged in the common performance of a task. These people must be equipped with instruments and have a definite environmental basis for their activity. We know also that in technique, law and ethics, rules are the essence of human organization. As we have seen, however, human groups do not organize for nothing. They have a purpose in common, they pursue an end, and thus they are bound together by a charter defining the purpose of their collaboration and its value. Right through our analysis it is evident that humanity, primitive and civilized alike, engages in work not only under the impulse of motives, but also for the satisfaction of their real needs. This we have called function.

The function of an institution is the effect which it produces in the satisfaction of human needs. To the three concepts of personnel, norms, and material apparatus, we must add those of charter and function. Figure 7 diagram sums up this argument in relating the several co-effective factors of human organization.

We could read it as follows: human beings organize under the charter, which defines their common aims and which also determines the personnel and the norms of conduct of the group. Applying these norms and with the use of the material apparatus, the members engage in activities, through which they contribute toward the integral function of the institution.

Let us briefly define the concepts used in our institutional

| CHARTER | | |
| --- | --- | --- |
| PERSONNEL | | NORMS |
| MATERIAL APPARATUS | | |
| ACTIVITIES | | |
| FUNCTION | | |

*Figure 7*

analysis. The charter is the system of values for the pursuit of which the group has organized. It may consist simply of a legal document, or, in the case of traditional institutions, it may be based on history, legend, or mythology. The personnel of an institution is the group organized on definite principles of authority and division of function and distribution of privilege and duty. The rules or norms consist, as we know, in all the acquired skills, habits, legal norms, and ethical commands. The distinction here made between norms and activities is justified. The norms represent the ideal patterns of behavior, the activities their actual realizations. The distinction between charter and norms is based on the more fundamental character of the former. It defines the constitution of the group, its value and purpose for the members, as well as the command, permission, or acquiescence of the community at large.

The diagram would be as useful in ethnographic field-work as in comparative studies where it supplies the common measure of comparison. It is related to our previous analysis in that the entries *personnel, norms, material apparatus* correspond to the instrumental phases of culture. The charter, as well as the verbal prescriptions referring to the norms, belongs to the integrative class in our hierarchy of imperatives. The function is related to our theory of hierarchical needs in general.

The importance of the concept of institution as the legitimate concrete isolate of cultural analysis is seen also through the fact that we can draw up a list of the main types of institutions valid for all cultures. At first sight such a list would not look impressive, in that it appears entirely as common sense. In reality it supplies the student of culture with one of the most valuable proofs that universal laws of structure and process can be established in his field. The main types of institutional organization can be listed briefly under the following headings:

1. Family and derived kinship organizations
   (Extended family; kindred groups, clan)
2. Municipality
   (Local group; horde; village; township; city)
3. Tribe as the political organization based on territorial principle
   (Primitive tribe; polis; state; state-nation; empire)
4. Tribe as the culturally integrated unit
   (Primitive homogeneous tribe; nation)
5. Age-group
   (Age-grades; age hierarchies; professional age distinctions)
6. Voluntary associations
   (Primitive secret societies and clubs; advanced benevolent, political, and ideological societies)
7. Occupational groups
   (Primitive magical organizations; economic teams; artisan guilds; professional associations; religious congregations)
8. Status groups based on the principle of rank, caste, and economic class.

The analysis of this list would obviously require a textbook of cultural anthropology in full comment. Here I only want to point out that an institution like the family may change considerably from one culture to another. It is possible, nevertheless, to give a minimum definition which would serve in any comparative study as a common measure and for any type of ethnographic or sociological field-work as a general guide. The family is the group consisting of husband and wife, parents and children. It is based on the charter of marriage contract, concluded on the foundation of the marriage law and religious sanctity of this bond as it is concretely formulated in each particular culture. This contract implies not only the definition of the relation between the consorts; it also determines the legitimacy and the status of the children.

The combination of the law of marriage and the law of kinship prevalent in any culture constitutes the minimum definition of the family. It is obvious that the family fulfills several functions: reproductive, educational, economic, legal, and often also religious and magical. Nevertheless, it is clear that the main function of the family is the culturally redefined production not merely of human infants, but the supply of young citizens of the tribe. The economic appurtenances, the legal prerogatives, the definition of authority, and distribution of authority are all contingent on the main function. We can, therefore, define this briefly as the transformation of biological reproduction into culturally defined continuity of the group. We could supply analogous minimum definitions in terms of charter and function of all the other entries in our table. This example must suffice. This shows that in each case we can define the integral function of an institution, while it would also be possible to show that the aggregate working of the community as a whole, that is, its culture, is carried along by the combined activity of all the institutions. These problems, however, refer already to the detailed and specialized province of social anthropology, and cannot be more fully developed here.

## IX.  CONCLUSIONS

An attempt was made here to define cultural determinism, the influence of man's culture on man's behavior. We have seen that human beings act within the framework of institutional organization, and that the determinants of their activities can be defined in terms of what was described here as the hierarchy of needs. Our analysis of the various needs and particularly their relation proves that although cultural determinism supplies all the final motives of behavior, culture, in turn, is determined all along the line. We were not driven into the assumption of such concepts as cultural relativism, nor would we have to resort to research for specific tribal or racial geniuses or entities. We have seen that the driving forces of all behavior

are biologically conditioned. The indirect instrumental satisfaction through culture engenders new needs of an instrumental
and symbolic character. As we have seen, however, both the
instrumentalities and the symbolic systems submit to certain
general principles which we were able to formulate.

Does this mean that we are denying here the diversity of cultural phenomena as encountered in various types of environment, at various levels of evolution, and even within nearly
related cultures? By no means. The stress which was laid here
on the uniformity is due primarily to the fact that we are here
concerned with methods of approach, with common measures
of comparison, and with instruments of research. These had
to be built upon elements which are constant, recurrent, and
which, therefore, lead to generalizations of universal validity.

The very concept of function, which was dominant throughout our analysis, however, opens the way for the introduction
of variety and differentiation, as well as for the assertion that
there is a common measure in this variety. In a fuller descriptive statement of what anthropology teaches us about human
nature, such differential characteristics would obviously have
to be introduced. Some of them would undoubtedly lead us
back to the differential influences of environment. We would
find that the very basic needs have to be satisfied differentially
in a desert, in an arctic environment, in a tropical jungle, or
on a fertile plain respectively. Other divergencies are accounted
for by the level of development. Over and above such distinctions, we have to register fully and clearly that there occur in
human cultures strange hypertrophies of custom, specific types
of value, or else dominant interests in one or the other within
the range of the instrumental imperatives. In some cases we
can account for them by a gradual integration of accidental
events which gave to the development of a culture a specific
twist. In such cases we could say that an historic explanation
of such a hypertrophied economic institution as the Melanesian
*kula* or the North Western American *potlatch* can be given. In
many cases the anthropologist, following the famous student
of physics, has to admit simply and honestly his ignorance:
*Ignoramus, ignorabimus.*

As in all other studies, however, it is first necessary to establish the basis of research in formulating the universal principles of cultural analysis and thus providing a thoroughgoing classification of facts. On this basis it is then easier and more profitable to discuss the minor or partial problems of the subject matter, the deviations and the regional characteristics of cultures. I trust that in this essay a contribution is made towards the task of building the foundations of a scientific approach to anthropology and other social studies.

# THE FUNCTION OF THE
# SOCIAL SCIENCES

## *by* Carl L. Becker

IN ANY discussion of the social sciences there arises, of course, the inevitable first question, or pair of questions: is history one of the social sciences, and in any case are the social sciences really sciences. I shall not attempt to answer these questions further than to suggest that the answer depends a good deal upon definitions and points of view.

Science may be defined, in the original sense of the term, as a systematic body of demonstrable knowledge. The particular methods of ascertaining knowledge will depend upon the nature of the subject matter about which knowledge is desired; and the methods that are found suitable to the several branches of science are in fact so varied that it is difficult to say with much precision what "the scientific method" really is. The one thing that all scientists have in common is not a special technique, but a special attitude of mind towards their several enterprises. This attitude is simply the desire to know, in respect to the particular matter in hand, what is true about it, irrespective of any practical or esthetic or moral implications that may be involved in the truth that turns up. This does not mean that the scientist in any branch of learning is indifferent to these implications, but only that for the purpose of his inquiry he must disregard them. If one asks how he can afford to disregard them, the answer is that his enterprise proceeds upon the fundamental assumption that knowing what is true is itself a primary value upon which all other values must in the long run depend. In this sense history and the social studies are branches of science —that is to say, the pursuit of knowledge for its own sake.

There are, nevertheless, two important differences between

the natural sciences and the social studies which make it desirable (for the purpose of this essay, at least) to separate them into two categories, which we may label respectively science and history (including in history the other social studies). One of these differences has to do with the nature of the subject matter, the other with the method of apprehending it.

The natural sciences are primarily concerned with the material world (including living organisms in so far as they are parts of the material world), and their aim is to disclose the structure and behavior of material things in generalized terms (in terms of mathematics so far as possible) which will be true irrespective of variable conditions of time and place. In dealing with his subject matter the work of the natural scientist is greatly facilitated by the fact that he is not emotionally entangled with it: he does not care how his subject matter behaves, his subject matter is indifferent to what he does to it, and ignorant of what he has learned about it. Fortunately for the physicist, the atom cannot acquire a knowledge of physics. The physicist can, therefore, proceed on the assumption that any knowledge he may acquire about the behavior of the atom will not modify its behavior and thereby invalidate conclusions based upon its behavior up to date. The social scientist cannot make this assumption, at least not without important qualifications. For his subject matter is the behavior of men in the world of human relations; and men are not, like the atom, indifferent to what is done to them or ignorant of what is learned about them. On the contrary, the subject matter of the social scientist can find out what he has learned about its behavior in the past, and as a result of that knowledge behave differently in the future. This is the fundamental difference between the natural sciences and the social studies; whereas the behavior of material things remains the same whatever men learn about it, the behavior of men is always conditioned by what they know about themselves and the world in which they live.

This difference between the natural sciences and the social studies in respect to subject matter gives rise to a corresponding difference in respect to the method of apprehending the subject matter—a difference between what may be called the scientific and the historical approach to knowledge. Generally speaking, the natural scientist is disposed to ask of any situation how it functions in a general or a universal context, the social scientist how it has developed in a time sequence. The statement needs to be qualified, no doubt. The social scientist is not always exclusively concerned with development in a time sequence, nor is the natural scientist always indifferent to it. It is well known that the geologist gives us the history of the earth, the biologist describes the evolution of plant and animal life, on a time scale that dwarfs the historian's temporal span to the measure of a passing moment. Even physics, according to Whitehead, cannot be properly understood without taking account of the history of physical concepts. Obviously, since everything is related to something else, anything can be apprehended in terms of its behavior in a general context; and since everything has a history, anything can be apprehended in terms of its transformation in a time sequence.

Everything has a history—true enough in one sense. But in another sense only man has a history. The earth has a history in the sense that certain things have happened to it as an object in time and space; but knowledge of that history, not being a possession of the earth but only of the geologist, plays no part in shaping that history. Man is not thus limited. Man is the only organism that is aware that it and all things have a history, the only organism, therefore, that can acquire some systematic and enduring knowledge of what that history is, the only organism, accordingly, whose activities are modified by that knowledge. Only man has a history in the sense that his own knowledge (or what he accepts as knowledge) of the history of all things, including himself, is an essential factor in determining what his own objective history has been and will be.

The social studies are concerned with the history of man in this sense. They are primarily concerned with man as a social animal, that is to say, with his social activities as conditioned by intelligence and inspired by conscious purpose. They aim to disclose not only what man has done in the world, but also what he has thought about the world and his doings in it. The subject matter of the social studies therefore includes the history of the social sciences. It includes equally the history of the natural sciences. The social studies and the natural sciences have each a long history, and at every stage the history of the one is closely related to the history of the other. A brief survey of certain aspects of that history and that relation, as manifested in western civilization, may throw some light on the essential function of the social studies in the life of man.

I I

When we think of anything we ordinarily think of it in relation to other things which we know or believe or imagine to be located in space and to have happened in time. In other words, we live in a time and space world and think in a time and space frame of reference. For an omniscient intelligence there would be an exact correspondence between the real and the ideal time and space world, between the things that actually exist and have happened and the things that are known or believed to exist and to have happened. But for finite minds the correspondence can never be exact at every point. The time and space world is what it is, but for finite intelligence it is in effect what it is known or imagined to be. Other things equal, the development of intelligence, in the individual and the race, is largely a matter of pushing back the limits of the time and space world as known—that is to say, largely a matter of substituting for the things that are believed or imagined to exist in space and to have happened in time the things that actually exist and have actually happened.

In thus extending his time and space world, the individual in civilized society can do very quickly what it took the race a very long time to do. The earliest men, like each of us in early childhood, lived and thought in a very restricted time and space world. They knew little or nothing about any region beyond the country in which they lived, little or nothing about any event that could not be remembered by the oldest men in the community. On this point we may take the statement of Alexander Goldenweiser (*Early Civilization*, p. 402).

In all prehistoric communities, those, that is, without written records, the continuity of cultural life from generation to generation is carried by two vehicles: on the one hand by the objective continuity of material culture, on the other, by tradition, the knowledge of facts and events as carried in the minds of individuals and communicated by the spoken word from father to son.

The historic depth of such tradition is slight. It is communicated by fathers and grandfathers, and it reaches back to their fathers and grandfathers; and beyond this span of some three or four generations, tradition does not extend with any degree of accuracy. After this, moreover, the historic interest or inquisitiveness of the early group breaks down. The world of fathers, grandfathers, and great grandfathers is a world of the concrete and the significant. Then comes the . . . mythological period, good to play with and to dream about, but of little consequence for the realities of life.

The knowledge of facts and events, historically so shallow, is also closely limited geographically. The width of the cultural span is no less restricted than its depth. The group is thoroughly conversant with the human, animal, and material factors of its immediate environment. Outside of this a very fragmentary and unreliable set of data is available referring to the peoples and the regions with which some sort of contact is maintained. But there the world of humanity ceases. Beyond is the void, the realm of imagination, with its grotesque creatures and fantastic happenings.

This is an excellent description of the primitive man's time and space world in terms of his matter of fact knowledge of it. But the distinction which Dr. Goldenweiser draws between this restricted world of knowledge and what lies beyond (the "mythological period" of remote Time-Passed on the one hand, and the "void" of outer space on the other), although valid for him and for us, is a distinction which the primitive man himself was probably not aware of. The creatures and happenings which he finds in the world beyond the matter of fact, however grotesque and fantastic they may appear to us, are for him an integral extension of the world of matter of fact and by no means devoid of consequence for the realities of life. For the primitive man, like the immature child, like the civilized man for that matter, is not content to live wholly within the restricted world of matter of fact knowledge, since he finds it too monotonous to be satisfying, too immediately experienced to be wholly intelligible, and too precarious to be safe. Inevitably, therefore, he enlarges it imaginatively, by projecting into the outer world of nature and the remote world of Time-Passed those activating agencies and events which his limited experience assures him must be there, and which, being there, provide him with a rational explanation and a moral justification for his own activities.

The forces which primitive man projects into the outer world of nature are those with which experience has made him familiar. He knows that he himself can exert force whenever he wills to do so; he observes in the outer world certain effects that occur independently of his will, effects that appear to be more or less uniform in their occurrence and impersonal and mechanical in their genesis. According to Caveth Read (following Westermarck), the primitive man distinguishes, more or less vaguely no doubt, these two kinds of forces—the one in some measure uniform and mechanical, the other in some sense personal, volitional, and capricious. The primitive man's recognition of the mechanical forces Read associates with the word Magic, his recognition of the volitional forces with the word Animism. This is to say that primitive man's response to the one kind of force is to believe that, since it is uniform and mechanical, it can be in some measure understood and controlled; while his response to the other kind of force is to believe that, since it is volitional and capricious, it can at best only be propitiated or outwitted.

For controlling and propitiating the unseen forces primitive man constructs an elaborate ceremonial which provides him with precise rules of conduct appropriate to all the familiar occasions and the unforeseen emergencies of life. The origin of this ceremonial he does not know. He knows only that it has always been adhered to and that to depart from it would be disastrous. It is the way ordained, which has somehow come to him out of the dim Time-Passed before the great grandfathers. To explain how the way came to be ordained, and to give it a sanction not to be denied, he therefore projects into the unknown Time-Passed the same volitional forces which, being conscious of possessing them himself, he projects into the outer world of the Time-Present. In the Time-Passed, where the imagination can operate more freely, the volitional forces are more easily personalized; so that in societies that emerge from the primitive at least, the projection takes the form of an ascending genealogy, running from the great grandfathers through the heroic ancestors and the god-like kings to the gods themselves, and to the original chaos out of which the world and men and all things emerged.

In this or in some similar manner primitive man, inspired by the desire to make his life more interesting, more intelligible, and more secure, creates imaginatively a time and space frame of reference beyond the limits of the known matter of fact. Science and technology, religion and philosophy, history and the social studies, as they have developed through the ages, are but differential elaborations and corrections of primitive man's imaginative reconstruction. Science and technology derive from primitive man's matter of fact knowledge (the essence of science) of simple familiar things (tools, weapons, utensils and the like), and from his attempt, through Magic, to understand and control the forces implicit in material things. Religion and philosophy derive from primitive man's desire to adjust his conduct to the personal forces behind appearance, and from his attempt, through propitiation and sacrifice, to enlist the aid of their powerful but capricious volitions. History and the social studies derive from primitive man's desire to know what has happened in the Time-Passed—the epic story of the origin of man and the world, the doings of the gods and the god-like kings and the heroic ancestors—in order to understand how his elaborately patterned social life came to be what it is.

### I I I

History, the oldest of the social studies, begins with the epic story. As known to the ancient Greeks, the epic story is preserved for us in Hesiod and Homer. Hesiod's *Theogony* relates the beginning of the world and of man; his *Work and Days* sketches the decline from the golden age of King Chronos, when men lived like gods free from toil and grief, through the lesser ages of silver and of bronze to the iron age of evil unrestrained in which Hesiod lived. In Homer the epic story is associated with an actual historical event—the Trojan War; the *Iliad* describes the doings of gods and men in the last year of the war; the *Odyssey* relates the adventures of Ulysses on his return from the war to his home in Ithaca. For the Greeks of Homer's time the *Iliad* and the *Odyssey* were history, poetry, and scripture all in one, that is to say, history simply—the record of what had happened. Not until written records had been long in use could the Greeks (or any people) clearly distinguish between history and fiction, between the event as it actually happened and the event as it is later remembered or imagined to have happened. Yet in the sixth Century the Greeks were already beginning to doubt the truth of Homer's story. Since there were no written records contemporary with the Trojan War by which Homer's story of it could be tested, how could they ever have doubted the truth of the story?

For history and the social studies the question is a fundamental one. The answer is to be found in the fact that what men at any time will believe about past events does not depend solely upon human testimony preserved in written records contemporary with those events. It always depends also in part upon whether the events testified to are the *kind* of events which they believe can happen in the world as they know it: what I have called the time frame of reference must be filled with the kind of things and events that can be harmonized, without too much difficulty, with the kind of things and events with which the space frame of reference is filled. In the sixth century the speculations of the Ionian philosophers and more precise knowledge of the geography and history of Asia were making the Homeric story sound remote and unreal. Hecataeus (and after him Herodotus), traveling in Egypt, found it incredible, for example, that the gods should be walking over the hills of Hellas and taking an active part in the affairs of Agamemnon and Achilles at a time when the affairs of Egypt (according to records kept by Egyptian priests) were being managed wholly without benefit of gods, or even of god-like kings. It seemed to him that the kind of things that did not happen in Egypt at a certain time were unlikely to be happening in Greece at the same time. It even seemed to him that the kind of things that were not happening at the present time were unlikely to have been happening in any past time. He therefore ventured to say: "the stories of the Greeks are numerous, and in my opinion ridiculous."

The stories might be ridiculous, but they were too much a part of the substance of Greek thought to be wholly dispensed with. To deny the truth of them altogether, without putting something in their place, would leave the time frame of reference for Greek thinking empty of content. In the absence of written records contemporary with the events related, the best the Mythographers could do was to rationalize the stories by eliminating what was incredible in them. For example, Horodorus could say that Apollo and Poseidon did not, as the story had it, actually build the walls of Troy for King Laomedon, but that Laomedon built the walls himself, paying for them out of the sacred treasure accumulated in the shrines of Apollo and Poseidon. No one could know whether Laomedon built the walls or not, but Horodorus could believe that he did build them and pay for them in the way indicated because that was the way walls were likely to be built and paid for in his own time. Thus the stories were rationalized, and the gods so far depersonalized that the Time-Passed could be filled, if not with events that actually did happen, at least with events that might have happened, with the same kind of events that were known to be happening in the Time-Present.

If Greek ideas of the past were modified by current scientific ideas, the reverse of this was also true: Ionian science, so far from springing full-blown out of the void, was influenced by traditional religious beliefs. The Ionian philosophers were concerned with *physis*, the ultimate nature of the universe. According to Thales, the universe is "alive"; and Anaximander conceives of the genesis and permutation of the four elements (earth, air, fire, water) in animistic terms. "Things perish into the things (the four elements) out of which they have their birth, according to that which is ordained (*physis*); for they (the four elements) give reparation one to another for their injustices." Earth, for example, appropriating air, fire, and water to create the human body, makes reparation for these robberies when death dissolves the body into the four elements. Anaximander's *physis* seems to be derived from the primitive conception of *Moira;* and his four elements are reminiscent of the dominions which, by casting lots, Destiny confers upon the gods—to Poseidon the "heavy sea," to Hades the "misty darkness," to Zeus the "aether and the clouds." Therefore, says Poseidon, "never will I live according to the mind of Zeus; . . . let him remain quiet in his own third part." Anaximander's four elements are scarcely more than the provinces of the gods with the gods left out; and the injustice of the elements one to another is but a less personal conception of the encroachment of Zeus on the dominion of Poseidon.

Anaxagoras and Leucippus reduced the four elements to "seeds" or atoms whose movement and permutations ceaselessly create and dissolve all things. But whereas for the latter atoms in motion is an ultimate fact to be accepted, for the former the world of atoms in motion is "set in order" once for all by a non-moral *nous,* mind or intelligence, which then withdraws leaving the mechanism to run on its own. Leucippus' conception of atoms in motion, an inspired guess, was as far as Greek science could go in the absence of an experimental technique to verify the existence of atoms and measure their movement; and until Zeno and Epicurus gave wide currency to his ideas, the main current of Greek thought followed the lead of Anaxagoras. Heraclitus deprecated analysis and emphasized the unity of all things, finding the ultimate explanation in Anaxagoras' *nous,* or something less impersonal, in life or soul as a dynamic force operating in time. Socrates criticized Anaxagoras for confining the operation of *nous* to the initiation of a mechanical system, and employed the argument from design to prove that God or Right Reason is an activating agency continuously at work in the world of man and nature. Plato reduced the world of appearance to the ephemeral and the unreal—shadows in the cave projected by the universal Idea, the unseen but ultimate and enduring reality; and even Aristotle, although giving far more credit to the material world than Plato would allow, retained the concept of an activating transcendent intelligence.

## I V

This refurbishing of the time and space frame of reference, effected by Greek thought in the sixth and fifth Centuries, provided the conditions which shaped classical conceptions of history and the social studies. In so far as the gods had withdrawn from the immediate direction of human affairs, sanctions for the good life had to be found in the purposes and actions of men. It is well known that classical historians, even those who were not merely annalists or antiquarians, were primarily concerned with particular events (for the most part political and military events), and with the conscious purposes and deliberate decisions of leaders prominently associated with such events. Rarely do they look beyond the immediate context of the particular situation for an explanation of the events they relate; those impersonal forces, generated by "economic and social conditions," which for the modern historian provide the essential "causes" of events, they either did not look for or could not find.

Perhaps one reason is that the time frame of reference was too restricted. For the fifth Century historian "antiquity" was a concept with a rapidly diminishing factual content. Herodotus, although regaling his readers with an ironic account of the rape of fair women, could trace the known origin of the Persian wars no further back than the time of Croesus. Thucydides found it possible to sum up, in fifteen pages of acute analysis, all that could be positively known about the early history of Hellas. For Herodotus and Thucydides there was no long Time-Passed, filled with credible events, with which "modern" history might be compared or its long time significance apprehended. For later historians the time scale was longer. Polybius and Livy and Tacitus could contemplate modern history against the background of the Oriental monarchies and of Greek and Hellenic civilization. But of these Polybius alone understood history as a co-ordinated whole; and even he, in attempting to find a general explanation of that unique phenomenon, the Roman conquest of the world, found it, not in "economic and social forces," but in "Fortune" which had "guided almost all the affairs of the world in a certain direction." For classical historians the time frame of reference was still so restricted that the history of mankind, beginning with civilizations already highly developed and throughout exhibiting civilizations not highly differentiated, could more easily be understood in terms of a repetition of similar events than in terms of an integrated process.

But the chief reason classical historians did not find the causes of historical events in impersonal forces is that they were not looking for them. They took it for granted that since a man was free to choose between courses of action, the adequate cause of the course of action pursued was to be found in his deliberate decision to pursue it. Polybius identified "cause" with "purpose," and clearly distinguished between cause and beginning. A beginning of anything is "the first attempt to execute . . . plans on which we have decided, . . . its causes whatever is initiatory in our judgments and opinions." Thucydides makes essentially the same distinction, although less explicitly. "The real though unavowed cause" (or "the most genuine pretext," according to Cornford's translation) of the Peloponnesian War "I believe to have been the power of Athens, which terrified the Lacedaemonians and forced them into war; but the reasons publically alleged were as follows." Thucydides rarely goes beyond the "reasons publically alleged," although he must have known that often enough they were ostensible rather than real reasons, because he was determined to relate nothing that he did not know to be a fact. He therefore presents two sorts of facts: what was done and what was said, the events and the speeches. These were all that could be positively known; and Thucydides was convinced that if he could find out exactly and set down plainly what was done, and what reasons the chief actors gave for doing what they did, his history would be "an everlasting possession" because in time to come no man would "be at a loss to know what was the origin of this great war."

This conception of causation was the application to history of Aristotle's doctrine that "man is the original source and parent of his acts"—the doctrine of "final causes." An object which a man desires is the "final cause" of the series of acts which he judges appropriate to attain the object. The desire and the actions taken are conditioned (not caused) by character; and this closed circle of character, desire, and action contains the adequate explanation of the events that occur. No other explanation of events was yet available. After all, Zeus had not wholly abdicated, since *nous* functioned as vicegerent; Whirl had not yet become effectively king, since it had not yet assumed the form of intelligible natural process or regulative natural law. The result was that classical philosophers and historians, rejecting the ascendancy of Zeus but unable to identify natural law with anything more tangible than Right Reason, could find an adequate explanation of historical events only by substituting for the uncaused volition of the gods the (antecedently) uncaused volitions of men, aided or frustrated by the operation of Fate or Fortune—that which, although ordained, is unknown because unpredictable.

The juxtaposition of Foresight (in the sense of sound judgment of a known situation) and Fortune (in the sense of that which could not have been foreseen—Fate or the intervention of the gods or mere chance) is a recurring theme in classical histories. For classical historians it provided both an adequate explanation of historical events and a sufficient reason for studying such events. So commonly was history regarded as politics teaching by example, that Polybius finds it useless to elaborate the point. "All historians, one may say without exception, . . . have impressed upon us that the soundest education and training for a life of active politics is the study of History, and that the best and indeed only method of learning how to bear bravely the vicissitudes of Fortune is to recall the calamities of others." Classical historians were not looking for a general law or dialectic of history to which, by understanding it, men could adjust their thought and conduct; they were looking for examples of the operation of Foresight and Fortune in particular situations, from which, in similar situations, those in charge of political affairs might profit.

So long as historical events could be regarded as being caused by the rational and moral judgments of exceptional men, there was every reason for supposing that social relations were established and transformed by the same causes. Social relations, in their economic and ethical no less than in their purely political aspects, were identified with the organization of the state; and for fifth Century philosophers the aim of Politics, the all-inclusive social discipline, was to make manifest to men the ethical and rational purposes essential to the organization of the good life. Aristotle, the most realistic and fact-minded of Greek philosophers, professed to base his *Politics* on an analysis and comparison of all constitutions known to have existed; and he was quite aware of the infinite variation and persistent transformation of actual political and social systems. But even Aristotle was not primarily concerned with disengaging from the actually existing systems a general theory of the social process. Like all Greek philosophers he was dominated by the idea that Becoming is an incidental and imperfect attribute of Being. "For what every being is in its most perfect state, *that certainly is the nature of that being.* . . . Besides, whatever produces the final cause of the end we desire must be best; but a government complete in itself is that final cause and what is best." The nature of the state is thus to be discerned in its ideal rather than in its actual form. From his analysis and comparison of actual constitutions, Aristotle accordingly derives, not a theory of the social process, but the types of state that are best because based on right principles. There are three of these—Monarchy, Aristocracy, and Polity, each of which is good because each "has in view the common good"; but each of these, on account of human frailty, tends to degenerate into forms based upon wrong principles— Tyranny, which has in view the good of one; Oligarchy, which has in view the good of the rich; Democracy, which has in view the good of the poor. Such clear-cut distinctions were surely never found in actually existing states. They are, no less than Plato's *Republic*, ideal forms laid up in Heaven, constructs of

Right Reason designed to guide men in the deliberate purposeful construction of the good society.

V

So long as the small city states of the Greek world retained their independence it was possible to suppose that society might be shaped by rational means to moral ends: on a political stage so limited philosophers might become kings, or kings philosophers. But this momentary optimism was inevitably dispelled by the conquests of Alexander and the subsequent creation of the Roman Empire. The rational decisions of reasonable men, incapable as it turned out of shaping the destiny of an Athens, would obviously be even less availing against that "Fortune" which had shaped "almost all the affairs of the world" to an end which no man had willed. Swept along by forces beyond their control, men therefore found refuge in acceptance and resignation, or in the aid of super-human powers.

The prosperous and cultivated classes of the Graeco-Roman world found refuge, for the most part, in acceptance and resignation. The attitude was rationalized for them by Zeno and Epicurus. Both philosophers accepted the atomic system of Leucippus; but whereas Zeno taught that a man's acts were mechanistically determined (so that the master could no more help beating his slave for a fault committed than the slave could help committing the fault for which he was beaten), Epicurus taught that a man was free, within narrow limits fixed by nature and social convention, to choose the rational course (the slave could have avoided the fault, the master could have avoided beating him for it). Yet the practical import of their teachings was much the same. Both counseled acceptance of a world forever the same and forever beyond man's control, the aim of the wise man being to attain individual peace and tranquillity: according to Zeno by steeling his sensibilities against its injuries; according to Epicurus by cultivating his sensibilities for the enjoyment of its rational pleasures.

Acceptance and resignation in a social world beyond man's control implied a suitable philosophy of history. Such a philosophy was easily derived from the traditional epic story of a decline and fall from the primitive Golden Age. The cultivated mind, rejecting the Golden Age of the past as a poet's dream, and unable to regard the Golden Age of the future as anything more than a futile hope, could best understand the historic process as a series of cyclical changes, an endless repetition of the process of regeneration and decay, an eternal recurrence, in different forms, of the same goods and evils. The rational soul, according to the Philosopher-King, Marcus Aurelius, "goeth about the whole universe and the void surrounding it and traces its plan, and stretches forth into the infinitude of Time, and comprehends the cyclical Regeneration of all things, and . . . discerns that our children will see nothing fresh, just as our fathers too never saw anything more than we. So that in a manner the man of forty years, if he have a grain of sense, in view of this sameness has seen all that has been and shall be."

Only the prosperous and the cultivated could afford this pessimism. The dispossessed and the outcast, deprived of present security, could find compensation only in the future, and in the future only with the aid of super-human powers. Of many religions which offered them this compensation, Christianity, and after the seventh Century Mohammedanism (essentially a variant of Christianity) were the ones which, promising them most, ultimately won the allegiance of the peoples formerly comprising the Roman Empire. With the decline of prosperity, the collapse of Roman political authority, and the consequent decay of classical culture, society returned to relatively primitive conditions; and Christianity and Mohammedanism replaced the older religions and philosophies because, in times when life was harsh and precarious, they provided a conception of man and the universe which tempered pessimism with hope.

Christian doctrine especially (in a less reticulated form Mohammedan doctrine also) was at once a revival and a modification of primitive ideas. Grafted upon the Hebrew epic, it revived the concept of a past Golden Age, which it identified with God's creation of the world and man made perfect in the Garden of Eden. It revived the correlative concept of a decline and fall, through man's disobedience to God's will, from his perfected state; and, borrowing from pagan historians and the Book of Daniel, it identified the subsequent history of mankind with the succession of the "Four Empires," of which Rome was the latest. But the birth of Jesus was regarded as a turning point in the history of mankind—the beginning of the end of the decline and fall. For Jesus was taken to be the Christ (the Messiah of Hebrew tradition), whose appearance represented, not the God-like king of the House of David, but the intervention of God himself, in order to establish the "Fifth Empire," the Church temporal which, succeeding to the "Fourth Empire" (Rome), would prepare the way for the Second Coming of Christ, the judgment and destruction of the world, the emergence of the Church Triumphant. Thus Christian doctrine (and Mohammedan doctrine too) irradiated pessimism with hope by projecting into the future a new Golden Age, the life everlasting in the Heavenly City in which all men, through faith and right living, could find compensation for the evils and frustrations of the temporal state.

This conception of the history and destiny of mankind, deriving from the Christian story and a mutilated classical tradition, dominated the social and political thinking of Europe for a millennium. Its authority was least questioned and its influence most pervasive in western Europe, where until the twelfth Century the decay of classical culture was more pronounced and the material conditions of life were more primitive than elsewhere. The revival (from the twelfth Century) of material prosperity and the rise of the universities was indeed accompanied by a varied and brilliant intellectual activity; but an activity which, although often highly critical and skeptical in a superficial and verbal sense, was chiefly concerned with reconciling pragmatic knowledge and experience with the fundamental presuppositions of the Christian faith. After the thirteenth Century even the most acute and resourceful dialectic proved inadequate to this task, so that gradually, almost imperceptibly, the Christian philosophy of the origin and destiny of man lost its commanding position, and at last faded away into the realm of myth. Many influences contributed to this result. The most important for our purpose are associated with a notable expansion of what I have called the time and space frame of reference—an expansion effected by geographical exploration and discovery and the growth of scientific and historical knowledge.

The names of Columbus and Copernicus may be taken as symbolical of those activities which, between the sixteenth and the nineteenth Centuries, so greatly enlarged the space world in which Europeans could pursue their enterprises and the space frame of reference which conditioned their thinking. Columbus and his successors—a multitude of navigators, traders and colonizers—expanded the geographical world known to the ancients from the narrow circle of Mediterranean countries to include the five oceans and the major countries of the globe. What a few Greeks had inferred, that the earth was a planet in space, was now demonstrated; peoples and countries hitherto only vaguely and fantastically imagined were now given familiar form and substance. But if Columbus and his successors thus enlarged the earth as a habitat for man's practical activities, Copernicus and his successors deprived it of its traditional primacy in the cosmic scheme. With the gradual verification and final acceptance of the Copernican cosmogony, the earth could no longer be regarded as the center of the universe, but only as a minor planet in a minor solar system in one of a thousand million galaxies of stars.

Meantime, there occurred an equally notable expansion of the time frame of reference. As the earth was enlarged for man's practical activities and its significance diminished in the cosmic scheme, the history of man's activities came to be known over an ever-longer period of Time-Passed. From the twelfth to the eighteenth Centuries many influences turned the attention of scholars to the study of pragmatic history—the revival of classical learning, interest in national origins, religious disputes which could be settled only by investigating the history of the Church from apostolic times. By the eighteenth Century the history of Europe could be visualized, in a series of concrete and connected and credible events for some two or three thousand years past; so that, whereas Thucydides could sum up all that was certainly known about Greek history before his time in fifteen pages, Gibbon required six volumes to tell what he knew about the fall of the Roman Empire. During the nineteenth Century historical research became one of the two major approaches (natural science being the other) to an understanding of human life. Recorded history was pushed back, another two thousand years, to the origins of "civilization" in Babylonia and Egypt, and evidence was uncovered of the life of man, in primitive and savage forms, during some hundreds of millennia before the beginning of recorded history. In these remote times no golden ages were discovered. On the contrary, man himself ceased to be clearly distinguishable from the higher anthropoids, and his origin was lost in the stream of animal and plant life which could be projected back, in various identifiable forms, over geologic ages that reduced the time of recorded history to the measure of a passing moment.

The significance of this expansion of the time and space frame of reference for modern thought does not reside in the mere expansion itself. Plato and Aristotle could readily conceive of a world infinitely extended in space, and without beginning or end in time. But the modern mind, by virtue of the increase and refinement of knowledge, was able, bit by bit, to furnish these outward spaces and backward abysms of time with concrete and verifiable things and events—stars the magnitude and location of which could be determined, the movement of which could be predicted; men and events in a long Time-Passed that could be concretely named and described and clearly visualized. The significant thing is that the modern mind, within a greatly expanded yet finite frame of reference, still found itself, however far removed in time or space, dealing with the concrete and familiar world of experience. Within this expanded frame of reference, filled with the concrete and the familiar, the modern man could, as it were, stand apart from himself, could regard himself and his activities more objectively, in longer perspective, in relation to the outer world of nature and the endless succession of generations before and after; so that, ceasing after a time to be too much frightened by the "eternal silence of the infinite spaces," he could at last contemplate himself as a creature which, by virtue of temperatures prevailing temporarily on the earth, had emerged without credentials or instructions from a universe as unaware of him as of itself, and as indifferent to his fate as to its own.

A conception of the cosmic process which reduced the human race to a chance deposit on the surface of the world, with "conscience enough to feel that it was vile, and intelligence enough to know that it was insignificant"—such a world-view should seemingly have left men with a sense of complete frustration. Often enough it did so. But generally speaking and in the long run it had the opposite effect—the effect of liberation: it enabled man to feel that he could dispense with the assistance of the gods and shape his own destiny. For if man was discovered to be a negligible item in the cosmic scheme, it was after all man's intelligence that had made this momentous discovery. An intelligence capable of so significant a discovery surely could not itself be insignificant, but should on the contrary be capable of subordinating the knowledge it had acquired, and might still acquire, to the attainment of its own purposes. There was thus no occasion for despair, but rather for hope, in a world-view which disclosed an intelligence capable of understanding, and by understanding, mastering both itself and the world that had carelessly spawned it.

As early as the eighteenth Century the conviction that men could shape their own destiny closer to the heart's desire became an underlying assumption of modern thought. This conviction derived partly from historical, partly from scientific knowledge. Scientific knowledge, grounded upon the discoveries of Galileo and Newton, indicated that the outer world of nature, so far from being subject to the contingent and the unknowable, was everywhere moved by forces that, operating always in a uniform manner, could be measured and made use of. The subsequent progress of science and technology more than confirmed this assumption: demonstrated in fact that the physical universe, however indifferent to man's fate, was equally indifferent to its own, and for that reason would lend itself, without anger or retaliation, to rational understanding and manipulation in the service of human needs. The universe was obviously a purely natural phenomenon; and man could therefore dispense with the assistance of the gods, since he could himself control the outer world by discovering the universal "laws" which nature or nature's God had impressed upon it.

As scientific knowledge enabled men to believe that the outer world of nature could be made to serve his purposes, so historical knowledge freed him from the pessimistic notion that time was the enemy of man. The first men, so far from having been specially created a little lower than the angels, had apparently emerged, by a natural process of evolution, only a little higher than the anthropoids; and the subsequent history of mankind, seen in this long perspective, whatever temporary disasters or cyclical returns might be noted in it, was in the long run obviously not a decline and fall from original perfection, but a slow and painful rise to relatively civilized and humane living. The Golden Age could thus be transferred from the past to the future, and instead of being conceived as a perfect state granted to men by divine powers could be regarded as an earthly utopia of man's own devising. "The Golden Age of humanity," as Saint-Simon said, "is not behind us; it is yet to come, and will be found in the perfection of the social order." The perfection of the social order would be brought about by time and deliberate human purpose: by taking thought man could always add a cubit to his stature, it was even conceivable that time would add a cubit to his stature whether he took thought or not. At all events the increase and refinement of scientific knowledge would enable him to subordinate the natural world ever more effectively to human use; while the increase and refinement of historical knowledge, gathering up and appropriating the experience of mankind, would enable him through the better understanding of his own nature and the world of human relations, to modify what was contingent and adjust himself to what was inevitable in his social environment.

This conception of the universe, and of man as an integral part of it, had a profound effect upon the study of history and politics. History could no longer be naively conceived as a repetition of similar events of which the causes were to be found in the free (antecedently uncaused) volitions of leading statesmen and warriors. On the contrary, historical events were, so to speak, embedded in the total social activities of the communities where they occurred; and the social activities of communities, like the behavior of the material world from which man had emerged, could be fully understood only as a natural process, an unbroken tissue of interwoven actions in which any particular action was related, as effect to all preceding actions, and as cause to all succeeding ones. Ideally, no action or event could be regarded as uncaused, or as not itself being a cause, although neither its causes nor its effects might be fully known. Ideally, the causes of any series of events were to be regarded as implicit in the events themselves, and not to be identified with certain particular events separated out of the complex and taken as the sole or primary activating agencies. Practically, it is true, the ideal could not be fully realized. In the actual writing of history, from lack of evidence and in order to grasp such complicated phenomena at all, it was necessary to stress certain "influences" as more important than others, or as symbolical of the integrated complex of influences. But the aim would be to realize the ideal as far as possible; and this meant that the causes of any complicated series of events, the Peloponnesian War or the French Revolution, would be looked for, not in the volitions of outstanding individuals, but in the total complex of impersonal "conditions" which determined the volitions of all the individuals who were the "bearers," as the Germans say, of the event.

The Christian story of man's origin and destiny offered for contemplation and faith a complete philosophy of history. As the Christian story in its historical aspects was discredited and more verifiable knowledge of man's activities over a long period was disclosed, it was inevitable that the traditional philosophy should be replaced by new ones—many attempts (in terms of moral, political, economic, or social phenomena) at a more rational and factual explanation of the trend and significance of the evolution of social forms from the earliest times. But in the measure that the causes of historical events were seen to be implicit in the complex conditions of time and place which determined the volitions of men, any philosophy of history, or even any explanation of particular civilizations, called for more intensive study both of the volitions of men and of the conditions which determined them in particular situations. It was no accident, therefore, that as the modern conception of man and nature gained credit, the various "influences" (material, social, psychological) which were thought to determine the volitions of men, and thereby shape historical events and social phenomena, should have been made the subject of special study. So, for the most part in modern times, the several social sciences were differentiated and given autonomous status.

The origin of the social studies can of course be traced back at least as far as the Greeks, but until modern times the all-inclusive social discipline was politics and the approach to politics was ethical rather than scientific. The study of politics, as Plato and Aristotle understood it, embraced the economic and social as well as the strictly political aspects of community life. For this reason the English word sociology has been suggested as the proper equivalent of the Greek word politics. Politics is nevertheless the better term. For inasmuch as the Greeks identified society with the state, and the good life with the good state, the study of politics was for them primarily concerned with forms of government, and the chief value of such study was to disclose those ideal or "best" forms which alone could guarantee the good life. The assumption underlying this conception of politics was that men of good will, informed by knowledge and directed by reason, could in some real sense attain the good life by deliberately constructing such ideal or practically best forms of government. The knowledge requisite for this task certainly included an understanding of the economic, psychological, and moral influences that determined the conduct of men. But such influences could not be profitably considered apart from the political structure: so far from having an independent function in determining the political structure, they were factors which the philosopher or statesman would have to take account of in constructing any form of government, but which at the same time he could modify and direct to good ends in the measure that the state which he constructed attained the object of all good states, which was, as Aristotle said, "that the subjects of it should be happy."

The assumptions which gave validity to this conception of politics were partly discarded in Roman and medieval times. With the disappearance of the small, self-sufficing *polis* it became less easy to identify society with the state, or to regard the individual outside of it as either above or below humanity. Stoic philosophers gave to the individual, as a member of the human race, an existence and the possibility of attaining the good life quite apart from the state to which he might be subjected; and preoccupation with practical problems of equity among diverse peoples enabled Roman jurists to differentiate natural jurisprudence from positive law and temporary political decrees. The medieval schoolmen retained the ethical approach, subordinating politics to morality and both to religion and theology; but the individual, as a child of God, was endowed with a worth which no temporal power could confer, and the good life for him was identified with allegiance to the Church and membership in the society of Christian men. Thus, although politics and ethics were even more inseparably united than in classical times, society was differentiated from the state, becoming a more universal, a natural or supernatural entity within which the state functioned and to which it was subordinated.

The separation of politics and ethics has usually been credited to Machiavelli. Certainly he may be said to have initiated it. Living at a time when the Roman Church was losing its commanding position and the society of Christian men was giving place to diverse national cultures and competing military monarchies, he was able to isolate and analyze the state as sheer power, completely divorced from moral and legal sanctions. The successors of Machiavelli were less machiavellian than Machiavelli; but Bodin and Grotius rationalized the existing "Great Power" system in terms of the concept of the sovereign state, and in the eighteenth and nineteenth Centuries the study of politics, responding to the influence of natural science, assumed its modern form—the realistic, factual description of the genesis and development of forms of government, as conditioned by and functioning within particular "societies" at particular stages of historical evolution.

With politics separated from ethics and confined to the sphere of government, the differentiation of other social studies followed as a matter of course. The Industrial Revolution disclosed, both to scholars and to statesmen, the importance of men's economic activities in determining events; and political economy, beginning with practical statistical inquiry, the "Political Arithmetic" of the seventeenth Century, was formulated in the eighteenth and nineteenth Centuries as the science of man's behavior in respect to the production and distribution of wealth. But "society," although embracing the political and economic activities of men, could not be understood in terms of these activities alone; so that a more comprehensive "science of society"—a science which, as conceived by Comte, "supplies the only logical and scientific link by which all our observations of phenomena can be brought into one consistent whole"—was called for. As understood by Comte himself, the science of society aimed at nothing less than a definitive philosophy of history, a "positive" explanation of all human experience in the past as the necessary basis for the rational organization of society in the future. The successors of Comte were less courageous because more aware of the difficulties of so stupendous a task. The result was that the new science of society became in the process of specialization too diverse in subject matter and technique to be easily definable: less a science than a co-operative enterprise which, with genial hospitality, admitted to its broad domains the social theorist and the statistician, the social psychologist and the student of the sociology of knowledge, the historian of ideas and of concrete social situations—and no doubt would have admitted the anthropologist, if he had exhibited any disposition to enter.

Thus history and the social studies have been differentiated. The differentiation, it is true, is not very clear-cut; true also it is that the techniques employed in the several fields of study are diverse and ill-defined. Nevertheless, history and the social studies in the course of their differentiation, a differentiation associated both as cause and effect with the emergence of the modern conception of the universe and of man as an integral part of it, have acquired a common approach and a common aim: they have all abandoned, in theory at least if not always in practice, the ethical for the scientific approach in order to learn what is true, apart from what is commendable, about the nature and activities of man as a social animal. The general assumption underlying this attitude is that exact, scientific knowledge of what, under known conditions in the past, men have as a matter of fact done is in the long run the only valid point of departure for determining what, under present conditions, they can and should do—the only sure foundation for constructing the good state and thereby attaining the good life.

## V I

In the long history of man on the earth there comes a time when he can hold permanently in mind the necessary relation between what he has done, is doing, and proposes to do. From that moment his activities, ceasing to be wholly at the mercy of immediate impulse, become in some measure ordered and purposeful. From that moment, accordingly, in order to make his life more interesting, more intelligible, and more secure, he experiences a profound and persistent need—the need of freeing himself more effectively from the immediate and the ephemeral by cultivating a trans-personal, social memory of things not directly experienced. This need is best satisfied by knowledge, but even in the absence of knowledge it must be satisfied; and in primitive societies, where matter of fact knowledge is limited to the narrow circle of immediate experience, a world beyond the matter of fact—an outer world of nature, a historical world of Time-Passed—is imaginatively created in terms of magic and the epic story. The primary function of science is to satisfy this need more effectively by enlarging the narrow circle of the known; so that in the course of time, with the slow but persistent accumulation of matter of fact knowledge, the imaginative creations of magic and the epic story are gradually replaced by the more carefully tested and better reasoned structures of the natural and the social sciences.

The rational structure of science has made the life of man more intelligible, and should make it more interesting and secure. Whether it does in fact make it more interesting and secure depends upon the purposes for which the knowledge available is used. Assuming that knowledge is power, power can still be used for good or evil ends. Natural science places at man's disposal immense power—mechanical power which can be accurately measured and released either for the preservation or the destruction of life. Knowledge made available by social science is power too, but power of a quite different sort—not mechanical power which can be stored up in a capsule or a machine gun and distributed to all men, but the power of understanding available only to those who can, and in so far as they can, master the knowledge which confers it. And this power also, no less than mechanical power, can be and is being used, by those who possess it, for diverse ends—for purveying truth or falsehood, for promoting selfish interests or the common good, for serving the values that exalt the humane and rational qualities of the human personality or the values that deny and degrade them.

The function of science is to promote knowledge. But knowledge alone is not enough: the question of ends, of what to do with knowledge, remains. The scientist, as scientist, engaged in the task of acquiring knowledge of a particular situation, is not concerned with the use which may be made of that knowledge; and in this sense science is divorced from politics. But the knowledge which science places at the disposal of the community cannot itself be divorced from politics, since it inevitably becomes a means of attaining practical political ends; and no man (least of all the scientist himself, as a responsible member of the community) can afford to be indifferent to the practical political ends which scientific knowledge is used to promote. The function of social science is to promote knowledge of man as a social animal, and the social scientist, even as scientist, is concerned with practical political ends, since practical political ends are essential aspects of the behavior of man as a social animal. As means of promoting knowledge, science, and especially social science, will therefore perform its function in vain without the aid of a political ethics capable of discriminating the social values which knowledge should serve.

# SCIENCE, NATURAL AND SOCIAL

## *by* Julian Huxley

SCIENCE, in the more restricted sense in which it is normally employed, in English-speaking countries, is that activity by which today we obtain the great bulk of our knowledge of, and contest over, the facts of Nature. This activity, like other human activities, has developed and evolved, and by no means all the stages in its evolution have merited the title of "scientific." In remote prehistoric times, our early ancestors worked by trial and error combined with simple intuitive common sense. On the side of control, this phase was characterized by an almost imperceptible improvement in man's implements of which those in non-perishable stone remain to us as a record. This pre-scientific approach, however, was combined with the non-scientific methods of magic control that we call equally unscientific rationalizations in the field of explanation.

Once agriculture had given the possibility of settled civilizations, with written records and specialized classes, the hand-to-mouth methods of common sense could be replaced by something much more elaborate. Science was born—witness the astronomy and geometry of ancient Mesopotamia and Egypt. But science in this phase was still, to our modern view, unscientific in two major respects—it was traditional and it was esoteric. Scientific knowledge was confined to a limited group among the priesthood and it was cast in a mold of tradition which rendered change and progress slow. Being associated with the priesthood, it was also intimately bound-up with non-scientific practice and non-scientific interpretation—magic and theology.

The era of groping trial and error lasted from the first dawn of essentially human intelligence, as marked by true speech, to the beginnings of settled civilization—perhaps a million, perhaps half a million years. The next, or traditional-esoteric phase, lasted for thousands instead of hundreds of thousands of years. After some three or perhaps four millennia, the Greeks (for whom the way had been prepared by the Minoans) suddenly burst free from the prison of secrecy and traditionalism, and proclaimed the freedom of intellectual inquiry. The "birth of science" is usually dated here. This is but a half-truth. At best it was the acquisition of freedom and self-consciousness by the scientific spirit, not the emergence of a wholly new activity to be called science. And in the second place, the type of science which it inaugurated differed radically from modern science in several ways. It was (as an effect of the slave economy of the Greeks) almost entirely derived from industry and practical application; it was exceedingly speculative and (doubtless largely because of technical limitations) did not lay the same stress on experimental verification as we do; and it had not invented the modern methodology of publication of data and methods as well as results and conclusions.

During a later period, a combination of Greek intellect and ingenuity with the practical spirit of the Roman *imperium* made of Alexandrian science something much more like modern science in outlook and methods. But this was swallowed up in the anti-scientific Christian flood and the collapse of Roman civilization.

During the Dark Ages of the West, the Greeks kept the scientific spark alive, and by means of their mathematical inventions, paved the way for immense improvements in the technique of scientific research.

Natural Science in its modern form, though its onset was not quite so sudden as is often made out, can fairly be said to date back no further than the seventeenth Century—some two millennia from the onset of the Greek phase. With Bacon as its St. John the Baptist, it developed its gospel and its ministry; curiosity for its own sake, but also interest in industrial techniques and practical content; freedom of inquiry; experimental verification in place of authority; full publication and abundant discussion. With these a truly new phase was inaugurated.

Today, it seems that we are in the process of launching a new phase—one in which social phenomena as well as natural phenomena are to be made amenable to scientific understanding and rational control, the modern phase of Social or Human Science.

As with natural science, it has had its earlier phases. It too passed through the phase of trial and error, in which social organization shaped itself under the influence of unconscious adjustment together with non-rational rules of conduct and non-scientific interpretations of human destiny. It also had its traditional phases, often tightly bound up with philosophical and theological interpretative principles, as for example in the climax of the Middle Ages. And it had its birth of free inquiry, its parallel to the Greek phase of natural science—but two thousand years later, in the philosophers of the seventeenth and especially the eighteenth Century.

Finally, its modern phase which is now dawning, has had like the modern phase of natural science, its scattered precursors, its Roger Bacons and Leonardos. And it has had its precursor in the restricted sense, its equivalent of Bacon in the Renaissance. Many, I am sure, would put Herbert Spencer in this position; but I believe that the true John the Baptist of Social Science is Karl Marx. Herbert Spencer, for all his academic knowledge—or perhaps because of it—was more in the position of an Old Testament prophet. His work was essentially analogical. He demonstrated that Social Science was an inevitable development: but his notions of what form it could actually take and what methods it should employ were vague and essentially erroneous.

Marx, on the other hand, developed a system directly based on social facts and directly applicable to them. He did not prophesy a Messiah, he indicated the Messiah. As natural scientists tend to undervalue Bacon because he himself did not make discoveries or work out experimental techniques, so social scientists tend to underrate Marx because his system is a dialectical one, ready-made and complete with an answer to any problem, not sufficiently empirical and inductive for their scientific taste. It is doubtless true that, as occurred in the case of natural science, the social scientists must go their own way to work, regardless of doctrine or theoretical system; a precursor cannot take the place of the Messiah or the gospel he indicates. But at least Marx, like Bacon, gave expression to a new outlook and a new method of attack, and helped materially to alter the intellectual climate so as to make it propitious for the scientific workers in his field.

The question immediately poses itself as to why the extensive emergence of social science into large scale and efficient operations has been delayed so long. The triumphs of natural science both in discovering radically new knowledge and in applying it practically to satisfy human needs have been so spectacular that it would seem natural and obvious to extend the same methods that had there been so fruitful to the field of social phenomena.

The answer is a very simple one: the methods are not the same. The scientific spirit remains unaltered whether it is contemplating a nebula or a baby, a field of wheat or a trade union. But the methodology of social science is inevitably different from that of natural science. It is different and must be different for one fundamental reason—namely, that in the one case the investigator is outside his material, in the other he is not. Man cannot investigate man by the same methods by which he investigates external nature. He can use the methods of natural science to investigate certain aspects of man—the structure and working of his body, for instance, or the mode of his heredity; but that is because these are shared with other organisms and because they are partial aspects which can be readily externalized. But when he starts investigating human motives, his own motives are involved; when he studies human society, he is himself part of a social structure.

What consequences does this basic difference imply? In the first place, since many social phenomena have no close biological counterparts, man must in respect of them be his own guinea pig. But this is impossible in the strict sense. He is unable to make fully controlled experiments. Even if an absolute despot or a fully totalitarian state were to subject a group of people to rigorous experimentation—by depriving them of alcohol, for instance, or by adopting a-new form of education—the results would have only a limited application. The smallness of the group, the compulsion exercised, the inevitable limitations on the contacts and full social activity of the group, would make it impossible to apply the results directly to an entire normal society, however regimented. The difficulties are of course infinitely greater in any free society. Large-scale social phenomena are also not only unique in detail, but in essence. Geological phenomena are unique, but they do not show the same quality of progressive change: they are in most features repetitive. Thus even the method of comparative study, as in geology or comparative anatomy, is only partially applicable while that of repeatable and controlled experimentation, as in physics or genetics, is not applicable at all to major social phenomena.

A second, more technical difficulty is in a sense a consequence of the first. Causation in social science is never simple and single as in physics or biology, but always multiple and complex. It is of course true that one-to-one causation is an artificial affair, only to be unearthed by isolating phenomena from the total background, and reducing the differences between two processes, in experiment or in thought, until but one remains. Nonetheless, this method is the most powerful weapon in the armory of natural science: it disentangles the chaotic field of influence and reduces it to a series of single causes each of which can then be given one weight when the isolates are put back into their natural interrelatedness, or when they are deliberately combined (as in modern electrical science, and its applications) into new complexes unknown in nature.

This method of analysis is impossible for social science. Multiple causation here is irreducible. The problem is a two-fold one. In the first place, the human mind, whether by nature or because of long conditioning by common sense and later and more intensively by the use of natural science, is always looking for a single cause for a phenomenon. The very idea of multiple causation is not only difficult for it to grasp, but definitely antipathetic to it. And secondly, even when the social scientist has overcome this resistance and faced the problem in theory and in general, extreme practical difficulties remain. Somehow he must disentangle the single causes from the multiple field in which they are operating. And for this, a new technique is necessary.

Next, and in many ways even more important than the first two together, comes the question of bias. Under this head I include anything appertaining to the investigator which may deflect his scientific judgment. It is the equivalent of experimental and observational error in natural science. In natural science, elaborate methods have now been worked out for error. There are statistical methods for discounting both sampling error and personal error; the limits of accurate measurement are determined for different types of instruments; the procedure of controlled experimentation has been reduced to a fine art; chemical reagents and biological material are tested for their purity and uniformity. The procedure of the discounting of error in natural science by these procedures has proven difficult enough. But to discover how to discount bias in social science will be very much harder. Let us look at some of the ways in which bias manifests itself. In the first place, the social scientist absorbs certain ideas from the culture in which he has grown up. If he sets himself to investigate that culture, he must discount his class bias, his social bias, his nationalist bias. If he is investigating an alien culture, he must use a great effort of imagination to overcome the very fact of its alien quality: group bias will tend to make him find alien methods ridiculous, illogical or inefficient, while the familiar methods of his own culture will tend to be accepted as more natural and sensible than they really are.

Then there is the inherent genetic bias imposed by his own temperament. For certain purposes, investigators in social science are their own instruments to a much greater extent than in natural science: and the instruments differ in their very construction.

Next we have the bias introduced by the peculiar psychological development of human beings. They can only resolve their inevitable conflicts during childhood and adolescence by relegating a great deal to their unconscious, whether by the psychological mechanism of suppression or that of repression. Roughly speaking, the former introduces bias by leaving gaps in a man's knowledge and outlook, whereas in the latter the gaps are accompanied by strong emotional distortions and resistances. Such emotionally-toned bias is naturally much the more serious. The scientific study of sex, for instance, has been much retarded by repressional bias—witness the reception given to Havelock Ellis' great work, and the extraordinary resistance offered to Freud's ideas.

Bias of this type has the additional danger that those who make an effort to discount it may readily swing into over-compensation—a bias of opposite sign. The investigator whose youth was tormented by intolerant religion is apt to discount the social importance of religion far too much: the convert to Freudian methods is liable, in discounting his own early sexual repressions, to under-estimate the social value of repression in general.

Bias has also been encountered in natural science, but only when its findings came up against emotionally held convictions —only, that is, when it has had social entanglements. We may cite the prohibition of anatomical dissection, the proscription of Galileo's findings, the hostility to the Darwinian theory, the Nazi distortion of racial anthropology, the Soviet attack on modern genetics. The present wave of general anti-scientific feeling, so noticeable during the past decade, has been due in part to an emotional reaction against the social misuse of science as in the employment of poison gas and war technique in general, partly to a general feeling that scientific findings, by sapping the traditional view of man's place in the universe and in society, are undermining the basis of ordered society—again a resistance to change the emotionally-charged foundations of our own existence.

Finally comes the most fundamental difference of all, a difference which is the parent of the difficulty caused by bias.

Values are deliberately excluded from the purview of natural science; but social science must include them. Values and all that they connote of motive, emotive, qualitative hierarchy and the rest, constitute some of the most important data with which the social scientist must deal. But how can science deal with them? Science must aim at quantitative treatment: how can it deal with the irreducible absolute of quality? Science must be morally neutral, dispassionate: how can the social scientist handle the ethical bases of morality, the motives of passion? Bias arises from his being called upon to do so; but the primary difficulty is a much more fundamental one.

Let us be frank with ourselves. There is a sense in which, because of this qualitative difference between its data and those of natural science, social science can never become fully and rigorously scientific. To understand and describe a system involving values is impossible without some judgment of values: and still more impossible without such value-judgment in the other scientific function, that of control.

However, this is not quite so serious as at first sight appears. Even in natural science regarded as pure knowledge, one value-judgment is implicit—belief in the value of truth. And when natural science passes into control, a whole scale of values is implicated. The application of natural science is guided by considerations of utility. Utility is itself a value-judgment; but there are different kinds of utility—utility for profit, utility for war, utility for food-production, for health, for multiplying power, for amusement and education.

The application of science through the instrument of laisser faire economic systems has brought us to a position in which we are being forcibly reminded that these different utilities may conflict, in other words that we are faced with a difficult problem of value-judgment.

Thus, rather crudely, we may say that in respect to the problem of values, social science in its aspect of knowledge is faced with the same difficulties as is natural science in its aspect of control. The value-problem begins earlier for social science, in the pure instead of the applied stage, that is all.

The difficulty is thus in a sense an artificial one. Its consideration has reminded us that natural science is not such a pure disembodied activity as is often assumed. Language is in part responsible for the assumption. There is no such thing as natural science per se. The phrase is a shorthand description of those activities of human beings which are concerned with understanding and controlling their natural environment. And, just as simple one-to-one causation is a fiction, only approximated in artificially isolated systems, so the emancipation of natural science from considerations of value is a fiction, approximated by the possibility of temporarily and artificially isolating scientific activity from the other activities of man. Nonetheless, both these are useful fictions, dangerous only if we erect them into realities over against the true realities of the universal interdependence of phenomena and the unitary nature of human activity—the one a field of material interaction, the other a field of interrelated values.

The essential differences between natural and social science thus boil down to this—that the phenomena with which social science deals are less readily isolated, and that as an activity it is more closely entangled with human values.

These differences, however, even if only quantitative, are very real, and it remains true that social science must develop its own methodology if it is to become an efficient instrument.

In regard to multiple causation, we may look forward to the extended use of the techniques of mathematical correlation. These have already been developed to a high pitch for dealing with problems of multiple causation in physical science (e.g. the relation of crop yield to the numerous environmental factors concerned) and special methods have been elaborated by Spearman and his school for dealing with psychological questions.

The use of probability methods is also indicated. Here again, these have been developed to a high pitch for use in natural science, notably in physics and biology, and it is only a question of adapting them to the problems of social science.

Mathematical methods also enter into another technique which is now being rapidly developed in social science, that of the questionnaire, and especially the set of questions asked by a trained interviewer. The questionnaire method is widely used, but the reluctance or inability of large sections of the public to fill its elaborate forms restricts its sphere. The method of set questions in the hands of interviewers is being employed with great success, notably in the United States, to gauge public opinion both with regard to commercial products and to questions of public interest. The success of the method in this form depends chiefly on two factors—the proper framing of the questions, and the obtaining of a truly representative sample of the population to answer them. It is in regard to the latter point that the mathematical theory of testing errors plays an important role.

The framing of the question to be asked is a matter rather of skill and common sense than of science. Some questions do not admit of a significant answer, nor any answer at all: others will defeat their own ends by influencing the form of the answer. The investigators who interview the questionees must also be properly trained if the results are to be accurate. In any case, the method of questioning a representative sample of a large population can only be applied to a restricted set of problems, though within its limitations it may become extremely efficient. In one field, that of the straw ballot, it is developing such uncanny accuracy that it is infringing upon practical politics. Some people are asking whether a properly conducted straw ballot could not be profitably substituted for the trouble and expense of a full election; while others feel that the announcement of a straw vote may itself influence the course of the subsequent election. Psychologists are busy devising modifications of the questionnaire method so as to build up objective rating scales (objective, that is, for the population of which the questionees are a representative sample) for various value-judgments.

In addition, they are essaying to assess the distribution among the population of various qualities of value. Intelligence-testing has been practiced, and is now approaching full scientific validity. Attempts are also being made to assess temperament and even more elusive qualities.

The method of mass observation constitutes an attempt to obtain objective information on various aspects of public opinion and behavior which elude the method of yes-or-no questioning. Inquiries may concern the reaction of the public to a particular place, like the Zoo or the National Gallery; to a particular event, like the Coronation; to a particular activity, such as smoking or the time of rising; or to a general direction, like that of war. Numerous investigators take part, and note down either the remarks they overhear, or the answers to questions and reactions in discussion, made by their acquaintances or by casual encounters.

In some cases, composite pictures which could have been obtained in no other way have resulted from the use of this method. But in general, its technique, both as regards sampling and questioning, will have to be refined a good deal before it can claim to be scientifically dependable.

Another set of methods which is being developed to cope with the complexity of social problems is that of anonymous group working, repeated drafting, and circulation of preliminary draft results for comment and criticism. A combination of all three seems to yield the best results when tackling large and many-sided problems, such as the structure of a natural science like health or a big industry like steel or agriculture, the organization of leisure, international adjustments, etc.

Joint work is on the increase in natural science, but here largely because of the quantitative burden of routine procedures in subjects like biochemistry or genetics. We may distinguish such work as team-work. Group will here be used in the sense of a body of people pooling their different knowledge and skills to cope with qualitatively differentiated problems. Group work in this sense is also to be found in natural science, as where geneticists, geologists and statisticians make a united attack on some problem of microevolution, or an embryologist and a biochemist combine to study development. But it is far more necessary in social science. Anonymity is often desirable to enable the participation of public servants or well-known men whose opinions might be distorted, or discounted in advance. It may also be desirable for an essentially opposite reason, to give the weight of a recognized study organization to the work of young and unknown men whose findings would otherwise tend to be disregarded.

In both these ways, anonymous group working, as well as

securing greater efficiency, helps to discount bias of one sort or another.

Provided that a good drafter is available together with a chairman and a few members who will give regular attendance, group membership can be fluid, and specialists invited for one or a few meetings as required.

Repeated drafting is a substitute for experimentation in problems where the experimental attack is ruled out. As soon as a preliminary survey has been made of the problem in its entirety, a draft is circulated for discussion at the next meeting. The gaps and errors are thus brought to light from the subject of the next period of work, when the process is repeated. Three, four, or even more complete drafts may be required before publishable conclusions are reached, just as new sets of experiments must be planned and executed to deal with tentative conclusions and new points arising in a piece of research in natural science.

Some or all of the successive drafts may also be circulated among a comparatively large number of outside experts for written criticism. The collection of such comments often brings to light new points and unexpected points of view which the group, in its preoccupation with its own trend of thought, has overlooked. It affords a method of enlarging the group without the time-consuming business of large-scale discussion.

In other cases, the actual investigator may be a single man, while the group element is provided by interviews and by circulation of drafts. This method is best adapted to problems which are of large geographical scale and local diversity, though it may also be used for those which are qualitatively diversified in themselves. It was adopted, for instance, in Lord Huxley's *African Research Survey,* and in the supplementary volumes to it on African research and capital investment. Where the subject matter is highly technical, as in the above mentioned case of African research, repeated circulation of drafts for civilians by a large number of experts is imperative.

It may be prophesied that the working out of techniques of this sort, made necessary by the nature of the data of social science, will have fruitful repercussions in certain fields of natural science, such as evolution and comparative biological study in general, where the present bias in favor of experimental work and specific results is leaving vast bodies of published data awaiting the synthetic treatment which only organized group attack can provide.

I have already mentioned certain substitutes for the controlled experimentation of the natural sciences. But experimentation as a method is not ruled out in social science, though it must take different forms. Regional or group experimentation is the most obvious method. Two regions or groups are chosen which are as similar as possible, and certain measures are introduced in the one, while the other serves as control. The Carlisle experiment in liquor control was an early attempt in this method, but unfortunately it has been allowed to drag on without any serious attempts either to draw theoretical conclusions or to frame practical policies on the basis of its operation. The T.V.A. in the United States is perhaps the largest social experiment ever undertaken, at any rate in a non-totalitarian country. The area involved, however, is so large that strict controls are difficult to find. Education is a field in which regional experimentation could be very fruitful. We hear a great deal about educational experiments; but for the most part these are not experiments in the scientific sense, merely new ventures and they lack the crucial feature of scientific experimentation.

As the spirit of scientific planning extends into government, we may expect to see regional experiments tried out in many fields. Medical and health service methods would afford another excellent field problem; new techniques like that of Stapledon for converting rough moorland into pasture should be tested on a regional scale for their social effects as well as for their technical efficiency. The social results of cheap electric power could be made the subject of local experiments much more rigorous than that of the T.V.A. Different methods of developing backward tropical territories by international or national chartered companies, by public works schemes, under the local administration, by the establishment of corporations, and so on, could and should be made the subject of carefully planned regional experiment.

The fact that in social science man is his own guinea pig has a number of methodological implications, both for social science research and for its practical application. In a sense, the scientist must always secure the co-operation of his material, however inert. The chemist must discover the conditions in which his pure substances will oblige him by reacting: the geneticist's results will be obscured if his cups or culture-bottles interfere with the fertility of his mice or flies; the student of growth will be misled if he cannot coax his animals to maximum performance. But the social scientist often requires true co-operation from his material, in the sense of understanding the reason for his work and voluntary participation in its course. Education as a social experiment can never succeed without properly equipped teachers, specially trained in pedagogy. The interview method will give entirely misleading results without interviewers skilled in the technique of their job.

In the field of application, propaganda and public relations may be of prime importance. A good example is the Cancer Campaign recently initiated in the United States. Cancer has been presented to the public in such a way that they feel a real interest in it as a social problem, and are collaborating in the attack upon it. The vast problem of malnutrition will never be solved unless the public be made to take a similar interest in it. The British Medical Association has made a beginning in this field with its milk campaign: but it is a beginning only.

In general the whole technique of propaganda, persuasion, and public relations needs the most intensive study before the findings of science can be socially applied. When does propaganda defeat its own ends by putting up counter-resistance? What are the relative values of reiteration and variety of appeal? Of the printed word, the cinema, and the radio? Of rational persuasion as against mere suggestibility? Of intellectual comprehension as against a sense of active participation? We do not know, and until we know, our progress toward efficient social structure and a fuller life will be fitful and slow. In many ways, the enlistment of public co-operation is to social science what the enlistment of capital investment is to natural science: it provides motive power for application.

There remains the question of bias. Here, there is no ready method at hand. It took generations for natural science to work out the technique of discounting experimental and observational error: it will take generations for social science to develop that of discounting the errors due to bias. The first step is obviously to make the world aware of the existence of bias and the need for its discounting. Where human affairs are still handled in a pre-scientific spirit, bias is apt to play a very large practical role, especially the bias in terms of your own group, whether class, nation, religion, or race. Such bias produces powerful rationalizations, which are then used to justify policies of the merest self-interest. The enslavement of Negroes was justified on the basis of the scriptural authority for the menial destiny of the Sons of Ham; the brutalities of the Spanish conquests in the New World on the basis of the unique superiority of Christianity; of the Nazi persecution of Jews on the racial superiority of Aryans. The group bias of the prosperous classes in early nineteenth Century England manifested itself in astonishing assertions about the inherent inferiority of "the poor"; the same bias is evident in certain aspects of the eugenics movement today. The general assumption that your own group standards and methods are right and sensible while other beliefs and forms of behavior are wrong, silly, or at best inferior, has determined much of the relations between the great imperialist powers and the backward peoples of the earth.

Another widespread and disastrous form of bias arises from psychological conflict and tension.

Unconsciousness in respect of moral lapses, the desire to see the infliction of vindictive punishment, the unconscious reluctance of many parents to see the harsh school discipline of education under which they suffered replaced by more human methods, the emotional basis of militarism—all these and many other undesirable determinants of human conduct are the result of bias arising from repression or emotional conflict and inflicting lasting distortion on the psyche.

In these fields, bias is thus an urgent subject for investigation by social science, and the application will here lie in making its findings universally known and accepted by the public in general and by administrators in particular.

But even in scientific circles bias may play a surprisingly large part. A good example is the resistance of the great majority of medical men during the early part of the last war to admitting any cause for breakdown among soldiers save physical shell-shock and malingering. The uncritical assumption, even among scrupulously careful workers, that differences in intelligence between social classes, were genetic and not due to nutrition or other social factors, is another. Again, we have the thesis of anthropologists, like Lévy Bruhl, that savage mentality is in some ways qualitatively different from and inferior to our own, whereas it is actually only operating in different material and social conditions.

No golden rule can be laid down for the avoidance of such pitfalls, beyond the obvious step of realizing that they exist. Beyond that, special methods must be worked out in each field.

There are still voices raised proclaiming that social science is a contradiction in terms, that human affairs are not intrinsically amenable to the scientific method. They are, I believe, wrong. They are confusing the methods of natural science with scientific method in general. Social science differs inevitably from natural science in many important respects, notably in its lesser capacity for isolating problems, and more generally in its lesser degree of isolation from other aspects of human activity and its consequent greater entanglement with problems of value. It must therefore work out its own technique and its own methodology, just as natural science had to do after Bacon and the eager amateurs of the seventeenth century had recognized natural science as a new form of human activity.

Let us not forget that the working out of this technique and this methodology by natural science took a great deal of time and is indeed still progressing. During the phase of modern science, the amateur was largely replaced by the professional. University laboratories have been supplemented by governmental and industrial institutions, whole time research has become a new profession, and the team has in many spheres replaced the individual: co-operative group work is beginning, and the large-scale planning of research is in the offing.

The criteria of accuracy have meanwhile steadily improved, and mathematics has put new tools and indeed new outlooks at the disposal of the natural scientist.

Finally, the enormous growth of applied science has had effects of the utmost importance on pure research. It has done this partly by providing new instruments which would otherwise have been unavailable; one need only mention the gifts of the wireless industry to such unexpected branches of science as certain aspects of physiology. And partly by supporting new lines of research the needs of wireless again have revealed new facts concerning the upper atmosphere, while the study of plant pests and human diseases has brought to light new modes of evolution.

We need have no fear for the future of social science. It too will pass through similar phases from its present infancy. By the time that the profession of social science, pure and applied, includes as many men and women as are now engaged in natural science, it will have solved its major problem of new methods, and the results it has achieved will have altered the whole intellectual climate. As the barber-surgeon of the Middle Ages has given place to the medical man of today, with his elaborate scientific training, so the essentially amateur politician and administrator of today will have been replaced by a new type of professional man, with specialized scientific training. Life will go on against a background of social science. Society will have begun to develop a brain.

# THE BODY PHYSIOLOGIC AND THE BODY POLITIC

### by Walter B. Cannon

AT THIS bewildering time, when ancient customs are not respected, when new forms of society are being advocated and tried, when doubts cloud plans for present and future action, it is pertinent to inquire whether we might seek and find a social organization which would yield more of the benefits of security than we now enjoy. This search is natural. In the evolution and behavior of living beings the trend toward security has been one of the outstanding features. The oyster's shell, the bird's quick wings, the tiger's teeth and such human devices as clothing, houses and the varieties of insurance illustrate the universality of provisions for assured existence. The search for security is also important. In the relations among men in civilized nations there are many harrowing uncertainties. Industries are destroyed by inventions; business catastrophes create misery as hosts of laborers are suddenly thrown out of employment or realize that they hold precarious jobs; wars inflict on great populations death or painful and debilitating wounds and spread far and wide wretchedness and want. Under such stressful conditions masses of men may be led into precipitate and violent action. No wonder, then, that we look for a more stable society. Yet there are values we would not lose in the effort to gain greater stability of social organization. We would by all means wish to avoid the blight of a fixed rigidity of occupations or classes. We would wish also to avoid any check on human ingenuity directed toward advancing the welfare of mankind. Those consequences would be blighting. Freedom must be preserved—for fresh discoveries and contrivances, for novel enterprise and for the emergence of eminent ability whatever its origin. A social order assuring not security alone, not freedom alone, but both security and freedom, is the desirable goal.

If we examine any social or industrial group we note that it presents two sorts of relations, internal and external. The family, for example, must have regard for the intimate accommodations among its members in the home; and it must encounter in its environment the school, the regulations of local government and other conditioning agencies. Industry, likewise, must arrange for adjustments within and without; inside the walls of its plant it must consider the numbers and activities of its employees, their superintendence and their pay; and outside it must be on the alert for altered demands for its manufactured goods, for maneuvers of its competitors, for shifts in the community, for changes of style and for governmental requirements. Even among nations inward and outward concerns are distinguished routinely; some officials are assigned to meet the problems and to administer the country's interior affairs, other officials are assigned to study its relations with other powers, i.e., to attend to foreign affairs.

Observe that states of stability and instability in the nation, in industries and in homes are closely linked. When a break occurs in the even course of activities of larger aggregations, having widespread influence, the harmful consequences are likely to reach down to the ultimate units in the social structure, human beings. They, who are least influential in the very complicated social and economic hierarchy of influences, are the almost helpless victims. Recognition of that fact is the stimulus for the efforts to devise an organization of society which will furnish a greater assurance than hitherto that mankind shall not suffer distress and privations which are of human origin and which might be avoided by applying human intelligence.

For purposes of later discussion it is pertinent to note at this point that in the functional organization of our bodies there are relations and activities which can be distinguished as external and internal. Our *external* activities are directed towards modifying our surroundings or changing our position with regard to them—manufacturing merchandise, or engaging in hard play, or working for food and shelter—indeed, they include all the voluntary uses of our muscles. Such outwardly directed actions, however, have effects within; they use up our stores of energy-yielding material, they produce acid which might clog the working parts, they increase the amount of waste which must be discharged. These alterations, unless corrected, are capable of interfering to a serious degree with the efficiency of our bodily performance. It is the function of the *internal* activities of the organism to prevent or correct these alterations and maintain stability; thus our bodies are held in a fit state for continued action, or are made ready for special efforts when critical situations arise. Furthermore, the internal activities preserve a fitness for work despite variations in the outer world, such as excessive heat or cold, that might be deeply disturbing. The remarkable effectiveness of the regulative processes of the body's department of the interior in preserving fitness is one of the marvels of biology.

Wonderment over the maintenance of steady states in the human organism increases when we consider that we are composed of substances that are in the highest degree unstable and are commonly responsive to extremely slight modifying influences. The retina, for example, is many hundreds of times more sensitive than the most sensitive photographic plate, and brain cells are instantly dependent on a continuous supply of oxygen-bearing blood. A persistent stability of these supremely labile parts appears even more astounding when we recognize that the organism is an open system, receiving periodically from the outer world material for its repair and for the doing of work, and giving forth continuously the products of its own decomposition. We should observe, furthermore, that this stability is manifest not only in adulthood but also in the early decades when the body is undergoing a manifold increase of size, and that it is steadfast at all stages of life, although powerful alterative forces may be operating from both within and without. Here is an outstanding achievement, the result of evolutionary processes during immeasurable eons of past time. We are warranted in examining this supreme triumph of organization by nature for possible light on present defects of organization by man.

The most important device which enables our bodies to preserve steady states, notwithstanding conditions which might hamper or be destructive, is the constant character of the circulating fluids of the organism, especially the circulating blood. Our living parts are bathed by these fluids. We exist, therefore, not in the air which surrounds us—we are separated from that by a layer of inert material. We exist in a fluid matrix which provides us each with a private internal environment. Just in so far as this internal environment or fluid matrix is kept from noteworthy variations, there are no internal adjustments to be made; the internal organs can perform their functions undisturbed by the ups and downs of external circumstance or by possible consequences of our own strenuous activity.

A few examples will make these statements clearer. There is, first, the steadiness of our body temperature, a trait we share with most other mammals and with birds. Though these forms may be exposed to wide variations of temperature without they preserve an equable degree of heat within. The development of a nearly thermostable state in higher vertebrates should be regarded as one of the most valuable advances in biological evolution. Animals which maintain an approximate uniformity of temperature are released from the limitations which might be imposed by seasonal changes; they are not forced to escape either from the torpor of winter's frost or the stroke of summer's torrid heat. Again, there is the steadiness of the mild alkalinity of the blood. A slight shift to an acid reaction would result promptly in coma and death; a slight shift to a more alkaline reaction would bring on convulsions. We avoid both these dangerous possibilities because of arrangements which preserve a striking constancy of the acid-alkali relations of the internal environment. Another example of steadiness is seen in the sugar concentration of the blood. If the concentration rises to a moderate degree the sugar is wasted by spilling through the kidneys; if the concentration falls to a low level convulsions and coma ensue. These hazards might arise in prolonged and vigorous exercise. Then much heat is set free by the contracting muscles, also a large amount of acid is discharged from them, and blood sugar is abundantly utilized. In spite of the possibility of serious consequences—coma, convulsions and thermal damage—they rarely occur. Regulatory processes slip into action and preserve in the fluid matrix a relatively constant state. So characteristic is this constancy, and so peculiar are the processes which maintain it, that it has been given a special name, *homeostasis*.

Homeostasis is accomplished by different means according as processes or materials are involved. For instance, a process of discharging heat from our bodies is always going on at a moderate pace. If the bodily temperature tends to fall the discharge of heat is checked and at the same time there is greater heat production; if the temperature tends to rise the discharge is accelerated. Thus by varying the rate of a continuous process a relatively stable thermal condition is maintained. Similarly, in preserving the mild alkalinity of the blood, governing agencies are nicely adjusted. If a slight amount of acid begins to accumulate, as happens in exercise, breathing becomes more rapid, the heart beats more frequently, the circulation is hastened, more oxygen is delivered to the active organs to burn nonvolatile acid, and simultaneously the faster processes rid the body of the resultant excess of volatile carbonic acid. Again homeostasis is preserved.

In so far as materials are concerned steady states are assured by storage in times of plenty and release from storage in times of need. We take in provisions occasionally, we are using them constantly. When food is plentiful, for example, starchy reserves are stored in the liver. If now the sugar in the blood becomes reduced, these hepatic reserves are drawn upon and thereby a safe concentration in the blood is maintained. Excessive increase of material in the blood is avoided by overflow. Too much salt, too much water or too much sugar, taken at one time, are not allowed to accumulate and alter the relative constancy of the internal environment. The kidneys, acting as a spillway, permit the surplus to flow out of the body.

In relation to the maintenance of homeostasis three points may be emphasized. First, it is noteworthy that a special portion of the nervous system has become established that co-ordinates, in an automatic manner, the variable processes and the material reserves which are involved in keeping a comparatively uniform consistency of the blood. Second, this nervous organization is mainly for emergency use. Experiments have demonstrated that there can be, to a considerable extent, local autonomy in the functioning of the co-operative parts. The liver, for example, can by itself store and release its carbohydrate reserves; the island cells of the pancreas can act independently to manage the use of sugar in the organism; and the heart can perform its functions as a pump quite isolated from nervous government. Third, when stability is threatened, even to an apparently mild degree, extremely sensitive indicators are affected which promptly bring into operation the proper corrective agencies. Thus the oscillations on either side of a homeostatic norm are slight. Indeed, the responsible organs of the body react to any disturbing condition as if they were directed toward preserving a steady state in the internal environment.

Besides the regulatory arrangements which work for stability we should recognize the significant fact that our bodily organization is set up, as a rule, with a large margin of safety. Except in parts of the brain we are not built on a scant and skimpy plan. For example, we have two kidneys, we need only one; we carry much longer intestines than are actually required; half of the lung area, half of the thyroid gland, more than half of the pancreas can be removed without markedly altering the uniform state of the fluid matrix. When we consider the possible damage to organs by accident or disease this liberal mode of construction is obviously important for the persistence of the organism.

Another arrangement making for stability is, interestingly enough, characterized by temporary alteration of the fluid matrix. That is manifest when bodily welfare is imperiled by enemies. If there is a bacterial attack the number of protective corpuscles in the blood is augmented, or an antitoxin is developed to counteract a circulating toxic substance, and the body temperature rises in fever as part of the defense. If larger foes appear, requiring flight or combat, fear or rage is aroused, emotional reactions which are attended by a remarkable and commonly the greatest possible mobilization of the bodily forces for physical struggle. Even though fierce muscular conflicts between man and man or between man and beast are rare in civilized countries, the internal adjustments appropriate for victory are fully retained in us and are ready for instant response. The body is unified, integrated, for a single purpose—survival. Blood sugar is increased, the heart beat is accelerated, blood is specially distributed to the active regions and is circulated at a faster pace, respiration is deeper and more frequent, extra corpuscles are set moving to carry more oxygen, and adrenaline is discharged to reinforce the adaptive nerve impulses. Of course, all these reactions profoundly disturb the internal environment; they disturb it, however, to render the organism more effective in a contest which may issue in either life or death.

In violent struggle non-volatile acid waste is produced in muscles more rapidly than available oxygen can burn it. The accumulation of unburned acid may in the end greatly lessen muscular efficiency, but when there is an emergency that risk is run. It is obvious, however, that when the emergency has passed, extra oxygen must be delivered to remove the liability created by the waste, i.e., an "oxygen debt" has been created. That debt is not deferred by the body; it is promptly paid by persistent deep breathing and rapid blood flow to provide an oxygen delivery of the requisite amount. Thus a condition which might seriously limit freedom of action is soon abolished. Whether foes be small or large, therefore, an admirable readiness and ability to assemble protective forces are disclosed. And after danger has vanished normal homeostasis is quickly restored.

A final notable feature of bodily organization is the preferential care of certain organs when internal conditions take an unfavorable turn. Of these the brain and the heart are the two most privileged. Both are specially dependent on a continuous supply of oxygen; the brain because it contains nerve cells which are exquisitely sensitive to oxygen lack, and the heart because it requires oxygen for its ceaseless pulsing. In a condition which reduces the oxygen delivery, as after a severe hemorrhage, these two organs are soon receiving a normal blood flow, but at the expense of other parts. In starvation also, heart and brain are spared while other structures are slowly consumed.

Mention of the favored treatment of the brain makes pertinent at this point an interpretation of the significance of physiological homeostasis. It is a condition which in the course of organic evolution has been only slowly acquired. Among lower vertebrates, for example, most amphibians are bound to a nearby water source lest they desiccate. And during the long winter they must lie sluggishly at the bottom of an icy pool. Reptiles, having developed a dry skin, may move freely over the land without danger of a disastrous water loss, but they too are rendered inert for months by seasonal cold. When higher vertebrates, during stupendous ages of evolution, acquired a constant temperature and other constancies of the internal environment, when the functions of the body were more and more liberated from disturbing or limiting conditions, what is the advantage that was gained? The answer to that question is that homeostasis has released for the exercise of their peculiar services the higher functions of the brain. If we had to attend momentarily to preserving a proper alkaline reaction in the blood, or preventing its sugar concentration from falling dangerously low, or checking harmful variations of body temperature, we should have time for little else. In the myriads of millennia during which vertebrates were evolving, these functions developed and became automatically controlled. And to the degree that the control was perfected, man, in his complex external environment, has attained freedom of action. Thus our bodies disclose a type of organization in which both stability and liberty have been achieved.

We have previously noted that there are other organizations —domestic, industrial, governmental—which, like the human organism, face problems of internal and external adjustments. Their external adjustments relate to circumstances which may profoundly affect many included units or groups. In a similar situation, as we have just seen, our bodies, by the evolution of a self-regulated internal economy, have become to a high degree liberated from deranging external influences. Can this sort of liberty be achieved in human society? Historical evidence clearly reveals that human society has been undergoing an evolutionary development; and observation indicates that even in civilized nations it is still in an early stage of that development. Wherever complicated functions are performed there appear to be general principles of organization which are more or less realized. It may be that our bodies, which are the culmination of ages of experience, have learned secrets of management that are worthy of our study. We must admit that organisms have long shown abilities beyond the present reach of human ingenuity—for example, the compounding of elaborate chemicals (proteins, fats, carbohydrates), the contrivance of self-reproduction, the nice control of a gradual increase in size of a manifold structure. Only within our memory has man learned to fly as birds have flown for millions of years. Indeed, the manner in which our bodies have found both stability and liberty may have lessons for larger and less perfect organizations.

The resemblance between the body physiologic and the body politic has long attracted the interest of philosophers, biologists and historians. Among sociologists, economists and men of affairs, however, the analogies have been largely discredited, because, it is said, the comparisons have not contributed to the understanding of social structure. The failure to be helpful seems to have been due to pressing to an absurd degree resemblances in the minutiae of that structure. We are not illuminated by a likening of manual laborers to muscle cells, manufacturers to gland cells, bankers to fat cells and policemen to white blood corpuscles. On the other hand, analogies may be instructive if, instead of a comparison of structural details, there is inquiry into relative functional accomplishments in the physiological and social realms. Naturally, on undertaking this inquiry a physiologist must proceed not as an expert in the social realm but as a layman. In the realm of physiological organization, he finds that, despite inherent structural instability and despite constant exposure of unstable organic stuff to powerful destructive forces, an almost incredible steadiness has been achieved. Are not the principles exemplified in the workings of our bodies sufficiently fundamental to have social applications? Might not the outstanding achievement of bodily homeostasis, the means of which have been revealed by fairly recent discoveries, be indicative of ends to be sought, and the means of attaining them, in social evolution? An attempt to answer these questions may not present to students of society any new ideas; the success of the physiological organism, however, may add emphasis to some ideas which are already well recognized. With this admission of hazard in the venture, standing as a boundary post between observed facts and possible pertinencies, a comparison of the body politic and the body physiologic is undertaken.

What corresponds in a nation to the internal environment of the body? The closest analogue appears to be the whole intricate system of production and distribution of merchandise. It would include the means of industry and commerce—the agencies of manufacture and agriculture, the rivers, the roads and railroads, trains and trucks, wholesale and retail purveyors —all the factors, human and mechanical, which produce and distribute goods in the vast and ramifying circulatory system which serves for economic exchange. Into this moving stream products of farms and factories, of mines and forests, are placed, at their source, for carriage to other localities. In the operations of this stream one is allowed to take goods out of it only if one puts back into it goods of equivalent worth. As a rule it is not possible to do that immediately, or to furnish the full replacement value exactly when goods are removed. Money, therefore, is used to facilitate the process of exchange, or credit may serve as a temporary substitute. Thus money and credit become a part of the internal environment of society.

The bodily analogue has been regarded by some as indicating that just as there is fixity of the units (i.e., the cells) in the internal organs, there must be fixity of the human units in the diverse parts of the social structure. That condition, however, is not essential. Emphatically, the essential condition is *functional*—a continuity of service. Men are needed, of course, to operate farms, factories and railroads, but so long as these services are maintained, men may move freely from one position to another. As we shall see later, society, unlike man, is not limited by death; society lives on, for indefinite time, precisely because the human units are replaceable. In social organizations, therefore, the closest analogues to the parts of the body are not the ultimate units, the human beings; the closest analogues are the functional groups—the special trades and professions and the various labor types. They correspond to the bodily organs.

On the assumption that industry and commerce constitute the internal environment of society, what has the experience of the physiological organism to suggest as a result of its own attainment of stable states?

It suggests, first, that the primary condition for freedom from the operation of disturbing forces, both within and without, is a maintained constancy of the internal environment. According to that required preliminary the moving commercial stream should deliver continuously, to units which are recognized as serving society, at least the necessities of existence—food, shelter and protection and assured assistance if there be injury or disease. Constancy would involve also reliable opportunity for every man to have uninterrupted work and the payment of a wage or other recompense sufficient to permit him to obtain from the stream what he and his dependents actually require. Only in recent years have some of these practices begun to be respected. Others are only discussed. In these regards the body biologic has developed further and become more effective than the body politic in its organization for internal homeostasis.

A second suggestion which physiological organization offers is that trends toward dangerous shifts of stability should be noticed at the start and controlled immediately. We have seen that any even minor tendency toward such a shift in the bodily organism is quickly detected by delicate indicators, and corrective processes are at once evoked to prevent further change and to restore the former state. In society these regulatory devices are little known or are lacking altogether. We do note that a crude sort of oscillation occurs: loose government is followed by reform and that in turn by loose government again; a boom ends in a depression, and after recovery there is another boom. These swings of social mood by their cumulative effects can cause intense distress. Deeper insight into what starts them, what stops them and how they can be avoided is highly desirable. Furthermore, in the body politic an initial disturbance, instead of promptly arousing protective and corrective factors, often starts a harmful process which spreads through a community with accelerating speed. Thus, when a run on a bank begins, it is self-intensifying. As the claims of depositors force a closure, fears are aroused, and the run extends to other banks, until a national moratorium may be required to permit recovery. Still another example of self-aggravating damage to social stability is seen when stock prices decline; margin calls which are sent out provoke a further fall of the prices and the sending out of further calls; an unchecked circuit of injurious behavior ensues, ending in panic. In short, when danger threatens, stabilizing agencies do not act on the instant to guarantee security; instead, disruptive factors have full sway. The situation demands research on economic fluctuations and on modes of governing them, for the human organism has demonstrated that in an extremely unstable structure there are ways of maintaining steadiness. It is of interest to note that efforts have been made to find sensitive signals of perilous economic tendencies and to set in motion corrective measures. Thus, an index of velocity of deposits was intended as a warning of excessive business activity; and theoretically the condition might be remedied by raising the discount rate. Control of this remedy, however, is subject to influences playing on human prejudice, and its operation will probably remain imperfect until greater knowledge and experience permit more precise decisions.

A further hint offered by bodily homeostasis is that industries and commerce should be organized to operate smoothly in caring not only for routine but also for emergency conditions. In the organism storage of excess material when it is plentiful and release from storage as want arises provide for variable supplies and variable demands without altering the uniformity of the internal environment. The prime value of these methods has recently been recognized by both government and industry. Within the last few years the establishment of agricultural and commodity credit policies, which allow the withholding of surpluses in fat periods, for sale in lean periods, illustrate governmental recognition of the importance of uniform distribution for both producers and consumers. Also commercial storage by preserving perishable foods, by permanent sterilization or by freezing, has been much developed of late, with the result that former seasonal glut or dearth in the markets has become almost obsolete.

In the organism smooth operation under variable demands is achieved also by changing the rate of continuous processes. Those processes are characteristically conducted at a moderate pace, an arrangement which permits them to be varied, i.e., slowed down or speeded up according to requirements. In the body politic the control of processes still has far to go. Instead of a change of rate a frequent alternative is a total stoppage of the process; men are thrown out of their jobs and drift in idleness. How industry and commerce can be adjusted to inconstant or temporal demands has not yet been discovered. Various schemes for co-ordinating production and consumption and for assuring regularity and continuity of employment prove that thoughtful men are deeply concerned with the fear, the despondency and the hardship which result from uncertain economic existence. Control to a greater degree than now prevails might lead, however, to more extensive liberty of action, as control by stop-and-go signals has eliminated traffic jams and promoted free movement, or as control of infections has enormously expanded the liberties of mankind by providing safe food and drink and by isolating the carriers of disease. More control is tolerable if it results in greater human freedom.

Instant readiness for defense against dangerous and destructive enemies is also suggested by the body. We have noted that, when faced with the necessity of physical combat, nearly every part of the organism is almost at once intensely aroused to defensive action and that, for gaining victory, mobilization of the internal forces is likely to reach the utmost limit. No "oxygen debt" is allowed to persist that might be a source of weakness if an emergency should arise. Again observe that security is a primary objective. In a world where predatory nations, powerfully armed, are ready to attack, the ideal of security often is not adequately respected. Internal forces are not trained for action. Protective instruments of warfare are lacking. At a time of crisis industry is obliged to begin to construct buildings and design tools and machines to manufacture the instruments which the crisis demands. Compare this unpreparedness with the preparedness of our bodies, which through many generations of little use still retain the elaborate reactions of defense.

Physiological homeostasis would suggest, further, that stability is more important than economy. As previously remarked, excess of water or salt or sugar is thrown away when derangement of a steady state is approached. The violent shivering which attends a fall of body temperature is, in terms of obvious accomplishment, wasteful of energy, because the muscular contractions do no external work. They are useful, however, in producing heat and thus keeping uniform the fluid matrix. Further evidence that security comes before economy is revealed by the wide margins of safety found throughout the organism. Extra blood volume, lung capacity, blood pressure and cardiac power—much more than ordinarily required—all indicate generous preparations for meeting unusual demands, which might create disorder if they were not met. In personal and governmental practice, also, the principle of preferring security to economy has been to some degree recognized. Life insurance and accident insurance may be paid year after year with no advantage except a sense of being protected. Fire departments are maintained, and armies and navies are kept in fighting trim at great expense, again with special regard for safety rather than economy.

The idea has been expressed that functional groups in the organism, i.e., the various organs, compete with one another for nutriment. There is little evidence to support that idea, so long as the body is in a healthy and well-nourished condition. All groups receive adequate support, not only those which are routinely active, but also those which may be active at some time or occasionally. The reproductive organs offer a striking example of prolonged sustenance before and after functional service, and perhaps through an entire lifetime of no service whatever. Here again is illustrated a liberal treatment of valuable parts rather than strict economy.

In emergencies, when life is in peril, there is, as already observed, discriminative treatment of specific organs. Those on which the organism depends for the proper conduct of its external affairs and for the internal distribution of its supplies receive special care. During protracted starvation, for example, the brain and the heart remain unchanged in weight while other structures waste away in furnishing them with nutriment. And if there is a serious hemorrhage, which drops the arterial pressure and greatly reduces the circulation rate and thereby the oxygen delivery, the pressure is soon raised so that the flow is fast again in brain and heart; but this is effected at the expense of a normal blood supply to other parts, which suffer until the normal blood volume can be restored. In short, the agency which is on the alert for changes in the outer world and which reacts to these changes, and also the agency by which the fluid matrix as a common carrier is kept moving for aid to the body as a whole, despite privations, are supremely favored. In the body politic, likewise, administrative and distributive agents, charged with conducting important external or internal business, receive in time of crisis exceptional consideration. In warfare, for example, the general staff and the service of supply are protected from the perils of the fighting line. And in civil life members of essential functional groups are retained at their usual work instead of being drafted for military duty.

In surveying the evidence thus far presented we see that social, like biological organizations, are characterized by having external relations with the surrounding environment and internal relations among the operating parts or groups; that the higher biological organisms, composed of extraordinarily unstable stuff, have learned the secret of stability by developing wide margins of safety in their bodily structure and ample provisions for defense against dangerous foes, and pre-eminently by producing for their internal parts a common environment which is automatically held in a relatively uniform state by corrective factors set in action by delicate signals of deviation from that state. The body politic exhibits many processes which resemble those found in the body physiologic; the analogies are so close and so numerous, not only for nation but also for industry, as to intimate strongly that there are indeed general principles of organization, widely applicable to complex aggregations of collaborating parts. Although there are these analogous processes and systems in the social organization they are effective only within very broad limits in providing stable conditions. Without definite regulations for social homeostasis —without an equable flow of the necessities of life to all, without arrangements for variable demands for labor, without signals of economic danger when that danger impends—booms alternate with depressions, hunger alternates with abundance, and overtime work alternates with forced idleness. Also adequate defense against attack by insidious disease or by gross external foes is often neglected; and tight economy and maximal efficiency are demanded with little regard for the welfare of the units in the functioning groups on which the very existence of society must rest. In such respects the body physiologic has evolved methods of operation which are more efficient than those thus far prevailing in the body politic.

A question which properly arises is whether an organized control of the internal environment of society is consistent with human freedom. That control, would, indeed, involve assignment of power to store goods in times of plenty and to release them in times of need, to lay aside wage and job reserves to care for temporary unemployment, to train labor in new skills when they are required, to accelerate or retard essential processes of production and distribution according to demands or needs, to check perturbing and distressing shifts of price level, and to assure to all the opportunity for expert attention in case of illness or injury. Analogous arrangements exist in our bodies, with the possibility of local control by functional groups, to be sure, but ultimately under a central, automatic, co-ordinating system. Precisely because that co-ordinating system is automatic we are free—free from consciously meeting the exigencies of a variable outer world, and from attending to harmful variations of the inner world of the organism. If we were not protected against these perturbing states we should be either compelled to remain inert in a carefully and uniformly regulated chamber, or checked at every move by the need of attentively avoiding such perils as coma or convulsions. Just because there is an inner homeostasis the higher functions of the brain are released for their special uses—for work and play, for adventures, for research and exploration, for the production and enjoyment of literature and art and for all manner of social interests.

We should recognize that the functioning of the human brain has made social homeostasis differ markedly from physiological homeostasis. By use of the brain in seeking new devices we as discoverers and inventors are occasionally changing the internal environment of society. Only thus do we improve it. But an upset of constancy necessarily results. Railways replace canals, automobiles crowd out the horse and buggy, and now airplanes compete with previous means of travel. Such disruptive inventions profoundly derange the functional groups of a social system. Experienced workmen find that their skill can no longer be applied. During a period of transition thousands may be thrown out of work. Then the personal security which social homeostasis might provide would be, for many, sadly lacking. The brain, however, is not only an organ for discovery and invention; it is also an organ for adaptation and adjustment. As possessors of brains we should be able to apply them to finding ways to care for our fellowmen who will suffer from inventions having general social value. By planning employment which is expansible in non-technical directions, by extending processes of education and specialized training for new skills, by stimulating fresh enterprise, the distress due to penurious idleness can be greatly lessened. Already the humanity of such social conduct is being recognized by the state and by industry. A very important step toward establishing a sense of security will be taken when these and similar measures are regarded as necessary in order to avoid the harassing fears and anxieties and the needless pain of insecurity.

The peculiar service of the brain in adapting the organism to its external environment raises questions as to its role in the congeries of organs which constitute the body physiologic. Is the brain in a dictatorial position? Does its relation to the other organs suggest an unchecked dominance? It can, indeed, so act that it and all other organs of the body are destroyed, as in suicide. But if the brain performs its proper functions, it is revealed as acutely dependent on these other organs; a momentary inadequacy of the oxygen supply from lungs and heart abolishes the cerebral processes which are basic for consciousness, and a few minutes of that condition will produce irreparable damage, a state of idiocy. Idiocy results also if an almost incredibly minute amount of thyroid secretion is not routinely produced during the period of childhood. In short, the body physiologic is a collection of organs, the brain among them, which are interdependent and which, for the welfare of the whole, co-operate. Each one needs the others for perfect function.

The brain has almost no *direct* government of the autonomous homeostatic mechanisms; we cannot, at will, increase sugar in the blood, accelerate the heart or stop the secretion of digestive glands. On the other hand, if the brain does so direct behavior in relation to outer circumstance that the organism is endangered, the corrective self-regulatory devices will be supremely stimulated. Fever, inflammatory barriers, antitoxic agents, corpuscular defenders, all arise to check infective incursions; and against attack by beast or man emotional reactions summon the forces of the entire body for physical effort. In either case the internal economy as a whole is placed on a survival basis; reserves are lavishly distributed; even portions of the organism itself may be destroyed in meeting the emergency. In these critical conditions the functions of the brain are no longer free; they are confined to solving problems of survival; and creative activities in art and science, apart from those problems, are largely obliterated.

Such disastrous consequences of human conduct have their analogues in the calamities which fall upon nations when governmental leaders act in such ways as to bring on war. The body politic, to be sure, like the body physiologic, is then unified, integrated, and for one purpose—self-preservation. Men are mobilized for military service; women are called by industry and commerce to replace the men; hours of work are lengthened; the arts of peace are neglected; scientists cease their untrammeled labors and concentrate on inquiries of importance for the army and navy; immense resources which might be used to carry comfort and conveniences to the under-privileged or to lessen ignorance and disease are appallingly spent in reckless and malicious destruction; the lives of tens of thousands of citizens are extinguished, and privation and misery become universal. In avoidance of these calamitous disruptions of social stability the problem is that of finding conditions which are least likely to allow damage and destruction through acts of a functional group responsible for directing conduct related to external affairs.

Before touching on that problem we must consider an inevitable difference between the body physiologic and the body politic. The body physiologic must die. The body politic can live indefinitely. When death of the body physiologic occurs it results from failure of proper performance by one of its essential organs—for example, impaired activity or an ended service in kidneys, lungs or heart. Death is due, therefore, to dependence on irreplaceable parts. By substitution of new parts a machine may continue operating without limit of time. Likewise in social organization there can be unending continuity of efficient existence so long as there are arrangements for continual renewal of the functional groups. The body politic runs the risk of extinction, however, if one or another of its essential functional groups, like those of the body physiologic, is lacking proper provision for strong and useful replacement. There are illustrations of this possibility in the failure of a group in the body politic which is analogous to the brain in its highest functions.

The human cerebral cortex is the climax of biological evolution. The triumphs of its processes in solving the mysteries of natural phenomena, in transforming knowledge into power, in designing ingenious mechanisms, in making and using symbols in place of things, in providing means of perpetuating the past, and in guiding behavior through appropriate ways in the novel world which it creates, give the cortex the supreme position among the functional groups of the body. It happens, however, that among all the units of which our organs are composed the units of our nervous system are least replaceable, either immediately or by substitution. We have only a thin sheet of cortical tissue over the brain surface and it is so indispensable that if portions of it are damaged we may be paralyzed, or rendered blind or deaf or be utterly deranged. In the social body, also, the functional group which corresponds to the organ of intelligence—the revealers, the creators, the directors of affairs—are least easily replaced. It is of the utmost importance, therefore, that whenever unusual ability of social value is disclosed, no matter what its source, it should be allowed every chance to rise to its highest level of accomplishment. Thus the vigorous persistence of the social organism is best assured. Obviously the casting forth of highly gifted, irreplaceable units, its discoverers and interpreters, from a society, is an act partaking of social suicide. And obstacles placed in the ways of advancement to posts of managerial responsibility and direction, so that members of the administrative group are not supplanted by able successors, may lead to disaster. In that direction revolutions lie, and the fall of dynasties and the disintegration of empires.

The success of the body physiologic would seem to intimate that in the body politic there should be a thorough co-operation of functional groups, with the administrative groups dependent, like the others, on a common welfare. And the failure of the body physiologic to survive would seem to emphasize the importance of adequate replacement of functional groups as an elemental necessity for the social body's persistence. Its firmest basis for longevity and stability would appear to be a generally accepted mode of replacement, socially sponsored as being orderly and just. When a leader is thus chosen for responsibility he becomes a temporary advocate for public opinion. And when he is no longer representative he in turn can be replaced. Thus, in a democratic society, the diffused functional groups have possibilities of continuing the life of the social organization and of controlling their own circumstances. When an arbitrary dictator seizes power these possibilities vanish. The circumstances are now dominated by the personal pride or ambition or whim of a single man. Experience has shown that the social body, like the human body, is integrated by martial emotions and by preparations for conflict. A dictator, therefore, praises military powers, and rouses martial emotions by pointing to national insecurity or national destiny, and finally drives on to open aggression. Thus he obtains the support of a unified people. But despotic domination lacks precisely what is required for continuance of despotic rule—provision for replacement by an equally despotic ruler.

The use of insecurity by dictators as a basis for rousing hopes and fears and hatreds well illustrates the plasticity of people when they are uneasy and anxious. When they are in dire want, or are uncertain of support, or are fearful of their future, they are easily persuaded by anyone who firmly promises them relief. And if their distress is definitely attributed to a certain class or another nation, they are easily persuaded to hate and to call for vengeance. The unscrupulous demagogue grasps for power and becomes a menace because he knows that the needy are not free; he knows that they are sure to follow a course in which they are offered abundance. For any democratic society this situation is not without peril. Social homeostasis becomes, therefore, a consideration of prime significance. It is foolhardy to be smug and self-satisfied and disdainful of efforts to establish a more perfect social justice. As remarked before, human society is in the process of evolution, and probably is in what will be regarded as an early stage of that process. Stability of the internal environment of social organization has not been attained. So long as men have not the right to work and earn their bread, so long as they are left ignorant of vital information, so long as they are ill and not attended, so long as they are in misery and wretchedness without care, further evolution of society should not only be expected but sought, not only advanced by trial and error but promoted by applied intelligence.

We have seen that conditions in the nation, in industries and in homes are intimately related. Harmful consequences of unsteadiness in the nation finally bring misery to the ultimate social units, ourselves and our fellows. But steadiness in society as a whole and steadiness in its members are also intimately related. Just in so far as social stability fosters security, both physical and mental, of the members of the social organization, so also it fosters their higher freedom, assuring them opportunity for self-support, replacing fear by confidence and providing for health and reasonable leisure. These are the prime conditions for wholesome living, for the enjoyment of natural and created values, for the discipline and exercise of individual aptitudes and for the pursuit and acquisition of new knowledge. They are prime conditions also for safety of the body politic.

# MAN AND TECHNOLOGY

## by Karl T. Compton

SCIENCE, through observation of phenomena and controlled experiments, followed by correlation, hypothesis and theory, has given man an understanding of himself and his environment which has brought him satisfaction and release from the fears and superstitions which inevitably accompany ignorance. This understanding of Nature has also enabled him to utilize her materials and forces to his advantage, which is the field of technology and the subject of this chapter.

Volumes have been written to describe the marvelous advances of technology in recent years, and to set forth its benefits to the human race. To some, including the technologists themselves, the benefits seem so overwhelming as to preclude any reasonable argument on the subject. Others, including some who have suffered through technological unemployment, or who shudder at the destructive power of modern warfare, or who are temperamentally worried, or are suspicious of change, are inclined to question whether, after all, technological progress has increased human happiness. The realist would say that, for better or for worse, man will continue to seek and employ the most potent methods at his disposal for accomplishing his purposes.

Technology and its influence on employment and standards of living are, literally speaking, as old as the hills. The relics of primitive man, disclosed by the excavations of archaeologists, prove that he has used tools from the very dawn of history. In fact, the ancient civilizations are now described by these tools, as the Stone Age, or the Bronze Age. To a very large extent, man's standard of living has always been limited by the tools at his disposal.

As long as man has built roads and shelter he has practiced civil engineering. When the ancient Assyrians invented wheel-carts to carry their loads and when the Egyptians used inclined planes to raise the massive stones of their monuments they were mechanical engineers. And the old alchemists developed some rudiments of chemistry and metallurgy.

Technological unemployment, also, has existed ever since men have used mechanical devices to aid them to do their work more advantageously. When the Egyptian farmer installed a water-driven or ox-driven pump to irrigate his fields with waters from the Nile he became, thereby, technologically un-employed. The time which he previously spent in carrying water by hand, he could now spend in loafing or doing some other job. At the same time he could irrigate a much larger field and harvest a much larger crop than ever before.

With the development, first of water power, and then of steam power, and with the accelerated rate of discovery in sci-ence and its useful applications, these primary desirable effects of technology on employment and living standards have been multiplied enormously, and have, at the same time, disclosed some secondary complications which are definitely undesirable unless they can be avoided or compensated.

Perhaps the most inclusive statement of the effect of tech-nology on the human race is found in the estimate that three-quarters of the people now living on this earth,—some billion and a half persons,—would not now be living except for the modern technology developed in the last three hundred years. They would have died in childhood or later, or they would never have been born at all because their parents or grand-parents would have died through exposure, epidemics, lack of food, lack of medical care or other hazards of more primi-tive civilizations which modern applications of science have alleviated.

The basis for this statement is the admittedly very rough estimate of the world population just before the advent of modern technology about three hundred years ago. In per-haps a half million years of human life on the earth the pop-ulation had grown to about five hundred million. The limit to this rate of growth was certainly not in the rate of childbirth; it was, as always, in the close balance between death rate and birth rate, with death in childhood playing an obviously major role as regards future population. But in the relatively infinitesimal time of three hundred years since the advent of science and machinery the population grew three times as much as in all preceding epochs.

Undoubtedly the major elements in this population growth were increased food supply, improved methods of transportation and communication and reduction in premature deaths, all ascribable to technology in its agricultural, engineering and medical branches. Technology has dismissed the dismal doctrine of Malthus, once held to define the inevitable limitation to population.

To this one inclusive example can be applied in stark form most of the arguments for and against technology. If one believes that unhappiness is man's lot on earth, then truly has technology increased the sum total of human unhappiness enormously,—there are so many more people inhabiting this vale of sorrow. If one believes that each human soul has an imperishable value, then technology has increased the aggregate of these values. If one deplores (as all do) the increased destructiveness which technology has added to warfare, then one can at least take comfort and thank technology in the thought that death of thousands in battle is less heartrending than death of millions through disease and starvation. Unless one is a pessimist one can also take courage from the hope that war, disease and starvation will all be conquered.

In the hope for eventual elimination of war, technology may yet play just as significant a role as in banishment of disease and starvation, and in an analogous way by removing at least some of the causes. Some examples will make this clear.

For centuries China was subject to invasions to capture her riches, of which a principal one was silk; now we can make artificial silk out of materials which are widely accessible. For decades oil has been vital to the economy and defense of nations; now it can be produced from coal, which is much more widely distributed. At present the rubber plantations of Malay and the Dutch East Indies are a threat to their peace and safety; but as artificial rubber comes more and more into development and use this threat will be lessened. So, one by one, through substitutes produced by technology, the list of these natural resources which nations feel that they must control is being reduced. Every such technological triumph means one less excuse for war.

This is just one aspect of a more inclusive argument for technology as a substitute for barbarous or unethical procedures by which men have for centuries satisfied their ambitions.

From the days of the cave man, all through history up to the modern era of science, there were only two primitive recipes for securing the materials desired for the more abundant life. One was to work hard and long in order to produce more, and the other was to take the good things of life from someone else, by theft, conquest, taxation or exploitation.

To get the good things of life by taking them from others is a primitive instinct, undoubtedly developed by the age-old struggle for existence. We have all seen monkeys, or sea gulls, or wolves, or pigs snatching food from each other, fighting to possess it, or shouldering each other away from the trough. When human beings carry this philosophy too far beyond the accepted standards, as did Jesse James and John Dillinger, we call them "public enemies." But this same philosophy of taking what we want from others, by violence or trickery, or by legalized strategy and force has run all through history.

Remember when Moses led the children of Israel out of Egypt into the Promised Land. Joshua, sent ahead to spy out the land, brought back a glowing description of a "land flowing with milk and honey." This was truly the opportunity for a more abundant life for the Israelites, and they proceeded to smite hip and thigh the Hittites, Moabites and Philistines, to slay them by the thousands and the tens of thousands, and to take possession of their land, herds and cities. The ethics of the case did not disturb them, for were they not the "chosen people"?

Later, the Romans conquered the then known world, in order to extract tribute and slaves from the conquered nations, and to exploit the mines and farms of the world. Beginning with 1492, all Europe sought wealth through exploitation of the newly discovered lands of America, which they took from the Indians by conquest or treaty. Great Britain built up her world empire primarily for economic gain through trade and control of natural resources. A century or two ago the nations of the world were robbing Africa of its ivory and its gold, and capturing its people for slaves. We can all cite examples in our own generation of this same philosophy in international affairs, even to the use of the old excuse of the Israelites in that each nation tends to consider itself as a "chosen people," with special privileges over other peoples.

But it is not alone nations against nations which have followed this policy of seeking to profit at the expense of others. Let me suggest a few examples of this same primitive philosophy operating *within* our own nations today.

A speculator attempts to corner the wheat market so that he may reap a profit at the expense of the purchasing public. A trust, in the sense of a combination in restraint of trade, attempts to use its control of the situation to force its customers to pay exorbitant prices in order that it may make an abnormally large profit at the expense of the public. There is much of the same basic element in the doctrine, which has had some governmental sanction, that the farmers of the country should combine together to restrict production in order that prices of agricultural products may rise, thus forcing the public to pay special benefits to the farmer. Industries seek an analogous special advantage through tariff protection. A political party, when it wins an election, proceeds to displace postmasters and commissioners with its own followers,—to hand out patronage, as it is called, at the expense of the losing party. There has always been a tendency for the owner of a business to pay his employees as little as possible, taking all the work he can get out of them and paying the smallest possible amount in order that his profits may be large. For equally natural reasons, ever since the days of the Romans and perhaps earlier, there has always been a tendency for workers to organize to force the employer to pay higher wages for less work.

But, in recent times, modern science has developed to give mankind, for the first time in the history of the human race, a way of securing a more abundant life which does not simply consist in taking it away from someone else. Science really creates wealth and opportunity where they did not exist before. Whereas, the old order was based on competition, the new order of science makes possible, for the first time, a co-operative creative effort in which everyone is the gainer, and no one the loser.

For this reason, the advent of science and modern technology is one of the most important social events in all history. It marks the point at which men have come to understand themselves and the world they live in well enough to begin systematically to control the hidden forces of Nature to their advantage. Already applied science has done wonders to raise our standards of living and of knowledge, but these hidden forces are so great that we are assuredly only at the beginning of things possible.

The basic effects of technology can be illustrated very simply as follows: Suppose, by some new triumph of science, men are everywhere enabled to produce the products of their labors with tenfold the previous rapidity. It is evident that they can then have everything which they previously produced if they work only one-tenth as many hours per week. But this will give them an opportunity, in their spare time, to produce still other things which people want sufficiently to be willing to work and to pay for. They might, for example, work only half as many hours as they formerly did, and they would still produce five times as much of the desirable things of life.

Of course there are many other factors involved if this situation really leads to a general rise in the standard of living. For example, people must be educated to use their newly found spare time in ways that will be beneficial rather than harmful to their personalities. Here education, religion and legislation all have a role, but so too does technology, which provides education and recreation through transportation, communication, books and magazines, motion pictures and many other things which it has created and made so cheap as to be available to the common people. Then too, these products and the wealth which they represent must be properly distributed in order that the people as a whole may benefit,—another job for legislators, economists and scientists.

The extent to which technology is today aiding mankind to accomplish his purposes can be illustrated by the following facts. According to the latest figures available, the total mechanical power now used in the United States,—derived from coal, oil and hydroelectric sources,—amounts to 13.4 horsepower per capita of population. Tests also show that the average power which a man can exert throughout a working day is 35 watts, or about 1/20 horsepower. Thus every man, woman and child in the United States has working for him, in the form of mechanical power, the equivalent of about 270 slaves, on the average! So, through technology, men and women have largely become directors and operators of productive equipment, instead of toilers. True, they may still work very hard as directors and operators, and some kinds of work still have to be performed in the primitive manner by hand, but on the average, technology has multiplied our accomplishment by at least 270 times the amount we could have done by sustained physical effort alone.

Another way of illustrating the same point is to say that, for about two cents per day in the average home, the housewife can buy an amount of electrical energy equal to the total physical energy which a servant could deliver in ten hours of work. At electrical power rates in factories, the cost of one day's electrical equivalent of human energy would be still less.

An indication of the significance of this technological use of mechanical power is seen in figures which were published a few years ago, giving for various countries the average number of hours which a laborer must work in order to buy a basket of food containing one pound each of beef, bacon, bread, butter, potatoes and sugar, plus one quart of milk and one dozen eggs. Note the striking parallelism between this indication of *real* wages, and the technological development of the country as measured by its use of machine power.

| Country | Horsepower used per capita | Hours of work required to earn above food basket |
|---|---|---|
| United States | 13.4 | 1.5 |
| Great Britain | 6.6 | 3.75 |
| Germany | 6.0 | 3.5 |
| France | 4.3 | 3.5 |
| Russia | 0.9 | 23.5 |

Another way of indicating the effects of technological progress on the earnings of workers in the United States is to point out the steady rate of increase in the amount of goods which the laborer has been able to purchase with his wages during the last 100 years, which has been distinctive for the rapid increase in technological development. Of course wages have gone up rather steadily, as measured in dollars, but this is of no significance unless wages have gone up more rapidly than have the prices of the commodities which the wage-earner wishes to buy. In other words, it is important to know what has been the effect of technological progress on *real* wages. These are the facts. During the past hundred years the ratio of average wages to average prices of commodities has multiplied sevenfold. In other words, the average wage-earner in America can today buy seven times as much with his wages as he could 100 years ago. He can buy twice as much with his wages today as he could 30 years ago.

The fact that the intelligent leadership in the ranks of labor realizes this situation is demonstrated by statements both from the American Federation of Labor and from the Committee for Industrial Organization. Twenty-one years ago the American Federation of Labor expressed its conviction on this subject in the following resolution:

"Whereas, the increased productivity of industry resulting from scientific research is a most potent factor in the ever-increasing struggle of the workers to raise their standards of living, and the importance of this factor must steadily increase since there is a limit beyond which the average standard of living of the whole population cannot progress by the usual methods of readjustment, which limit can only be raised by research and the results of research in industry:

"Resolved, by the American Federation of Labor in convention assembled, that a broad program of scientific and technical research is of major importance to the national welfare . . ."

And the following statement is quoted from the Handbook for Committeemen of local lodges of the Steel Workers Organizing Committee, an affiliate of the C.I.O.:

"The Steel Workers Organizing Committee, as a progressive union, stands for a policy of security and plenty for all. In order for all our people, wage earners, farmers and other useful people, to have more, we need to produce and distribute more, not less. The American people possess almost unlimited natural resources. We have trained management and millions of wage earners able and willing to work. Under such circumstances greater production, guided by efficient management, means lower cost per unit. Lower costs tend toward lower prices. This enables our people to buy and use more goods. This, in turn, makes possible putting our unemployed back to work."

The booklet then goes on to say:

"How is it possible for the employer to pay labor more and still not have less himself? The answer is simpler than it looks. Almost any shop or mill is full of wasteful practices. There are many workers in any large-sized establishment who could offhand, as a result of their daily observations, give the management hints as to how it could save money and put out a better or a cheaper product. If this knowledge were collected and applied, the establishment would be better able to meet labor's demands.

"If a systematic study is made with the help of an expert—an expert working for labor as well as for management—a great many unsuspected ways of making economies can often be discovered."

Thus far in this chapter we have devoted attention to "over-all" situations and "long-term" trends. Now let us examine a few of the more immediate and specific effects of technology on man. This examination will refer to economic rather than to medical situations, since there is no argument over the value of medical science to man's welfare. Consider first some favorable features, which are given as specific examples illustrative of more general situations.

In the worst period of the recent depression the President of the General Electric Company reported to his stockholders that 60% of that year's business had been in products which were new within the preceding decade. In a national conference on "Technology and Employment" held in Chicago a little over five years ago, Mr. John W. O'Leary stated that one-fourth of the employees of American industry at this time owe their jobs to eighteen new industries which have developed since 1880. He also showed that the most rapid growth of employment is in those industries which have been advancing most rapidly along technological lines. Similarly, a survey by the National Research Council has shown unmistakably that the financial soundness and prosperity of various types of industries are generally proportional to their activity in research.

Unusually striking are the status and trends in an industry which is very typical of those which have been built on the foundation of technological progress,—the chemical industry. Here we find a faith in the ultimate economic values of science, like that demonstrated by a company which recently put on the market a new chemical product on whose research development it had spent more than a million dollars. The following two paragraphs are quoted from the 1938 October issue of the magazine *Industry*, based on records from the U.S. Bureau of Labor Statistics and the National Industrial Conference Board:

"Employment today in the chemical industry is 20% higher than in 1929 although manufacturing generally is still about 5% lower than the 1929 peak. [Written in 1938.]

"The chemical industry's average hourly wage, also average weekly wage, is 15% higher than for all manufacturing. The chemical factory worker earns on the average $31 a week compared with an average of $26 a week for all manufacturing industry."

Turning now to the unfavorable side of technology's influence on man, the subject of technological unemployment is probably the one in this category which has most impressed itself on the attention of the public during the past decade. No more intimate explanation of this problem could be given than that by Mr. John L. Lewis as quoted from his article in the *Tech Engineering News* of October, 1937:

"Labor, of course, is not unaware of the argument that the displacement of labor, through technical improvements in industry, is only a temporary phenomenon. The argument runs like this. Improved machinery means lower prices, and the savings thus given the consumer are available for the purchase of other commodities, which, in turn, demand more labor to produce.

"The fallacies in this argument are twofold. First, prices do not automatically reduce themselves with lowered production costs. Prices are determined by many factors, and everyone, except the confirmed classical economist, knows that, even when prices do reflect reduced costs, there may be a long 'time lag' before this occurs. And, second, labor is not a fluid, flowing from where it is not wanted to where it may be wanted, without loss or friction. Labor, on the contrary, is just a conglomerate of human beings, with the ordinary human craving for food, clothing, shelter, and family life. Thus, if a machine displaces ten skilled lumber workers in Seattle, the fact that, simultaneously, there are openings for ten skilled tailors in New York City, is no help to the ten jobless lumber workers in Seattle. In the first place, they probably would know nothing of the New York jobs; secondly, they probably couldn't afford to travel that far; and thirdly, even if these two serious difficulties could be overcome, the unemployed lumbermen couldn't qualify for the jobs offered. This, of course, is an extreme case, but broadly speaking, it illustrates what has been happening to American labor."

Mr. Lewis' own recommendations for amelioration of this difficulty are: first, better assurance that workers will receive a fair share of the benefits of technological progress; second, liberalization of social security schemes; third, strengthening of labor unions for both defense against industry and assistance to it as situations dictate; fourth, direction of technology with a view to its social consequences.

The problem is very difficult, for there is great danger that steps will be taken which will sacrifice future welfare for the sake of immediate benefit. But the problem assuredly requires the most intelligent and active handling that can be given it. Various methods are available for reducing the shock of technological changes, such as retraining workers, gradual change-over to fit the normal turn-over of personnel (as followed by the telephone companies in the introduction of automatic switching), pensions and unemployment insurance, efficient employment agencies for labor exchange, and co-operation between industries of a community to synchronize lay-offs in one company with new employment in another.

It is evident, although not realized by all who discuss the subject, that technological progress affects employment in two opposite ways and by two different methods. The first method is that of scientific research, invention and engineering developments, which create new products or new services and new industries providing employment along lines where no employment existed before. This is the primarily constructive side of technological progress and involves only advantage for everyone concerned, for the invested capital, for the labor which is employed and for the public which enjoys the benefits of the products or services produced.

The other method is by the invention and development of labor-saving machinery the purpose of which, of course, is quite frankly to reduce the amount of labor required to do a given job. Unquestionably and inevitably there will always be a tendency of a well managed business to make efforts along this line, and these efforts are justified because their basic objective is to make available to the public the products of industry at the minimum cost, consistent with the making of a profit in the business. The first effect of the introduction of labor-saving machinery is always to throw a certain number of people out of work. In most of the important situations, however, the ultimate and over-all result has been to increase the sum total of employment, because of the fact that the reduction in cost made possible by labor-saving machinery makes it possible for the public to purchase so much more goods that the amount of production increases and the number of people employed in distribution and sales increases.

Two outstanding illustrations of this influence are the lamp and the automobile industries. By marvelous ingenuity in the design of production machinery the manufacture of incandescent lamps has been transformed from a hand-glass-blowing operation into a high-speed machine production line. But the influence of this change has been so to reduce the price of incandescent lamps as to lead to their universal use in homes all over the country and has led to the development of a great variety of night-time activities which would have been entirely impossible without plentiful and cheap illumination. Similarly, the development of assembly-line production and the stamping out of large parts by huge mechanical presses has so reduced the cost of an automobile as to put it within the reach of a majority of the citizens of this country. In both of these cases the introduction of labor-saving machinery has had, as its ultimate result, the growth of an industry to a size which employs far greater numbers of men and women than could possibly have been employed under the more primitive methods of production.

Turning back again to the general consideration of technological progress, it is important to realize that this progress is always a slow process of growth by accretion. From time to time there are big ideas, but these must be supplemented by innumerable small ideas and experiments, some successful, some unsuccessful, but gradually leading to the clear perception of some large possibility and to the development of an art whereby this possibility can be made a reality. For the technological progress of the future there must be a long and steady investment of time and effort put into scientific discovery and engineering test, often without any particular apparent connection to what will later prove to be the practical application.

Perhaps the way in which technological progress goes can be somewhat vividly illustrated by giving a cross-section of some of the activities which were going on in the laboratories of the institution which the author of this chapter serves,— going on just before the present war emergency caused a substantial diversion of these efforts into other lines related to the national defense. The examples listed below are only a few out of nearly five hundred which were proceeding simultaneously.

A physicist who, like the alchemist, starts out to transmute chemical atoms but does it by bombarding them with electrified particles from a giant high voltage generator, discovers by-products which have therapeutic properties for medicine, develops a machine for producing rays for the treatment of cancer, and may have found a new method for producing and distributing electrical power. A student of cosmic rays turns his technique to the curing of that rare but deadliest of all diseases, radium poisoning, and in his spare time measures the age of rocks and collaborates in studies of surgical shock and goiters of the thyroid gland. A colloid chemist, out of his laboratory studies, suggests a promising method for reducing the size of floods on rivers, and simultaneously discovers a method for the reclamation of artificial rubber. A civil engineer, by studying the operation of a scale model of the Cape Cod Canal, aids in the plans for enlarging this canal so as to reduce its costs of maintenance and increase its navigability. A spectroscopist, while he is directing a mammoth program for the remeasurement of the wave-lengths of all the spectrum lines for all the chemical elements, develops a method for testing the feed which threatens to produce disastrous selenium poisoning in western cattle. A geologist, an electrical and a civil engineer reproduce in the laboratory the actual motions of an earthquake and devise a safer type of building construction. An organic chemist discovers a new germicide for medical use and a cheaper method for making an important acid. A metallurgist and a physicist discover the cause and cure of the bursting of tin cans containing canned foods and also develop an improved type of stainless steel. An electrical engineer invents machines for solving tedious and almost impossible mathematical equations which are important in scientific and engineering calculations. A biologist examines the various types of bacteria in the dust collected from hotels, hospitals, schools, homes, railroad trains and even from high up in the atmosphere. A meteorologist develops a more accurate method of forecasting the weather, and a method for extending the length of this forecast. A civil and a chemical engineer work together to develop a better quality of concrete and cement. A mechanical engineer invents a new safety device for airplanes, and another invents a method for the early detection of defective parts of machinery. An electrical engineer invents a lazy-man's device for shuffling cards by electricity and, lest he be considered too frivolous, also invents an automatic machine which keeps the sales records and accounts in one of the country's largest department stores. A group of electrical engineers and physicists design a method for the blind landing of airplanes through fog or darkness, and supervise the successful test of this equipment on one of the large airports. Another man invents a new type of engine; another a new refractory material for lining furnaces; another a new type of textile fiber; another a new type of glass for improving microscopes. And this is but a small portion of the activities proceeding in only one of the technological institutions of this country.

It would seem appropriate to close this chapter with a brief comment on the subject of what we as a people should do about technology if we were really intelligent about the subject and had the character to do the things which would lead to the greatest ultimate benefit from the enormous resources which still exist untouched in the field of technology.

If our wisdom and character were what they should be, we would see some striking contrasts to our present situation. We would see labor unions demanding the introduction of labor-saving and rapid production machinery in order that their members might achieve higher wages and shorter hours. We would see the political forces of the country more interested in demanding the creation of new wealth than in ordering its redistribution. In times of economic stress we would see the government strengthening its scientific services instead of curtailing them most severely of all services. We would see the agricultural problem tackled by a powerful scientific attempt to discover new uses for agricultural products rather than trying to achieve prosperity by curtailing production, or maintaining artificial price levels. We would see income taxes which would encourage rather than suppress the man who creates a great and useful industry and who uses his wealth in a far-sighted manner for the public good. We would see industrial taxation which would permit and even encourage far-sighted action by the companies, looking to the development of new products and services.

Unfortunately our state of civilization, as a group, still falls far short of any such Utopia of intelligence. But fortunately there are some individuals who have vision, understanding and altruistic spirit and who have also the ability and initiative of leadership and who therefore supply those essential elements of progress which are lacking in the body politic. In this group, the technologists, the scientists and the engineers of the world have positions of great opportunity and responsibility.

# FACT AND VALUE IN SOCIAL SCIENCE

## by Frank H. Knight

THE PROBLEM of method or procedure in the social sciences is raised and emphasized especially by their failure to parallel the modern achievements of the natural sciences, either in startling discoveries of truths unsuspected by commonsense, or especially, in laying the basis of techniques for transforming the character of life. This paper which I have been invited to prepare for this volume is an investigation of the reasons for this "failure"—or of the question whether it is correct to apply the term.

The position to be taken is, in the first place, that because of fundamental differences in the subject matter, and especially in the nature of the problems, in the two fields, no such revolutionary results were or are possible, in the nature of the case. Consequently, in the second place, the great need of the hour in the social science field as a whole is for an understanding of the nature of the material, the problems and the possibilities. Only on the basis of such an understanding can we expect so to define our concepts and choose our methods as to avoid not merely waste of energy, but the production of consequences which are positively evil. In the field of social policy, the pernicious notion of instrumentalism, resting on the claim or assumption of a parallelism between social and natural science is actually one of the most serious of the sources of danger which threaten destruction to the values of what we have called civilization. Any such conception as social engineering or social technology has meaning only in relation to the activities of a super-dictatorship, a government which would own as well as rule society at large, and would use it for the purposes of the governors.

In the social field, as elsewhere, knowledge is wanted both for its own sake and for use in the guidance of action. It is a serious reflection that the unsatisfactory state of affairs in social science has largely resulted from the very progress of science, the revolutionary development of techniques for acquiring knowledge, and applying knowledge, which is an outstanding feature and achievement of civilization in our own and recent time. It becomes the primary function of a discussion such as this to contend against the twofold fallacy which has been current, if not predominant, in social science circles. The root fallacy is that social science should be or can be a science in the same sense as the natural sciences in which the revolution referred to has occurred. It is argued that the problems of pure science on the one hand, and those of its application to life on the other, are to be solved by carrying over into the study of society the methods and techniques which have led to the celebrated triumphal march of science in the study of nature and the application of scientific knowledge of nature in technology. In other words, the philosophical basis of social science is held to be positivism, with respect to pure science, and instrumentalism or pragmatism when considered with reference to application in action.

In this connection in particular—more or less characteristically for social problems in so far as they can be solved—it would seem that a clear statement of the issue ought to be sufficient to resolve it definitively. It ought to be obvious that the relation of knowledge to action cannot be the same or closely similar, nor can knowledge itself, apart from the question of action, be at all the same, where the knower and the known are identical as where they are external to each other. In a genetic-historical view the fundamental revolution in outlook which represents the real beginning of modern natural science was the discovery that the inert objects of nature are not like men, i.e., subject to persuasion, exhortation, coercion, deception, etc., but are "inexorable." The position which we have to combat seems to rest upon an inference, characteristically drawn by the "best minds" of our race, that since natural objects are not like men, men must be like natural objects. The history of British-American social thought in modern times is particularly interesting in this connection. In general, it has represented the combination mentioned, of positivism and pragmatism—two philosophical positions with respect to the nature of man and his place in the cosmos, and specifically with respect to social action, which are at once contradictory between themselves, and equally indefensible as a basis of social action. For man, conceived in positivistic terms, could not act at all; and conceived in pragmatic terms, he could not act upon himself, which to do is in fact his most characteristic trait.

## I I

A survey of the problem of method in the study of society will naturally begin with the point of view of pure science, the achievement of knowledge and understanding without reference to any use to be made of them in action, and will then go on to consider the relations of science to action which, in one sense or another, are determinative in all fields, for theory as well as for practice.

The primary fact which limits the development of "science" in the strict "positive" meaning of the term, in the field of social phenomena, is the virtually infinite heterogeneity, and unpredictable variability in time, of the subject matter or data, i.e., human beings and their behavior, and social institutions. The basis of all science is classification, supple-nented by the analysis and measurement of attributes, by which differences in kind are reduced to differences in quantity or degree. From the point of view of classification, chemistry is the ideal natural science, while from that of measurement, physics is similarly the ideal-type. With reference to classification, the mere naming of an "object" as a sample of a certain purified chemical conveys to an informed person most of the information that would ever be desired about that object. In contrast, the designation of an object as a "man," or, say, a family, or a deliberative assembly, serves chiefly to raise questions. (Data of botany and animal biology range themselves along a scale between these two extremes.) The natural way of meeting such difficulties is subclassification; but this procedure soon runs into the familiar dilemma between size and homogeneity of statistical classes. Where individual objects or instances are highly unique, classification can only be crude.

The effort to analyze and measure—especially to find quantitative correlation between antecedent and consequent, which is the meaning of causality in science, encounters at the outset the difficulty that there simply is no real measurement of distinctively human or social data. It is doubtful whether these phenomena should even be called quantitative, so different must be the meaning of the term from that which it has in connection with physically objective magnitudes or variables. Human and social phenomena unquestionably present differences of degree. But in the nature of the case these differences can only be estimated, not measured. The nature of measurement is illustrated by the simple case of thermometry. It is not men's feeling of temperature which is measured, but some physical phenomenon which, as we learn by a complicated theoretical analysis of experimental data, corresponds in some way to the feeling of heat and cold. But it does not correspond at all accurately, or measurement would not be called for, or would lose its meaning. What is called measurement in the social sciences, including psychology, is the averaging of estimates, and the use of the term measurement is a misnomer.

The difficulties of classification and measurement, amounting to impossibility, if the terms are to imply any high degree of objectivity and precision, suggests and indeed rests upon, the essential fact that the data with which social sciences are concerned are themselves not objective in the physical meaning—are not data of sense observation. They consist of meanings, opinions, attitudes and values, not of physical facts. It is these subjective data or facts which are at once social in nature and of interest, to scientific as well as to vulgar curiosity, and especially from the point of view of action. They constitute the "reality" into which it is the function of social sciences to inquire. To be sure, there is always some correspondence or parallelism with physical facts; but as the example of temperature is sufficient to suggest, the parallelism is of a sort which rather accentuates the difficulties and limitations of scientific procedure. Not merely is the correspondence crude and imperfect; in addition, there are two sets of physical facts involved, and they are not closely or quantitatively parallel between themselves. These are respectively physiology and overt behavior. Expression and communication are generally included in the latter though only by something of a *tour de force*.

From the point of view of science, the situation presents a paradox; our difficulty is not so much the absence or inaccessibility of knowledge, but rather that we know too much. Knowledge of these subjective data has to be obtained through observation of overt behavior, or especially through intercommunication, doubtfully to be classed as observation. Hence the problem becomes primarily one of *interpretation*, the uncertainties of which are notorious. The crux of the matter is the relation between *motive* and action. And as suggested, we not merely know this relation very inadequately, but we *know*— at least as certainly as we know the nature of physical data themselves—that there is no close or simple relationship, as a matter of fact.

The expression of motive in action, and specifically in language, gesture, etc., is subject to error. Men do not even at all accurately know their own motives, but in "fact" act in part experimentally, to learn what they want, and also deliberately change their own motivation as will be emphasized later. All this is in the nature of man as a knowing and acting entity, or as in part "free" or problem-solving. Thus motives are analogous to the "forces" of mechanistic science, but not parallel. There is no such strict and necessary correspondence between the "force" and its "effect" as there is where forces are known only by inference from their effects. Motives differ in being also known from other sources, communication and interpretation. Moreover, as we also know, men do not always try to express their motives to others at all accurately, either in communication or in overt action, but very often explicitly attempt to conceal or to deceive. The contrast between physical objects and such a choosing, struggling and scheming emotional and romantic entity hardly needs explicit mention. The limitations in the use of physiological data as a source of knowledge of motivation, or of feelings and emotions as facts, or for the prediction of overt behavior, are equally familiar and even less call for elaboration. One need only think of this method of investigating the feeling of temperature.

### I I I

As soon as we look concretely and realistically at the problem of knowing about man and society, and specifically that of getting the knowledge we actually want, either for its own sake or in connection with action, we confront the simple fact that our subject matter has to be interpreted in terms of a highly pluralistic system of conceptions or categories. The root of the difficulty is that we know, and are interested in, men, in contrast with "nature," not merely or primarily as known and as acted upon, but also and especially as knowing and acting. It is hardly mysterious that this contrast between man and nature as known, or the identity and mutuality of relation between man as knower and man as known, makes a profound difference in the activity and results of knowing. Men "exist," so to speak, in several different universes of reality, between which philosophy has so far built no adequate thought bridges, and does not seem to be in the way of doing so.

It is an indisputable fact that man is a physical object, a mechanism, and that the phenomena into which he enters are in considerable part to be explained by the same physical sciences which we use in interpreting inert objects. And just as indisputably, man is a biological organism, more specifically one of the "higher" animals. Hence he is also in part to be explained by the biological sciences, in their whole range from the lowest plant life to the most highly evolved animal species. Of course this raises the issue whether unconscious biological phenomena might ultimately be explained as physical phenomena merely. The question cannot be argued here, beyond noting that biological science does constantly use teleological categories, such as struggle and adaptation, and that it is sheer dogmatism to assert that they could be reduced to purely physical or positive content.

Next, it is as indisputably a matter of "fact," in the inclusive sense, that man and human phenomena present characteristics which any discussion must and does recognize as sharply different from those of non-human biology. Man as investigated is, like man as investigator, a being who *thinks*, and who acts on the basis of thinking, who *solves problems* of many kinds, in a way which sharply differentiates him from any other organic species, and which we have to assume is not characteristic of inanimate nature at all. Other distinctions will be developed in the detail allowable, as we proceed. It should at once be clear that man is at the same time many different kinds of being or entity, which are not reducible to any one kind. The appeal of the contrary notion is readily explained. Man as intellectual inquirer is characterized by a craving for simplification and unification, for "monism" as against pluralism. And since "he" cannot deny that "man" is a physical being, this craving leads him to deny that he is anything else. And of course the "triumphal march" of physical science and technology, already mentioned, contributes largely to the strengthening of the prejudice. But why these considerations should actually lead men to accept knowledge of man as a physical being and deny to him the characteristics which he, the inquirer, exemplifies *even in denying them*, must remain in the status of mystery, as far as the present writer is concerned.

We enter upon the domain of social science when we name the next familiar distinguishing characteristic of man—that he is a "social animal." But the social nature of man is utterly different from that of the animals which are properly and distinctively called social, such as the colonial insects. It is misleading to call man a social animal, since it is not as an animal that he is social. The social phenomena of the termite colony, for example, are based upon *instinct*, which positive science interprets as mechanism. Man is social as a feeling, knowing, thinking, desiring and acting *individual*. He is an individual in a sense categorically beyond the meaning the term has in any other connection. His social life must be interpreted in terms of individual interests and social interests, and especially in terms of *conflicts* of almost infinite complexity between diverse interests of both classes. Man, we repeat, is a *problem solver;* and the distinctive character of human society, from the point of view of the significance of knowledge for action, is that it presents problems, both to any society as such, and to the individuals who compose it, closely interrelated with their individual problems. In this respect, it presents a virtually absolute contrast with termite society—as far as we know, and as science must assume. And this characteristic, this fact, is vital for science, as description and interpretation, as well as in relation to action. These facts throw us back upon the notion of man as a motivated individual.

But the relation of priority between individual and society at the human level is a mutual one; each presupposes the other, a fact which accentuates the complexity of the problems. Human society presents another fundamental aspect, with respect to which it is in one sense similar to animal society, but in another sense sharply contrasting. It is largely "institutional" (in Sumner's "crescive" sense) in its basis and character. In other words, human behavior, individual and social, is to a large extent "traditional." In this aspect, behavior is nondeliberative, not problem-solving, and is even largely unconscious, and mechanical, like the behavior of termites. But the character of the mechanism is very different. It rests upon unconscious imitation. The "social inheritance" involved is distinct from the biological inheritance of instinct, and has played a vital role in human development.

Turning again to the individual, the analysis of human emotions, attitudes, motives, and rational nature, cannot of course even be surveyed in this essay. But one important detail of such an analysis imperatively calls for notice. Still another element in the pluralism of human phenomena is found in the fact that man as an individual, in one of his aspects, at one of the levels at which he exists, deliberately uses means, to realize ends which are given or are simply "there," while at another level he also deliberates about ends. The "possession" of individual ends, and of means, and of more or less knowledge as to how to use means to realize given ends, are the factors which make up and define the "economic man"; or, they serve to define economic behavior—two ways of saying the same thing.

Two facts need the utmost emphasis. On the one hand, every conscious subject is an economic man, and behaves as such in every conscious act. Every activity involves the use of given means, in accord with given knowledge, to achieve ends which are given or factual in some sense and in some degree. This is true of play activity, individual and social, as well as of work, and of the intellectual, esthetic, moral, and even the religious activities, as well as of those which we think of as connected with "subsistence." (This term has practically no meaning in connection with civilized life, for all human motivation is relative to *standards*.) The pursuit of all ends alike is "expensive," meaning that it requires diversion of means or *power* from other uses. And in so far as any activity is rationally purposive, it presents the problem of "efficiency," or the economy of power. That is, man is impelled to use power in such a way as to achieve the maximum possible realization of "ends-in-general," as given or desired, aggregated in terms of some common denominator of desiredness. (In all developed society, there is of course a conventional unit called money.)

The second fact referred to as calling for equal emphasis is that just as all activity is economic, none is purely or merely economic. For, while the three elements of economic behavior—means or resources, knowledge of their use, and ends for which they are used—may be taken as "given" for a given subject at any moment of action, in a larger view and a longer run they are not given, but changing; and the effecting of changes in them is commonly an essential and even a major factor in the motivation of the activity itself. This fact is especially important with regard to the "ends" of action. Under critical scrutiny, the given ends of action generally turn out to be not given, but themselves instrumental to *purposes*. And the essential character of purposes is not to be given or static, but to be inherently dynamic, progressive, looking toward indefinite growth in directions which are largely to be determined in action itself —action always including thinking.

## I V

These facts serve in a way as a bridge between the points of view of science for its own sake and science as a basis for action, in the social field. On the one hand, if we are to tell the "truth" about man, the most important truth, or fact, is that he is a free or problem-solving entity or being, or in a word, is *active*. This means that his doings as behavior events are ultimately more or less indeterminate, and cannot even theoretically be exhaustively predicted or described in advance. It is abstractly possible to formulate "laws" which will fit any past behavior or course of events, to any desired degree of accuracy. But, as already observed, we *know* that man is a deliberating and choosing subject, that human behavior differs from that of inert objects in that it involves effort and error, in a manifold sense. This fact of freedom is connected with and accounts for the peculiar heterogeneity and unpredictable variability in time already emphasized as factual characteristics of human phenomena. But the problem-solving characteristic has itself to be subdivided and considered at different "levels." We *know* again that men deliberate and choose with respect to the use of given means to realize given ends, and that they also deliberate about and choose ends.

Such deliberation or criticism of ends gives rise to many problems which cannot be explored here, but especially to the problem of valuation and of values. In all the folk-lore to which human thinking has given rise, in connection with human beings themselves, perhaps the most false and misleading single item is the common notion that men "know what they want," or that there is no arguing about tastes. It would surely be much nearer the truth to say that there is no arguing about anything else, or specifically about "facts." The principal thing that men actually want is to find out what they do really want; and the bulk of what they want, or think they want, is wanted because they think that in some sense they "ought" to do so, that it is "right." They "want" to be "in the right," in an infinite variety of meanings which cannot be explored here. (They also want to explore for the sake of exploring.) Such factors are at least as important for concrete motivation as is the achievement of any given end. This is another way of saying that the given ends are only provisionally given; ultimately they look beyond themselves to purposes, which have the antithetical character to given-ness. And problem-solving and choice at this higher level are correspondingly important as a source of indeterminateness in the phenomenal sequence of human events.

The distinction between personal desire and value, or "ought" in the most general sense, is one which is made by every human being, at practically every moment in his deliberative life, and most interestingly in the effort to prove a theory that the distinction has no validity, i.e., in maintaining "positive scientificism" as a position. Very little critical analysis is sufficient to show that other values have the same objectivity as truth, including scientific fact. As soon as any question is raised, the problem of fact is one of evaluation, and truth itself is a value. The distinction between individual wish or opinion and truth as a form of validity—indeed the most fundamental imperative or "ought," or "oughtness"—is presupposed in any serious utterance whatever (any but "conversation," which is perhaps the greater part of all actual utterance!). To say that there is no distinction, no *validity* beyond individual acceptance as a state of mind, would be to *say*, "I am not saying anything"; and this is surely a contradition, an absurdity and an impossibility far beyond the familiar example of A and not-A in formal logic.

These considerations serve, as already suggested, as a sort of bridge between individual and social phenomena and problems, and also between science for its own sake and science as a basis for action. For, to begin with, valuation is inherently a social activity, in contrast with individual motivation as simple desire. Values arise out of conflicts between interests, and out of reflection and discussion about these conflicts—the essential and distinctive feature of human social life, as already brought out.

It is only as asserted *rights* that interests in conflict can be discussed or treated as a *joint* problem—in contrast with a problem for each of the parties in conflict of overcoming the other party by some kind of force. A value is the solution of such a problem. Values are established or validated and recognized through *discussion*, an activity which is at once social, intellectual, and creative. No discussion can be carried on in propositions beginning with the words "I want" or even "I think"—without further implications which are their real meaning. And even these assertions themselves, in so far as they make any real sense, raise the question of their truth, which is a question of valuation, and one to be settled only by discussion as a social-intellectual-creative process. Truth is the fundamental type of value, and in an important sense includes all other values. For a "valid" valuation, in esthetics or morals (and in religion if that is recognized as a distinct category), takes the form of a "true" proposition. The general nature of validity is the same everywhere as in natural science itself, and the validity of valuation as a category should not call for discussion beyond "pointing," to any scientific discussion, or to what we are doing here and now, as an illustration.

This argument is fundamental for any "science" of human-social phenomena, apart from problems of action. Man is, in fact, a being who exists and behaves at all the levels indicated —to carry the process of making essential distinctions no farther than we have done. He is a mechanism, and a biological organism, and the "bearer" of a culture tradition. At all these levels, his behavior is to be described in terms of mechanism or scientific law, in one or another sense, the conception not being pressed too far. In addition, he is a being who solves problems in the sense of using means to realize ends. Even at this, the "economic" level, his behavior is not exhaustively describable in terms of science, for to assert that the solution of any problem, or result of any experiment or exploration, is given in advance is a denial of its character as a problem.

But man is also a problem-solving entity at the higher level of critical deliberation about ends, or free choice of ends on the basis of thinking, illustrated by the pursuit of truth. That is, he is a being who seeks, and in a real sense creates, values. The essential significance of this is the fact that man is interested in changing himself, even to changing the ultimate core of his being. This is the meaning of being active. It marks a categorical distinction between men and all other objects of knowledge. We cannot be sure that other objects are not conscious, or even that they are devoid of will; but if they have any conscious will-attitude toward themselves it is limited, as far as we can tell, to the *perseverare in esse suo*. They do not strive to change their own nature or character—or indeed to "convert" fellow-members of their species; and in so far as scientific categories apply, they do not undergo change at all, in their ultimate nature. In contrast with natural objects—even with the higher animals—man is unique in that he is dissatisfied with himself; he is the discontented animal, the romantic, argumentative, aspiring animal. Consequently, his behavior can only in part be described by scientific principles or laws.

Even at the level of economism, scientific description applies only to "perfectly" economic behavior, which both abstracts from all forms of error and also relates to motives assumed as given, but which in fact cannot possibly be accurately known, even to the behaving subject himself. These facts invalidate the common effort to reduce the evaluating process from qualitative to quantitative form, to a matter of "maximizing" aggregate fulfillment of desire, even for the individual. And of course such a maximizing theory completely eliminates any "obligation" to consider the interests of another subject beyond the point where the first person may happen as a matter of fact to be interested in the other, to a degree which takes precedence over any more strictly individualistic interest. Any social science which does not take full account of problem-solving activity at both these levels simply ignores the most important facts about its material.

## V

We turn to explicit consideration of the relation between knowledge and action, and of knowledge as a basis of action. It is in this connection especially that we encounter the categorical differences between social and natural science. The fact that there always is some relation between knowledge and action surely need not be argued or developed here, beyond noting, perhaps, that even the simplest experimentation is action, as is also all communication of knowledge in any form. Action may be instrumental to knowledge as well as conversely. Science itself, even considered purely as an end, is a part of the social and socially purposive life of man. It is through intercommunication that most of any person's knowledge is gained, that all knowledge becomes objective by verification, and that the capacity for rational knowing is developed in the individual, or that it was developed in the race.

All action by man, including expression or communication, begins with action by a purposive subject, with a motive, on his, or its, own body; and its next link is the use of bodily changes to produce changes in the world outside one's own skin. It is through, or *via* changes in the physical world that one human individual acts upon, or communicates with, another. This is theoretically important especially because at virtually every step in any action, the physical processes involved consist essentially in the directed release of potential energy, and in such changes there is no quantitative relation between physical cause and physical effect. There is no minimum limit to the energy in a spark which sets off a conflagration, and no maximum limit to the energy of the conflagration which it sets off. Hence, as far as physics is concerned, the degree of indeterminism needed for effective human freedom is infinitesimal and far beyond experimental detection.

The question of knowledge in relation to social action in the natural sense of "overt" action must be considered under two heads, action by man as an individual upon other individuals, and social action in relation to social problems. With regard to the first, the essential mutuality of both the knowing and the acting relationship means that the procedure employed takes such forms as suggestion, persuasion, coercion, and especially deception—and beyond these the cultivation of affection and trust—or such forms as communication of information, the rendering of reciprocal favors, etc. None of these procedures has any meaning whatever in the relation of men to inert natural objects. (As usual, the animals, especially the "higher" species, are in an intermediate position.)

In the second place, action upon other individuals by any individual, or exercise of power over them, in so far as it takes the form or has the meaning of a one-sided manipulation and use of them, is regarded, in modern free individualistic culture, as the essence of immorality. And this moral judgment is at least closely connected with the "fact" that the consequences of violating the principle may be expected to be undesirable to the actor himself. Even where the action is performed on behalf of the party acted upon, serious questions are involved: first as to the validity of the altruistic interest, and even more as to the presumption of knowledge of the other's interests superior to that of the other himself. And if the relationship is not ultimately mutual—as, e.g., between the doctor and patient—the person acted upon is at least treated as an inferior type of being, not a human person in the full sense. (E.g., treatment of criminals, children and the incompetent.)

## V I

We come finally to the most important consideration of all, that of social action proper. After all the introducing that has seemed necessary, this must be disposed of so briefly that the treatment may well seem dogmatic. But it surely ought to be evident that social action is not a problem of manipulation of an inert object-matter, by any subject, and hence is not one of "technique" in the proper sense of the word. That is, instrumentalist categories do not apply. In social action—action by any group, as a group—the really social activity, the solution of a social or group problem, consists in the establishment of agreement or consensus among the individuals who make up the group, as to what action is desirable. Consequently, the process is essentially that of *discussion of values,* the nature of which has already been suggested. Indeed, social action is not merely of the same form as the pursuit of truth, but that is always its essential character. To refer again to the former illustration, social action is what we, the parties to this discussion, are doing, here and now.

Social action in the proper sense is the solution of a social or group problem. With reference to overt action, which is to say, in the field of politics in the broad sense, it consists in reaching a decision in and by the group in question, upon the desirability of some change in its own character as a group. Agreement as a quest presupposes a question, a conflict of interest, a difference of opinion, and an objectively right answer (or at least a better rather than a worse answer) to be found by joint intellectual inquiry. More concretely, a social problem always has the content as well as the form of changing the "laws" in which the character of a group as a group is formulated and contained. In practice, social change is usually carried out by voting upon general objectives of policy and delegating individuals as agents of the group to formulate and to enforce specific laws. Thus all concrete action is carried out by individuals—apart from mob or lynch law, more or less characteristic at primitive levels. But in so far as the action is really on behalf of the group these agents are "responsible" to the latter. Social action always looks forward to embodiment in new institutional patterns or to culture change, and to related changes in the nature of the individuals who make up the group. It is a matter of group self-change, an activity even more remote from technical or instrumental intelligence, not to mention mechanical process, than is individual self-change—and the notions of social mind and social will and choice are correspondingly more repugnant to the reducing and simplicistic proclivities of our minds.

The little that can be said, i.e., stated in intelligible and unambiguous verbal propositions, about "method" in this field of value creation and self-change is vague and tenuous at best, and the meaning of essential terms is more or less figurative rather than literal. This is apparent in the literature of "criticism," in all the fields of value. It is especially clear in esthetics and ethics; but it applies also to "logic," including science itself, when it goes beyond the mechanical and more or less commonplace into issues which are really problematic. The problems of discussion or criticism or value creation by group intelligence cannot be taken up here. That is the task of philosophy, not of social science or its methodology. But social science must recognize and emphasize the reality of group action as well as individual action, and must attempt to say what can be said about it in terms of generalized description. Hence there can be no clear line between social science and philosophy. (In fact there is no clear line between natural science and its methodology, for at the growing point, where the really acute problems lie, these are essentially methodological and evaluative.)

These considerations would naturally lead into a discussion of the various positive—or more or less strictly and purely positive—social sciences, as sciences and in their relation to action, individual as well as social. Within the limits of this essay it is possible only to touch upon the problems raised. Discussion would re-emphasize the pluralism of categories required in the realistic treatment of human-social subject matter. The foregoing argument has shown that man must be described in terms of at least a half-dozen fundamental kinds of entity or being. He is (a) a physical mechanism; (b) a biological organism, with characteristics extending from those of the lowest plant to the highest animal in the biological scale; (c) a social animal in the traditional-institutional sense; (d) a problem-solving individual in the economic sense, an economic man; (e) a problem solver at the higher level of critical deliberation about ends; (f) a social being in the sense of the free association of individuals with characteristics (d) and (e). (He may also be to some extent a social animal, in the proper instinctive sense; but, if so, it is to such a limited degree that for present purposes it may be left out of account.)

It is evident that at least the first three of these types of existence can each be the subject matter of a distinct positive science or group of such sciences. And these sciences have already been more or less extensively developed. We do have more or less distinctively human physics and chemistry, human biology, and institutional science, sociology, or culture anthropology. And of the last, in particular, there are many branches, including institutional economics and descriptive ethics and esthetics. Each of these sciences deals descriptively with an aspect of human phenomena which is isolated and treated in the positive terms of "uniformities of coexistence and sequence," on the general pattern of a natural science. At least one further distinction must be made—a fourth type of scientifically describable form of existence recognized. Consciousness is not necessarily or always active, deliberative, or problem-solving. And to the extent that it is not of this character but is merely phenomenal (or epiphenomenal), it is possible, in theory (and more or less so actually) to describe consciousness in positive categories. Such description is the task and subject matter of another highly developed science—that of psychology—in the meaning indicated by the statement, which is its original and proper meaning, in distinction from various special physical and biological sciences such as neurology, physiology, and "behaviorology."

It is also evident that all these sciences must in a sense take account of the social nature of man. Yet they are not social sciences, with the exception of culture anthropology. This is in a sense *the* science of society, if the word is restricted, as far as the subject matter allows, to the category of a natural or positive science. It will naturally be subdivided along the lines of the major distinguishable branches or aspects of cultural life, such as language, law, religion, technology, economic organization, social usage and recreation. But it should hardly be necessary to emphasize that the content of culture anthropology as a positive science—namely, institutions—is not learned like natural science data through sense observation merely, but primarily through intercommunication and interpretation. In consequence, the results must be far less definite and precise than those of natural sciences, particularly with respect to the vagueness of classification and the absence of real measurement already emphasized. And the science can have no direct significance for social action in the society of the scientist himself; for if it results in such action, its conclusions are no longer true. It does, however, need to be emphasized that the phenomena of our own society are very largely of the traditional-institutional character, and this must be true of any society which is even intellectually conceivable, just as any real or possible society must involve human beings in all other "lower" aspects. The study of these phenomena may itself bring them above the threshold of social awareness and make them problems of social action.

A few words are called for regarding economics, at least as to the existence of a purely deductive quasi-mathematical science of theoretical economics or economic theory, in addition to the description of economic behavior patterns as institutional phenomena, already mentioned as a subdivision of culture anthropology. Economic theory as a branch of knowledge and inquiry deals with two main topics. The first is the abstract principles of individual behavior oriented to the maximizing of "want-satisfaction" through the correct allocation of limited given means among alternative modes of use. The second is the principles of *organization* of economic activity through the free exchange of services (or "goods" as the embodiment of future services) between individuals, giving rise to markets, and to the theory of the perfect market. Economic theory assumes—because it is an indisputable fact—that men do economize, and that economy is an ideal only partly realized in fact. They strive more or less successfully to achieve maximum efficiency in the use of means in realizing given ends. But these facts are and can be known only intuitively; they cannot be verified or established by sense-observation, as even the principles of mathematics can be—within the limits of accuracy and generality set by the labor and expense required.

The methodology, or logic, of various social sciences, in the abstract, and as far as they go as positive sciences, is not essentially different from that of the natural sciences, including the various mixtures of inductive and deductive procedure which these present. The main difference, as already noted, is in the large degree to which sense observation is replaced by intercommunication and interpretation. The relevance of the positive, or quasi-positive, social sciences for action, is essentially that of revealing and clarifying the "given conditions" of action —which again is true of the natural sciences also. The actual nature of the "given-ness" in this connection, and of action itself, and the relations between the two, belong, again, to philosophy rather than to social science as such. It is not the province of science to say what values society ought to strive to realize in action, anymore than it is in the case of natural science as the basis of technology. Science does not even explicitly tell how to realize any values. But it is its province to show by implication, through description of real and hypothetical courses of events, what would be the results of proposed lines of action—or what lines of action may be expected to produce any results accepted as desirable.

## V I I

In conclusion, a few words seem to be in order as to the relevance of this discussion as a whole to the present crisis in Western culture. The predicament in which free society finds itself at the moment arises precisely out of the fact that any free society must, by virtue of its nature as free society, reach agreement, by discussion, on fundamental values, wherever "serious" conflicts of interest arise. For, as already pointed out, it is only as conflicts of values or of "rights" that conflicts of interest can be discussed, and any solution of such a problem is in the nature of the case a value or mode of rightness. Now scientific enquiry has, and rests upon, a moral code, or in sheer fact a "religion"; and it is supremely important at this hour that scientists recognize this fact, and even more important that society consider carefully the moral code and the religion of science, and its general applicability in connection with social problems.

As we have already emphasized, truth is a value, and science itself is the type of the pursuit and creation of value as a social activity. The basic principle of science—truth or objectivity—is essentially a moral principle, in opposition to any form of self-interest. The presuppositions of objectivity are integrity, competence, and humility. The combination of the three gives the essential principle of freedom, i.e., problem-solving through rational discussion, a social-intellectual creative activity, the quest and definition of values. All coercion is absolutely excluded, in favor of a free meeting of free minds. Three aspects or forms of coercion particularly need emphasis. The first is the exclusion of persuasion which, as appeal to emotion, i.e., to *wrong* emotions (emotions conflicting with the love of truth or validity) is a form of coercion, and perhaps the "worst" form because the most insidious and therefore likely to be misconceived and adopted or condoned. The second form is coercion of any minority by any majority. Truth, or validity, is not a matter of a majority vote. The third point is that only in the most extreme cases can coercion be justified by considerations of "sentimental" morality, such as personal love, or the desire to do good. In general, these things have no more place in the solution of other value problems than they have in relation to science and truth. This is not merely a matter of moral idealism, but a *fact*, as to the nature of problem-solving.

The writer does not need to be reminded that serious questions are raised. "Real" discussion is rarely if ever "really" and purely discussion. Even scientists acting in their own field are frail men, and affected by original sin. They can only struggle, and "pray," for liberation from wrong emotions, dogmatism, sentimentalism, and the will to dominate, overcome and coerce, and especially to persuade—even in the interest of truth. And in the fields of economics and politics, social order is admittedly impossible without much coercion, in the ordinary use of the term. (International relations present the most serious problem in this regard.) Practical politics is necessarily a matter of compromise, of balancing evil against good. At least, the use of force might be largely—though by no means entirely—restricted to the negative form, coercive prevention of coercion. This was the central tenet of the older and genuine liberalism, which is unhappily tending to be overshadowed by the romantic craving for action, involving "thinking with the blood," which even appropriates the designation of liberalism itself. Space limits preclude more than mention of these topics. But surely, competent scientists ought not to be—as they too frequently are—heard favoring and advocating the placing of "intelligence" in charge of social affairs, not recognizing that this means putting *politicians* of some breed and brand in charge of all other people, including scientists.

# LOOKING FORWARD

## *by* Lewis Mumford

THE ACHIEVEMENTS of modern technology have been part of a culture whose central theme was the seizure and exploitation of power. But although the quest for power led to the ruthless exploitation of natural resources, the breakup of the natural balance of organisms, and the extermination of many valuable cultural traditions, it was not wholly a negative and destructive impulse. For up to the first World War this culture embraced people who lived in every part of the planet; and by means of an increasing interchange of trade, investments, and ideas, it brought over a billion people into a working partnership. In the field of politics there was a steady diffusion of power, through the spread of democratic and co-operative methods of control.

Unfortunately, technical improvements and economic facilities outran the moral capacities of the peoples who had fared best under this culture, and in particular of their governing classes. The very illusion of moral progress that was fostered by the prevailing optimistic philosophy of the nineteenth Century tended to conceal the vast hiatus between technological and social achievements.

The underlying axiom of this power culture was that the increased use of non-human sources of energy, and the increase of wealth through the mechanization of the means of production, must automatically increase the possibilities of human well-being. This axiom, as Mr. Arnold Toynbee has amply shown in his *Study of History,* has no factual basis. Though there is a close relation between technics and every other aspect of human culture, material abundance often goes hand in hand with social decay.

As a corollary to this prime assumption about the desirability of material expansion went the notion that the increase of "power and wealth" had no limits, because human desires were boundless and insatiable. This corollary was as baseless as the axiom itself: it was merely an illusion which assumed as given the very fact that remained to be established, the notion that human satisfaction increased in proportion to the number of human desires and to society's capability of satisfying them. That vulgar notion has been responsible for a great deal of human misery. For the experience of the race has abundantly shown that moderation and restriction are essential to human well-being in every aspect of man's existence. This is true on the physiological level, since three dinners at a time are not three times as satisfactory as one; and it is true on the moral level, where the moderation and equilibration of desire have proved organically satisfactory, whereas its inordinate expression, or inordinate contraction, leads to conditions of social and personal maladjustment.

When Lord Acton said, "All power corrupts and absolute power corrupts absolutely," he was referring mainly to political power. But what he said likewise applies to power in all its manifestations. The more energy that man commands the more important it is that this energy should be at the service of his whole personality and his whole culture, and not merely at the command of some narrow ambition or some limited goal. Now the fact is that science and technology, for the last three hundred years, have been at the service of narrow, and often, one must add, quite primitive notions of human development and human well-being. They have given power to the military and political and financial despots: they have fed their egos and justified their ambitions; they have further brutalized the brutal and corrupted the corrupt. As a result they have made mankind the victim of the machine rather than its benign commander and controller. Although many high and humane achievements remain, the animus of this civilization has been a predatory one.

The familiar doctrines of technological materialism are without a sound sociological or psychological basis; and that by itself would be enough to condemn them from a human standpoint. But there is still another way in which their insufficiency may be demonstrated; and this is by reference to the facts of historic development. Technological materialism itself represents a passing phase of human history. The great age of expansion which it fostered is now coming to an end; the conditions that turned men's attention exclusively to the conquest and exploitation of the material environment have been subverted by the very success of Western man's enterprise and invention. We are now probably living through the last great crisis in this power civilization. This crisis will either ruin Western Society entirely—and with it the very advanced technics of science and invention—or it will permit this culture to establish itself on a much broader human basis. In the second instance, the process of materialization, by which one may characterize our culture during the last three centuries, will give way to a process of "etherealization" to use a term coined by Toynbee: quantitative interests will become secondary to qualitative interests; and the great advances that were once made in the physical sciences almost exclusively will now be paralleled by progress in the domain of sociology and personology—sciences which themselves will no longer be dominated by the categories and methods of the physical sciences.

This change within the domain of thought is the counterpart of a wider social process; as it is, no less, one of the means by which further social developments will be guided and applied. If we are to understand both its significance and its necessity, we must understand first of all how completely our technological achievements in the past have been conditioned by the historic movement of expansion: the land expansion of the conquistador and pioneer, the mechanical expansion of the inventor, the industrialist, and the financier, and finally, the population expansion which was the source of the vital energy of Europe during the nineteenth Century.

The first thing to note about modern technics is that it is associated with the period of land expansion in the Western world, which began in the fifteenth Century, when Europe had reached the limits of its own frontiers. This period of discovery was accompanied by a steady pushing back of the physical horizons; and it was marked by the quick spread of the European from his original habitat to the remotest shores of Asia, Africa, and America. Here was an attempt to break away from the bounded and walled horizons of the medieval city; an attempt to treat the whole world as the habitat of Western man and as the object of his curiosity as well as of his cupidity.

This world-wide immigration and colonization was itself the complex product of economic interests, seeking to widen the area of trade, of a missionary impulse to spread Christian doctrine, which grew up again with the new preaching orders, and of new technical instruments for commanding space and time. The compass, the three-masted sailing ship, the sailing chart, the accurate ship's chronometer—the latter not invented till the eighteenth Century—made possible the era of exploration and colonization. It would be impossible to exaggerate the effect of the new spatial horizons upon men's minds. Samuel Morse's impulse to invent the electric telegraph dates from the moment when the lonely young American painter, in London, felt the gap between himself and his family, filled only by letters, to be an unbearably long one.

But the technical results of exploration and colonization were not one-sided ones. Though the Western European, by the nineteenth Century, had distributed his firearms and his friction matches, his iron hardware and his missionary pocket-handkerchiefs all over the map, he rapidly acquired, from the primitive peoples he conquered by his "superior" civilization, a greater abundance of resources and technical methods, which could be utilized by his advancing industry, than had been diffused by slower processes during the previous few millenniums. This account has never been accurately reckoned up, as far as I know: perhaps because its results would diminish Western man's self-satisfaction and conceit.

If, however, one goes no farther back than the fifteenth Century and takes nothing more away than printing from movable types from Korea, cotton fabrication from India, porcelain manufacture from China, rubber culture from the Amazons, and the new food crops that came from the Americas, the effect would be to bring the whole Western world to a literal standstill and to the verge of outright starvation. At all events, it is extremely doubtful whether anything that could be compared with modern technics could have resulted by the twentieth Century out of Western man's unaided imagination. The mechanical conquest of the planet, by means of the sailing vessel, the steamship, the railroad, the cable, the telegraph, the radio—and above all, perhaps, by gunpowder—was a means by which the technological contributions of hitherto isolated cultures were enabled to influence the whole Western world. This happened at a moment when Western man's interests were becoming almost exclusively technological and materialistic; and it therefore had an overwhelming effect.

Now, this period of land expansion has finally come to an end. What was true of the United States around 1890, as Frederick Jackson Turner pointed out, became true of the whole planet during the fifty years that followed: Siberia, Manchuria, and a few scattered outposts around the rest of the globe were the last regions to undergo the invasion and exploitation of modern man. The period of one-sided conquest now has come to its own natural terminus: the process of surface exploitation, of wholesale migration and colonization, with its careless wastage of capital resources and its greed for quick return belongs to the past.

We are now entering a period of settlement or rather of resettlement; and this involves the attempt to find a stable basis for living in the environments that have proved most favorable to human life. There are vast damages to be repaired: deforested areas to be restored to woodland, eroded soils to be built up, more organic patterns of living that are to be reinstated; and if science and technics are to benefit by the stimulus of other cultures, there must be a world-wide give-and-take, as between equals. Political skill must keep open the world-wide channels of intercourse and interco-operation, once established crudely at the point of a gun for the benefit of the Western exploiters.

But at this point it becomes obvious that the conditions for further technical advance, through the stimulus of other cultures and ways of life, rest not upon technicians and scientists, but upon political actions that lie far outside their immediate sphere of control. Once, the political instruments of cultural intercourse could be taken for granted: foreign scientists and explorers traveled freely in the remotest parts of the world, even without passports; unless they aroused purely local animosity they could come and go in safety and freedom. For the last twenty-five years the common vehicles of such intercourse have been one by one disappearing. The totalitarian states are even in times of peace closed regimes: the democratic states themselves have shared this vice in some degree, as compared with the open world which existed generally before 1914.

The danger should be plain. If each great state or empire becomes a rigid, self-contained unit, immune to outside influences and foreign ideas, the social basis for technological advance, which historically involves world-wide intercourse at all levels, will have disappeared. Doctrines of political and cultural isolationism—which are sometimes heretically preached even by men of science—are based upon historic ignorance as to the actual foundations of our present culture.

Now, world travel and intercourse rest ultimately on world trade. It is the passage of surpluses and specialties across frontiers that makes available the means of exchange that enables other people, besides the merchants involved, to travel freely and exchange their intellectual products. Where no such medium is available, .the investigator who wishes to become familiar with foreign thought or technics must either imitate Alexander, and come with an army, or he must follow Plato's reputed example when he went to Egypt and covered his expenses by taking with him a cargo of oil which he sold to the Egyptians. Otherwise only beggars can be travelers. Already there are states in existence where Plato's method would be impossible; even if he were not denied a visa or stopped at the frontier because he was not a believer in "Aryan" anthropology or in "Marxian" genetics.

If the closed totalitarian states should remain in existence for as much as another generation, the international structure of scientific thought would probably collapse. For even before the present war passed into its active phase, the tactics of the Russian, German, and Italian governments had made the procedures of so-called International Congresses almost a farce, for they were either used as a vehicle for fascist propaganda or decimated of some of their most valued contributors by these totalitarian governments.

To mark the change that has taken place here one need only compare the treatment accorded to the Belgian historian, Henri Pirenne, during the World War with that accorded to representative scientists and scholars in the totalitarian states during the last ten years. When Pirenne was taken in custody by the German government, after the occupation of Belgium, that fact was quickly known to the rest of the world; and the expression of outrage was universal. Danish and Dutch scholars dared to denounce it, no less than Americans. As the result of a world-wide protest, headed by President Wilson and the Pope, he was taken out of a prison camp and sequestered in a quiet German village, with no other duty than that of reporting to the Mayor once a day. That was in war time. Outrages a thousand times worse have been committed by the totalitarian governments against world-respected scientists, sometimes without the news coming out, frequently without arousing a single organized protest, always without world opinion being able to effect the slightest improvement in their position.

The problems raised by the termination of the period of land expansion have not yet been widely grasped; for uncontrolled colonization, immigration, trade—all the methods whereby the exploited resources were put ultimately at the disposal of a world community—have now to be replaced by a rational world organization empowered to redistribute the resources and to widen the economic and political basis of international co-operation. The need of the new age is to create balanced regional communities, which will be capable of operating within a worldwide framework: no longer sealed behind the military frontiers of the bellicose state. *Every movement toward regional or self-sufficiency is a betrayal of the positive achievements of the age of conquest, unless it is accompanied by an equal movement toward planetary organization.* Similarly every attempt to resume the age of conquest, on the Nazi pattern, by re-introducing the principle of dominance and by restoring inequalities and slaveries, goes deeply against the grain of civilized effort. This last movement is not the wave of the future but the treacherous undertow of the past.

Extensive exploration and conquest must now yield to intensive cultivation and regional development; not for the purpose of achieving an illusory self-sufficiency but for the purpose of making the fullest contribution ultimately to the life of mankind.

One could trace a similar movement toward stabilization and balance within the domain of the machine itself, as a result of the purely mechanical and economic factors that are in operation. In *Technics and Civilization* (1934) I called attention to some of these factors. But here I prefer to dwell on another development; or rather, on two current changes that must have a bearing on the future of technics and science. The first is the increasing importance of the biological and social sciences. Before 1850 it would be hard to point to a single important invention that rested directly upon a knowledge of the structure and function of organisms; but during the last two generations some of the most critical advances have come about through the direct application of the biological sciences. The telephone grew out of an interest in the mechanism of human voice production, and the telephone receiver was modeled directly upon the structure of the human ear; experiments with heavier than air flying machines resulted directly from Pettigrew's and Marey's study of the locomotion of animals.

Meanwhile, the application of biological knowledge to the raising of food and to the planning of the human diet has effectively altered the whole problem of man's health and his survival: genetics and the new discoveries on the physiology of nutrition have done far more to assure mankind of an adequate food supply than all the gangplows and automatic reapers and binders that the nineteenth Century boasted. We are now aware of many processes where chemical, biological, or social science will enable us to provide alternatives for the purely mechanical solutions that were chiefly available during the paleotechnical period. Most of these applications of biology are still in an early stage.

Let me give a simple illustration. By the use of costly apparatus and machinery it is possible to build a house without windows, in which the air shall be filtered, warmed or cooled, and circulated, and in which sun-lamps, applied at intervals, will make up for the need for natural sunlight: such a house will work almost as well in a crowded slum as anywhere else. Unfortunately, such an "advanced" technical form is compatible with hideous social disorder and economic waste—just as mechanical advances in war are, as in Germany, compatible with political barbarism. But with the full employment of other arts and sciences, such a house is actually a monstrosity. By utilizing current knowledge of meteorology, a house can be oriented and designed so that it utilizes to the full all available sunshine; by utilizing the political art of town-planning, the house can be assured permanent open spaces, pure air, freedom from noxious gases or effluvia without any provision of special machinery; by saving on the cost of mechanical equipment interior space and exterior gardens can be provided whose utilization and pleasure will help keep the occupants in health and psychological balance. In short, by employing all the knowledge at his command, the architect and planner of a modern community can reduce the expenditure on mechanical utilities, and create a far more effective human environment.

This simple example has a much wider bearing. The progress of the biological and social sciences will result in a shrinking of the province of the machine. Here, I believe, is a fact of deep significance: its implications have still to be grasped.

The coming utilization of social and political skills rests upon another condition, which held true even before the development of modern science; and that is, there is some relation between the degree of personal culture that prevails in a community and the quantity of physical goods it desires and commands. One can put this in a crude and comic form by saying that if all men were honest there would be no need for locksmiths and safes: if all men were co-operative there would be no need for handcuffs. In such simple relations it is easy to see that the achievement of a higher degree of moral culture would not result in a new form of machine: it would result in the elimination of a particular mechanical contraption.

What does this mean in the broader picture? It means that an effective transfer of interest to the realm of ethics and esthetics will result in a diminished demand for the machine and its products. If the use of speedy motor cars is the chief means of utilizing leisure, it is obvious that the output of motor cars, highroads, steel and concrete, and all the accessory supplies and services will increase: but if other means of utilizing leisure become popular, if more people paint and write and model and carpenter and garden, if more people study the stars or observe the behavior of children or become outdoor naturalists, there will be a lessened demand for swift agents of locomotion purely for the purposes of recreation. A transference of interest from the mechanical to the organic and human may be properly regarded either as a labor-saving device or as a brake upon production. At all events it introduces a new factor not embraced by the crude doctrine of "increasing wants." Such a change is one of the real possibilities that follows from a better scientific knowledge of the human personality.

Plainly, the process of etherealization has always been possible. There is plenty of historic evidence to show that it actually took place in Roman civilization, from the first Century B.C. onwards, and that it contributed quite as much as the invasion of the barbarians to overthrow that society. Perhaps the chief problem of our society is to make allowance for these submerged and blockaded human impulses, left out of the mechanical world picture, without permitting them to undermine and disrupt our whole civilization through their uncontrolled eruption.

The facts, at all events, should be plain. Those who have put their faith in mechanical inventions and in the power theme have failed to see that only a modicum of our constant human needs is encompassed by the machine or included in the territory it conquers. We know pretty definitely that men do not live by machines alone, and that the power impulse, however deep and ineradicable, is not a self-sustaining or a self-sufficient one. This is not to deny the importance of the machine in its place; it is merely to acknowledge the fact that it is not a substitute for art and love and fellowship and beauty and contemplative understanding. Many vital human needs have been frustrated by our one-sided overemphasis on the quantitative and the mechanical: this is true both in thought and in social and personal development. Indeed, as Karl Mannheim has pointed out, the hiatus that now exists between those parts of our life that have been rationalized by the machine and those parts that lie outside its scope, constitutes one of the gravest problems of present-day society. There has been, he points out, an uneven development of the human faculties. A diversification and balance of interests will itself be one of the elements that will save science from its own vices: the vices of isolation, non-communicability.

Beyond what is needed to provide what Aristotle called the material basis of the good life, our absorption in the machine deprives us of leisure, of the means of cultivating the arts and sciences for our personal illumination and enjoyment, and of the possibility of taking active parts as citizens in the shaping and direction of our polity. The machine today often serves as a substitute for activities that should be translated directly into biological, social, and personal terms. Our power and leisure are, in fact, empty of significance unless our leisure is used to build up those elements in the human personality and in social relations which are thrust aside or perverted by the one-sided pursuit of power.

The lesson of balance, which comes both from physiology and ecology, is one that has wide applications throughout our culture; it carries with it a demand for co-ordination, for interrelationship, and for intercommunication between the various domains which were once considered free, independent, and sovereign. (Dr. Walter Cannon has very ably elaborated this theme.) Need I point out that there is a close relationship here between the underlying political and social motives of the opening age and the framework of thought in which all our new tasks must be achieved? In both domains power politics and belligerent national sovereignty have produced immediate gains at the expense of the life and integrity of the whole. The age of balance will be one of world-wide federation and interlinkage —in thought no less than in political action.

The real question today is not whether stabilization will take the place of expansion, and symbiosis will replace a more or less predatory economy. The process of stabilization cannot be avoided. The real question is whether this will take place, in disorderly fashion, by a relapse to a more primitive underworld culture, like that envisaged by the Nazis, or whether the change will take place rationally and purposefully: in a fashion that will conserve all of man's great achievements in science and technics during the last three centuries, and bring them to a far richer fruition. But the future of science and technics cannot, in the nature of things, be an automatic continuation of the processes, methods, and beliefs that served the period of expansion. The age of cultivation has new needs and makes new claims. To satisfy these needs every part of our culture must be revitalized and re-oriented; and success here will demand political skill no less than philosophic vision; for thought itself bears an organic relation to life.

# 5. SCIENCE AND INTERNATIONALISM

# INTERNATIONAL LAW AND
# TOTALITARIAN WAR

## *by* Philip C. Jessup

TOTALITARIANISM, as the term is currently used, popularly connotes a negation of law. One need not be an advocate of or apologist for totalitarianism in order to disagree with so facile a generalization. Totalitarianism is by no means anarchic in the philosophical sense; it uses law and indeed attributes importance to the elaboration of legal theories and norms adapted to its own ends.

War, also, in the minds of many superficial observers, connotes a negation of law. The maxim *inter arma leges silent* is distorted to support this fallacious conclusion. As Judge Moore has pointed out, "In its origin, this was a maxim not of international law but of municipal law, public and private. It simply means that, under the stress of a contest by force, when men are struggling with arms in their hands for mastery, violations of law are bound to occur because the means of securing the observance of law are reduced to a minimum. . . . It signifies in effect that, when a contest by force prevails, the ordinary rules and methods of administration . . . give way to measures dictated by public necessity. The system by which the ordinary administration is superseded is called martial law." "Martial law," according to the famous *Instructions for the Government of Armies of the United States in the Field* (1863) "is simply military authority exercised in accordance with the laws and usages of war. Military oppression is not Martial Law; it is the abuse of the power which that law confers." From very early times the waging of war has been subjected to regulation which may be described as of a legal character, whether the regulation be national or international in scope.

A consideration of totalitarian war thus falls within the realm of legal science. The relation which international law bears to it and the effect which it has and has had upon international law are topics which concern the lawyer even though they affront the moralist and bore the hard-headed politician. I do not intend to discuss the question whether the architect of a better world order should concentrate upon the abolition or prevention of war instead of troubling with the regulation of war if it comes, although I shall point out that almost all plans for the elimination of war leave place for the equivalent of our present body of war law. At the time of this writing, war is the reality and its abolition is the dream. I shall try to explore the changing character of war itself as an instrument of policy and the changing character of the instruments of warfare, both in relation to international law.

It is unnecessary to restate the familiar divergent characterizations of war from the legal point of view. It is known variously as "an act, a controversy, a condition and a procedure." In the years immediately following 1918, there was a tendency, even among lawyers, to adopt an ethical or moralistic viewpoint and to regard war as an evil and even as an impossibility. Such an approach made inevitable the failure to solve the problem of the prevention or adequate regulation of war. Paradoxically enough, it was not until the signature of the General Pact for the Renunciation of War in 1928 that the world generally came to appreciate the fact that Clausewitz was correct in describing war as "an instrument of national policy."

The next difficulty was the over-optimistic assumption that a formal renunciation would so blunt the instrument as to make it unusable. National policy remained and was not renounced and, as writers like Shotwell have frequently emphasized, the international community failed to supply alternative instruments. It is none the less significant that the fact which cynics stress as the clearest indication of the futility of the Pact of Paris constitutes a notable triumph for that force of public opinion which inspired the Pact's proponents. I refer to the fact that since 1928 States in using *force* as an instrument of policy have sought to avoid resort to *war* in the technical sense. The legal subterfuge is obvious but its utilization is as much a tribute to the validity of the legal prohibition as was the invention of the "trust" to escape the legal restrictions on combinations in restraint of trade. To be sure, long before 1928 States sought to avoid the charge that they were waging war (particularly on small neighbors) because either at home or abroad a certain stigma if not definite illegality attached to war-making.

International law has recognized the legality of the use of force as an instrument of national policy in some circumstances and has characterized other uses as illegal. Thus the law has recognized the legality of armed intervention or of reprisals under some circumstances but not under others. Under customary international law, a resort to war was extra-legal rather than legal or illegal. This situation is puzzling to laymen but its historical explanation is clear. In its earliest stages, international law placed but little restriction on the use of force; gradually it was able to regulate certain uses of force and the law of intervention and of reprisals or retaliation took shape. International law was not simultaneously capable of dealing with the larger problem of war itself. Resort to war in this aspect represents the supreme problem for the solution of which international law was striving; success has not yet been achieved so far as customary law is concerned, although a great body of treaty law does offer partial regulation. Unable to regulate the resort to war, international law did continue the ancient process of regulating the manner in which it was to be conducted.

Jurists as well as laymen inevitably find difficulty in explaining how one can speak of an international legal system when that system contains the proposition that a state is at any time free, without committing an illegal act, to resort to forcible self-help to attain its desires. Two situations may be distinguished:

I. A State which has been wronged by another State resorts to forcible self-help to vindicate its rights.

Here one encounters no fundamental juristic difficulty. Permissible use of force for the vindication of individual right is not the negation of law but only the negation of that highly developed form of legal procedure which we associate with the internal structure of the modern state. The permissible resort to self-help is an institution found in many bodies of primitive law and it persists long after such bodies of law passed out of the stage which may technically be called primitive. While trial by battle may be distinguished from self-help, it was a legalized use of force for the settlement of legal disputes and as such technically remained available to suitors in English courts until 1819. In this category of situations, forcible self-help (war) is seen as reflecting a defect in the procedural more than in the substantive law. As a matter of defective procedure we lack adequate international machinery with power to determine authoritatively whether a State's allegation of infringement of its legal rights is sound in law. As a matter of defective procedure we lack international machinery to compel restitution even if the alleged wrong has been adjudicated. The right to resort to war in case of non-compliance with such an adjudication is implicitly recognized in Article 12 of the Covenant of the League.

II. A State resorts to forcible self-help not for the vindication of rights, but for the satisfaction of a desire to enhance its power or prestige or simply because it would like to have something which belongs to another.

So long as international law acknowledges that this type of self-help is not illegal (even if one takes the view that it is extra-legal), there is what Umpire Barge called a *vitium proprium*—an inherent vice—in the international legal system. It can be argued that the almost universal acceptance of the Pact of Paris for the Renunciation of War as an Instrument of National Policy has cured this vice. This argument is possible from the juristic point of view even if one admits that the unqualified reservation of the right of self-defense vitiates the political efficacy of the Pact. This is true because if the resort to war is allegedly based upon the right of self-defense, the case is immediately removed to our first category and the use of self-help is revealed in its procedural aspect as a means of vindicating a legal right.

The argument based on the Pact of Paris is, however, of doubtful validity unless one assumes that the Pact has created general as distinguished from conventional law. That assumption I am not prepared to make. Until such a principle of general law is established the inherent vice in the international legal system remains. Nevertheless, no matter how devastating this theoretically sound criticism of the international legal system may be, the fact remains that by and large for some three hundred years States have argued and acted as if the term "international law" were not a misnomer. It is, in reverse, the situation described by the English High Court of Admiralty in 1778: "A pedantic man in his closet dictates the law of nations, everybody quotes, and nobody minds him."

Totalitarian war, in the sense of war conducted by the whole state against the whole state of the enemy, is not new. Some writers are fond of comparing twentieth-Century warfare with the warfare of a period when hostilities were waged chiefly by mercenary soldiers and the life of the people who were not in the immediate path of the combatants was not greatly disrupted. It is probably correct to say that such professional warfare was an intermediate type both preceded and followed by a type in which the whole community or state was involved. Certainly the "modern" type of totalitarian war dates back at least to the eighteenth Century even though every war since that period has not been of the "all-in" type.

Judge John Bassett Moore in a recent article in the *Virginia Quarterly Review* epitomizes the argument of his classic *International Law and Some Current Illusions:*

The current titles "World War" and "First World War" merely betray a misconception of history. Marshal Foch ("Des Principes de la guerre," 1918. Preface IX) has truly said that the principles which govern the art are immutable, and that among them is the harmonious employment of all the national resources in men, materials, and money. It was so in the wars of ancient Persia, of Greece, of Rome, and of Carthage. At the close of the Thirty Years' War (1618-1648), the population of the old German Empire was reduced from sixteen million, or slightly more, to about four million, and only one city was left with its ancient walls. In the wars of the Spanish Succession (1700-1713), the losses of the belligerents, among whom were Austria, England, France, Holland, and Spain, were enormous in their totality as well as in their proportions; the population of France alone was computed to have fallen nearly fourteen per cent. In the Seven Years' War (1756-1763), in which George Washington fought as a British subject, although the general drain upon the belligerents, among whom were Austria, England, France, Prussia, Portugal, Russia, and Spain, and incidentally the British, French, Portuguese, and Spanish colonies in America, was less heavy, Prussia was estimated to have lost, simply on the field of battle, more than six per cent of her population. The losses in life and property and in commerce and industry in the wars growing out of the French Revolution (1792-1802) and the Napoleonic Wars (1803-1815) are beyond computation; . . .

Although historians may differ as to the correctness of particular figures during these earlier struggles, the point which Judge Moore makes is one which cannot be escaped.

In 1793 the British Government sought to justify cutting off all trade with France by describing the "unusual mode of war employed by the enemy himself, in having armed almost the whole laboring class of the French nation, for the purpose of commencing and supporting hostilities against all the governments of Europe." Moreover, it was said that the trade was being carried on by the French Government itself and could "no longer . . . be regarded as a mercantile speculation of individuals, but as an immediate operation of the very persons who have declared war." So in 1915, the British Government stated that, "The reason for drawing a distinction between foodstuffs intended for the civil population and those for the armed forces or enemy Government disappears when the distinction between the civil population and the armed forces itself disappears.

"In any country in which there exists such a tremendous organization for war as now obtains in Germany there is no clear division between those whom the Government is responsible for feeding and those whom it is not."

Parallel arguments as of 1939 and 1940 will readily come to mind. All of these examples are adduced merely to illustrate the fact that, contemporaneously, great wars of the past have been regarded as "totalitarian," although the term itself is of more modern coinage.

It is also interesting to recall that in one sense it is the traditional Anglo-American rather than the Continental European view which embraces the concept of the "totalitarian" nature of war. This is illustrated by the laws concerning trading with the enemy. The traditional Anglo-American view is that upon the outbreak of war, all private contacts with the enemy are prohibited except as particularly licensed; the European view holds that all private contacts are permissible except as particularly prohibited. Thus, the Supreme Court of the United States declared in 1814 that "The universal sense of nations has acknowledged the demoralizing effects that would result from the admission of individual intercourse. The whole nation is embarked in one common bottom, and must be reconciled to submit to one common fate. Every individual of the one nation must acknowledge every individual of the other nation as his own enemy—because the enemy of his country." Just one hundred years later, the Supreme Court of Germany though dealing with a somewhat different problem, stated: "German international law does not share the point of view of certain foreign legal systems, that war is to be so conducted as to result in the greatest possible economic damage to the nationals of enemy states and that these, therefore are to be robbed to a large extent of the benefits of the common civil law. On the contrary, the principle applies that war is to be conducted only against the enemy state as such, and against its armed forces, and that the nationals of enemy states enjoy the same equality with German nationals in regard to civil law as was the case before the war, in all respects, except in so far as statutory exceptions exist."

What has been said above must not be construed as involving a moral judgment or a denial that "totalitarian war" in its current meaning connotes the use of practices never countenanced by the Anglo-American system.

The peculiarities of the use of war as an instrument of national policy since 1928 are of a different order. Paradoxical as it may seem, one peculiarity of totalitarian war has been that in many of its manifestations it has not been total. The loss of life on both sides since the outbreak of the European

war in September, 1939, has been astonishingly low considering the forces engaged. In the current armed conflict between
China and Japan, Japan has not made full use of belligerent
rights on the high seas although she has had sufficient sea power
to establish an effective belligerent blockade and to intercept
shipments of contraband on continuous voyage to China through
Burma. Similarly, Germany in Norway and especially in Den-
mark has sought to pose as a "protector" rather than as an
enemy. In the recent Spanish civil strife, the very word "war"
was studiously avoided by most governments in dealing with
the struggle, belligerent rights were not recognized and the
obligations of neutrality were not accepted. During the Russo-
Finnish "war" of 1939-40, the United States did not proclaim
its neutrality, just as it refrained from so doing in the Sino-
Japanese conflict. Thus the non-total character of totalitarian
war has resulted in non-total neutrality on the part of other
states. From September 1939 until its full participation in the
fighting in May 1940, Italy carefully avoided the word "neutral" to describe its position and insisted that it was "non-bel-
ligerent." The United States at first espoused a total neutrality
but gradually drifted into a status which was called "limited
war" by one school and that of a "supporting State" by another.[1]

In the face of totalitarian war, the international lawyer is
confronted by a series of anomalies. In his report on the foreign
policy of the Soviet Union to the extraordinary session of the
Supreme Soviet of the U.S.S.R., made on October 31, 1939,
Mr. Molotov stated that:

The non-aggression pact concluded between the Soviet Union
and Germany bound us to maintain neutrality in the case of Germany being involved in a war. We have consistently pursued this
course, which was in no wise contradicted by the entry of our troops
into the territory of former Poland which began on September 17.
It will be sufficient to recall that on the same day, September 17,
the Soviet Government sent a special note to all the states with
which it maintains diplomatic relations declaring that the U.S.S.R.
would continue its policy of neutrality in regard to them.

---

[1] This essay was written just before December, 1941, and therefore does not
include references to the present state of belligerency.

The U.S.S.R. did not consider that it was at war with Poland. The United States, without assuming the status of a co-belligerent, established a joint defense committee with belligerent Canada under the Ogdensburg agreement of August 18, 1940, and exchanged with belligerent Great Britain fifty destroyers for a series of naval bases which apparently are to be jointly used. One is reminded that in 1917 El Salvador, while announcing that it would remain neutral, declared its sympathy for the United States in its war with Germany and declared that the United States could use Salvadorean waters for naval purposes. Similarly Uruguay announced at the same period "that no American country which in defense of its own rights should find itself in a state of war with nations of other continents will be treated as belligerents." The German Government did not consider that a state of war between Uruguay and Germany resulted from this decree. Other Latin American governments took somewhat similar positions in their attitude toward Germany.

Such cases are illustrative of the fact that international law is not yet a thoroughly developed legal system. International lawyers seek to fit governments into the traditional categories of belligerents and neutrals, just as English lawyers in the fourteenth Century sought to fit the cases of their clients into the forms found in the Register of Writs. The English lawyers met their difficulties by evolving devices such as the action on the case just as international lawyers may now be in process of creating the status of non-belligerency. Law is perhaps inevitably formalistic.

In the seventeenth Century a state was still catalogued as neutral although it supplied troops to one of the belligerents. Gradually the law insisted that the status of neutrality was maintained in such cases only if the aid were given in accordance with a pre-existing treaty obligation. Finally, such aid by a neutral to a belligerent was banned entirely but it was still lawful for a neutral to give certain kinds of help as, for example, to supply fuel to a warship within defined limits. What are considered anomalies in "neutral" practices of today are almost identical with common practice in the seventeenth Century. As late as 1759, Hubner wrote that the usages of nations required the classification of neutrality into "full and entire neutrality" and "limited neutrality." The latter type he admits is not really neutrality unless the obligation to help one side had been incurred prior to the outbreak of war. There is a familiar modern note to the plaintive statement of the English agent at Leghorn in 1655 when he wrote to his government that he did not know "how they stood" with Spain in view of the activities of Penn's fleet in the West Indies. In 1813, Sir William Scott found it proper to discuss whether in 1812 Sweden was "in a state of perfect neutrality." He noted that Sweden's conduct toward England "had been, for a considerable time, of a very unfriendly description . . . Sweden, therefore, by her conduct, afforded to Great Britain a legitimate cause of war." Great Britain proceeded to seize the island of Hanoe and thereafter Sweden declared war. Until the declaration was issued, Sweden was apparently in a state of "imperfect" neutrality. The transit of Germany through Rumania into Russia would have seemed proper to jurists of the sixteenth and seventeenth Centuries.

This apparent reversion to prototypes of past centuries is not to be attributed to a modern barbarity of states. The partial neutrality of Latin American states in 1917 and of the United States in 1940 is not a relapse into barbarism even though one does not accept at the other extreme the thesis that it is an evidence of the achievement of a higher form of international society in which law-abiding states decline to be "neutral" in the face of "illegal aggression." The Havana Convention of July, 1940 providing for the possible joint administration of European colonies in the Western Hemisphere and the Panama Declaration of September, 1939 establishing the Pan American neutrality belt, are reminiscent in some respects of the armed neutralities of the seventeenth and eighteenth Centuries, but they are not barbaric.

Advocates, as we all are, of a better world order, sometimes decry the effort to regulate the conduct of war because they consider such regulation futile and because they think that efforts should be concentrated on the elimination of war itself.

I have tried to suggest that even in the face of modern totalitarian war regulation is not futile. I shall now speak of the other part of the argument.

It is fair to say that most proposals looking toward the elimination of war contemplate the substitution of some kind of international police. This means that they recognize the possibility that in the international society, as in the national society, lawless persons or groups may have to be suppressed by force. In the international society, plans for an international police force must contemplate the use of the police against sizeable armed groups whether or not we speak in terms of a recalcitrant state rebelling against the international order. Just as it was difficult in 1937 to distinguish factually between war and the clash of Chinese and Japanese arms, so in 1947, let us say, it may be difficult to distinguish factually between war and the clash of international police forces and an "aggressor." It is not to be assumed that an international police force would carry out its function with anarchic barbarity. Presumably it would not use dum dum bullets, would not poison wells, would not resort to bacteriological warfare, would not kill prisoners or torture the wounded. National police forces are regulated, although the regulations are sometimes violated. The same would have to be true of international police forces. The situation might be comparable to that of civil war. *Mutatis mutandis*, one may quote Article 152 of the *Instructions for the Government of Armies of the United States in the Field*—Lieber's code:

> When humanity induces the adoption of the rules of regular war toward rebels, whether the adoption is partial or entire, it does in no way whatever imply a partial or complete acknowledgment of their government, if they have set up one, or of them, as an independent and sovereign power. Neutrals have no right to make the adoption of the rules of war by the assailed government toward rebels the ground of their own acknowledgment of the revolted people as an independent power.

Law often lags behind facts but if it does not correspond to facts, it is soon nullified or modified. Take air law as an illustration. In private law we find that the civil codes of many coun-

tries have long contained provisions indicating some right of
private ownership in the air space above a person's land. In
Anglo-American law, the same idea found its place in the frequent reiteration of the maxim *cuius est solum eius est usque
ad coelum*. All this was before the practical development of
aviation and involved the right to build overhanging projections, telephone wires and like problems. Since the development of aviation, the American courts at least have broken with
the old maxim and have rejected the idea of a property right
*usque ad coelum*. "We think it is not the law, and that it never
was the law," said the Circuit Court of Appeals for the 9th
Circuit in 1936 (*Hinman v. Pacific Air Transport*, 84 F. (2d)
755) . . . "We will not foist any such chimerical concept of
property rights upon the jurisprudence of this country." The
judges could not bring themselves to hold that a transconti-
nental plane committed thousands of trespasses as it soared
from Los Angeles to New York. In international law during
the first decade of the twentieth Century, the overwhelmingly
dominant view was that the air was free and no state had sovereignty *usque ad coelum*. With the development of aviation and
particularly the use of aircraft from 1914 to 1918, the prevailing view changed with great rapidity. As a result, the Air Navigation Convention of 1919, and subsequent legislative treaties
largely modeled upon it, recognized as an existing fact or rule
of law "that every power has complete and exclusive sovereignty over the airspace above its territory." The rule of sovereignty is admitted with practical unanimity today. Governments could not bring themselves to agree that foreign aircraft
could fly at will over their territories. The contrast may be
stressed: in private law, we start before the development of
aviation with the rule of property in the airspace and we end
after the development of aviation with the rule of freedom. In
international law, we start with the rule of freedom and end
with the rule of sovereignty. Both legal developments are comprehensible in the light of facts and contemporaneous interpretations of social and political needs.

In the law of aerial warfare, the development has been
neither so rapid nor so clear. At The Hague in 1907, govern-

ments could agree to a rule prohibiting the launching of projectiles from the air; the prohibition had a humanitarian appeal and military men were not concerned to preserve a weapon which then seemed unimportant. After the World War demonstrated the potential military importance of aerial bombardment, no agreement could be reached on the regulations proposed by The Hague Commission of Jurists in 1923. As a result, the present war broke upon a legal scene whose stage was not set with adequate regulation. Between the two wars there had been abundant humanitarian appeals and proposals to protect the civilian populations, but the other essential element of military utility had not been swung into line. Thus, although the United States Government expresses its revulsion against the bombardment of civilians through the imposition of moral embargoes, it is impossible for the international lawyer to demonstrate that it is illegal for a bomber to release its bombs upon a factory, a railroad center, a bridge or docks even if the bombs may kill numerous innocent civilians. But one may well argue that the bombing is illegal if the objective is merely to terrorize the civilian population. That proposition can be maintained, *inter alia*, upon two grounds:

1st. The advocates of totalitarian war have not succeeded in grafting upon international law the proposition that the distinction between combatants and non-combatants has been eliminated. If this proposition were true, an invading army could lawfully shoot or capture as a military prisoner, every civilian it encountered, just as well as every soldier under arms. I do not believe that is either the law or, as a matter of fact, the practice.

2nd. The law against indiscriminate bombing for purposes of terrorization is supported by both humanitarianism and military utilitarianism. The military judgment here expressed is a lay echo of informed opinion, but is believed to be correct.

One reason why aerial bombardment has defied detailed regulation is that the science prior to 1920 was in its infancy. Today it may be in a state of extravagant adolescence. Tomorrow, when it has reached maturity, and with maturity a greater degree of accuracy, I venture to think it will be regulated like dum

dum bullets and poisoned weapons and for the same reason that the ends of humanitarianism and of military utility will coincide.

The effect of totalitarian war upon this particular rule of international law may well be to clarify the definition of a military objective since the old test of a "defended" place which was utilized in the old rules governing terrestrial and maritime bombardment, has been definitely unsatisfactory.

It is not possible here to review the numerous laws regulating the conduct of warfare, although it is an illuminating record from the precepts "enshrined in the *Mahābhārata* and in the *Rāmāyana*" of ancient India, through the rules of Western European chivalry, down to such effective instruments as the Convention Concerning the Treatment of Prisoners of War, signed at Geneva, July 27, 1929. *Flagrante bello* it is difficult for the scholar to gather reliable data on the conduct of armed forces. But it is possible, though dangerous, to hazard the prophecy that international lawyers of the future will be able to record the applications as well as the breaches of international law during the current war. Changes in the international society will be reflected in the law governing both the resort to war and the conduct of war, whether war continues as a legal anomaly or as the regulated application of force to restrain lawbreakers; and legal science will become more adequate, less permeated with antinomies, only when it more adequately considers humanitarian ends.

# CONDITIONS OF
# INTERNATIONAL JUSTICE

## by Hans Kelsen

THE PROBLEM of international justice is only a special instance of the general problem of justice, a problem which has occupied the human mind as has no other. Since men have thought at all, they have put the question: What is just? And although the most illustrious thinkers, including Plato and Kant, sought an objective answer, valid for all, the question of the nature of justice is as far from being answered today as it ever was. The most famous definitions, when subjected to critical analysis, are revealed as empty tautologies on the pattern *"suum cuique."* It is our feeling that compels us to put the question: How should we behave for our behavior to be considered just? The intellect, however, from which we expect the answer can only say: you should behave as you ought to. However indispensable belief in justice may be for the volition and action of men, the problem of justice cannot be approached by cognition.

What does it really mean to say that a social order is a just one? It means that this order regulates the behavior of men in a way satisfactory to all men, that is to say, so that all men find their happiness in it. The longing for justice is the eternal longing of men for happiness. It is happiness that man cannot find alone and hence seeks in society. Justice is social happiness.

It is obvious that there can be no "just" order, that is, one affording happiness to everyone as long as one defines the concept of happiness in its original, narrow sense of individual happiness, meaning by a man's happiness what he himself considers it to be. For it is then inevitable that the happiness of one individual will at some time be directly in conflict with that of another. Nor is a just order then possible even under the supposition that it is trying to bring about not the individual happiness of each, but the greatest possible happiness of the greatest possible number of individuals. The happiness that a social order can assure, can be happiness in the collective sense only, that is, the satisfaction of certain needs, recognized by the social authority, the law-giver, as needs worthy of being satisfied, like the need to be fed, clothed and housed. But which human needs are worthy of being satisfied, especially which is their proper order of rank, the satisfaction of which needs should take precedence, all that cannot be determined by means of rational cognition. The decision of these questions is a judgment of value determined by emotional factors and is, therefore, subjective in character, as is every true judgment of value. It will be different according to whether the question is answered by a believing Christian, who holds the good of his soul in the hereafter more important than earthly goods, or by a materialist who believes in no after life; and it will be just as different according to whether the decision is made by one who considers personal freedom as the highest good, i.e., by liberalism or by one for whom the equality of all men is rated higher than freedom, i.e., by socialism. Even were there unanimity as to which needs of mankind it is the purpose of the social order to satisfy, and as to the order in which the satisfaction was to take place, it is still not possible in view of the present-day condition of social science, to indicate definitely the means by which the social order can best achieve its end. Hence, this question, as to the appropriate means, is also determined more by subjective judgments of value than by an objective insight into the connection between means and end, that is, between cause and effect; and hence, at least for the moment, the problem of justice, even as thus restricted to a question of the appropriate means to a generally recognized end, cannot be rationally answered. The issue between liberalism and socialism, e.g., is, in great part, not really an issue over the aim of society, but rather one as to the correct way of achieving a goal concerning which men are by and large in agreement; and this issue cannot be scientifically determined, at least not today.

The same is true of the different and very contradictory principles presented under the name of international justice, especially of the two formulas which just recently have been put in the foreground. They relate to the regulation of the territorial problem. According to one formula, the incorporation of a territory with a certain state should depend on the will of the individuals living in this territory. It is the principle of self-determination of peoples and the supplementary principle of the international protection of minorities. Both principles proceed from the supposition that all nations, races and religions are equal, and hence have an equal right to exist, to maintain their own culture, and to determine their own fate. The other formula is the claim to "Lebensraum." It proceeds from the supposition that there are superior and inferior peoples, and that the former, and only they, have the right to dominate a territory whose extent and natural resources suffice to assure a satisfactory, i.e., self-sufficient existence of its people, and that even at the expense of the inferior peoples. It is a principle which was applied in previous centuries only to the relation between Christian and heathen, between civilized and primitive peoples, but which today is invoked to justify the imperialistic claims of certain totalitarian states vis-à-vis other civilized nations.

To the extent that the opposition between the right of all peoples to self-determination and the claim of certain peoples to "Lebensraum" rests upon different ideas of the value of the peoples, this conflict is not capable of being decided by science. It is not so even if the claim to "Lebensraum" and the correlative claim to domination of one people by another presents itself with the argument that the domination is exercised in the interest of the people that is not able to govern itself, or with the argument that it is only a question of a special way different from self-determination, in this case a better way to assure the welfare of the dominated people. For, this justification, too, rests on a judgment of value which cannot be objectively verified.

In regard to the purpose of the social order, as well as in regard to the means to be used, there are not one, but many, and very different answers to the problem of justice. One might almost say there is no justice because there are too many conceptions of justice.

Regarded from the point of view of rational cognition, there are only interests, and hence conflicts of interests, whose solution is possible only by an order that satisfies one interest at the expense of the other, or which brings about a compromise between the conflicting interests. That only one or the other of these two orders is "just" cannot be established on the basis of rational cognition. But it can be established on the basis of our experience that only a social order whose function is, more or less, a compromise between the opposing interests, has a prospect of continued existence. Only such an order will be in a position to secure social peace to its subjects on a relatively permanent basis. And although the ideal of justice in its original sense as developed here is something quite different from the ideal of peace, there exists a definite tendency to identify the two ideals, or at least to substitute the ideal of peace for that of justice.

This change of meaning of the concept of justice goes hand in hand with the tendency to withdraw the problem of justice from the insecure realm of subjective judgments of value, and to establish it on the secure ground of a given, social order. "Justice" in this sense means legality; it is "just" for a general rule to be actually applied in all cases where, according to its content, this rule should be applied. It is "unjust" for it to be applied in one case and not in another similar case. And this seems "unjust" without regard to the value of the general norm itself, the application of which is under consideration. Justice, in this sense, is a quality which relates not to the content of a positive order, but to its application. "Justice" means the maintenance of a positive order by conscientious application of it. To the extent that the aim of every social order, especially of the legal order, is peace, justice, in the sense of conformity with law, i.e., legality, means peace guaranteed by the law.

It is a thoroughly conservative ideal. Its aim is the maintenance of an existing legal order, especially in the sense that necessary changes are not to be brought about by force. If a national legal order is in question, such changes are to be made not by revolution but by peaceful means, that is, in the way the constitution itself provides.

International justice means international peace, peace secured by international law. The international legal order is to be maintained, especially in the sense that necessary changes in the legal relations among the states are to take place peaceably, not by the use of force. International justice means prevention of war.

As general international law serves this purpose only very inadequately, the problem of international justice presents itself as the problem of an international organization by which peace may be more effectively assured and war more certainly prevented than is possible by general international law.

I I

What are the conditions of this international justice?

This question can perhaps best be answered on the basis of the experience we had with the League of Nations, the most comprehensive international community so far, whose aim, according to its constitution was "to achieve international peace . . . by the acceptance of obligations not to resort to war . . . and by the maintenance of justice. . . ."

It is self-evident that an international community that desires to insure peace must be as nearly universal in its scope as possible, that is, it must embrace as many states as possible; and it is today beyond question that the League of Nations was not able to achieve its aim primarily because the United States of America was not among its members. But the experiences of the League also teach that the universality of an international community which is to insure peace has certain limits. The peace to which the members of the League were in duty bound by its Covenant, was broken in general only by states whose political or economic constitutions were opposed to the political or economic constitutions of the other members. Dictatorships with more or less totalitarian or communistic economies were the breakers of the peace: fascist Italy, Japan with its military dictatorship, bolshevist Russia, national-socialist Germany. The last-named state was, it is true, no longer a member of the League, when it resorted to war against members of the League; but it had withdrawn from the League obviously because the principles upon which its political and economic constitution rested were not compatible with the ideal of peace of the League of Nations.

We can learn from this experience for the benefit of a future international organization:

There must be as far as possible political and economic homogeneity among the states forming the community. There is as little reason to expect communist or state capitalist states and states with a liberal economic system to exist side by side even in a fairly loose international organization as to expect democratic and autocratic states to combine in an enduring community. In this context one should not cling too closely to the traditional conceptions of democracy and autocracy. Both have changed their meanings in the developments of the last twenty years. One of the most important tasks involved in preparing the way for the peace of the future is to clarify these meanings. For this purpose the Constitution of the United States may be used as an example. It represents the best solution up to the present time of the problem which has appeared clearly in Europe in the clash of democracy and autocracy: How can a stable and effective government be combined with extensive participation by the people in the formation of state policy and with personal liberty of the citizens?

III

If we seek the causes of the wars by which the peace guaranteed by the League of Nations was broken, we find that they were primarily territorial conflicts. Whether the claims of the aggressors in the instances here under consideration were more or less justified is not here an issue. It is certain only that one of the essential conditions of a permanent community for the furthering of peace is the following:

A fairly satisfactory regulation of the territorial relations of the states forming the community. This kind of regulation is possible only if it is conducted as extensively and as honestly as possible, according to the principle of the right of peoples to self-determination. Where minorities are unavoidable, they are to be organized as entities with constitutional rights. The treaty establishing the international community must grant them the status of persons in international law so that they will have the right to call upon an international court in case of violation of the provisions protecting minorities. This regulation of the territorial problem is not suggested here because it is the only "just" one, but because it probably better than any other assures peace.

## I V

To understand one of the weightiest causes that contributed to the collapse of the League of Nations, and to be able to draw from it a lesson for the future, one must cast a glance at the development that lies back of national as well as international law.

The evolution of law from its primitive beginnings to its standard of today has been, from a technical point of view, a continuous process of centralization. It may also be thought of as a process of increasing division of labor in the field of the creation and application of law. The functions of law-creating and law-applying, originally performed by all members of the community, have gradually passed on to specified individuals and are now executed exclusively by them. In the beginning every individual, subject to the legal order, participates in all the functions of creating and applying the law. Later, special organs develop for the different functions. In the field of law the same process takes place as in that of economic production. It is always a process of centralization.

In the field of law this process is characterized by the surprising fact that the centralization of the law-applying function precedes the centralization of the law-creating function. Long before special legislative organs come into existence, courts are established, to apply the law to concrete cases. The law, thus applied, is customary law. Customary law is law created by a specific method. The peculiarity of this method is that the general legal norms are created by collaboration of all the individuals subject to the legal order. It is a totally decentralized means of creating law. During thousands upon thousands of years it was the only way of creating general legal norms. The application of the law, however, long ago became the exclusive function of special organs, of tribunals, was long ago centralized. No longer is each individual authorized to decide whether or not his rights have been violated, whether or not he will react by a sanction against another individual responsible for the violation of law. Such decisions have for long been entrusted to a judge, a special organ, different and independent from the parties in conflict. The general norms, however, in accordance with which the judge decides such conflicts, are not even now created by a central organ; they still have the character of customary law. Customary law forms an important part of the legal order even in technically highly developed legal communities.

The procedure of applying general legal norms to concrete cases involves three distinct phases. First, the conditioning facts must be established, especially the delict, the concrete violation of law; second, the sanction, provided by the general legal norm, must be ordered to be applied to the concrete case; third, this sanction must be executed against the individual responsible for the delict. The three stages of the procedure do not necessarily become centralized at the same time. Historically, the centralization of the first two stages has probably preceded the centralization of the third stage. The centralization of the employment of force, i.e., the procedure by which a concrete sanction is executed against the responsible individual, seems to be the last step. The application of law by courts replaces the legal status of self-help by blood revenge.

It seems, however, that the state of self-help was only gradually eliminated. In the early days the courts were hardly more than tribunals of arbitration. They had to decide only whether or not the delict had actually been committed as claimed by one party, whether or not one party was authorized to execute a sanction against the other if the conflict could not be settled by peaceful agreement between them. To bring about such a peaceful agreement, enabling the vendetta to be replaced by wergild, was probably the first task of the tribunal. Only at a later stage does it become possible completely to abolish the procedure of self-help, according to which the sanction is executed by the individuals whose interests have been violated by the delict. The execution of the sanction by a central organ of the legal community, authorized to punish the guilty individual, presupposes a concentration of the means of power, the existence of a central organ with all these means of power at its disposal. To centralize the execution of the sanctions, provided by the legal order, the legal community needs not only courts but also a powerful administration.

A legal community which has an administration and courts is a state; but a central organ of legislation is not an essential requisite of a state. The jurisdiction of statal courts is older than statal legislation. It is noteworthy that the French term "parlement" originally referred to a court.

The fact that the application of law is centralized much earlier than the creation of law, the legislation, is of the greatest importance. It seems to manifest a certain regularity of evolution originating in the sociological and especially in the sociopsychological nature of law. We may therefore presume with a certain degree of probability that the development of international law has the same tendencies as the development of national law. There is perhaps in the social field a certain analogy with the phenomenon called the bio-genetic law, that is, the law according to which the human embryo in the womb of the mother has to pass through the same stages of evolution through which humanity, i.e., men as species, has passed in the process of evolution from a lower to a higher stage of life. Thus perhaps the law of the universal, the international community, has to pass through the same evolution through which the law of the partial community, national law, has already passed. In fact, the first organized communities of international law, the first relatively centralized unions of states are organizations, the function of which is to settle conflicts. The first central organs in international life are international tribunals, instituted by international treaties. The function of these tribunals is confined to the establishment of the conditioning facts, to a decision whether or not in a concrete case the right of a state has been violated by another state. The decisions of these courts are not executed by a central executive power. In case the other state does not execute the decision of the court, the application of the sanction is reserved to the state whose right has been acknowledged by the court.

As a rule, the international court is not competent to decide all the disputes which may arise between the contracting parties; its competence is usually restricted to certain disputes exactly determined by the treaty of arbitration; and this treaty is normally valid for a limited period of time only.

These facts show clearly that the law of the interstate community develops in the same direction as the primitive law of the pre-state community, that the tendency toward centralization is in both cases to a certain extent parallel. They also suggest the direction in which a relatively successful attempt may be undertaken to secure international peace by emphasizing and strengthening the given tendency toward centralization. Natural evolution tends toward an international judiciary. The first step toward an enduring peace must be the establishment of an international community the members of which are obliged to submit all disputes arising among them to a permanent international court and to respect the decisions of this authority. The chief thing is to subject as many states as possible to the authority of an international court, competent to decide all conflicts arising among them. So far, no such enterprise has been successful, perhaps because it has not been seriously attempted. Until this end has been attained, however, the other much more far-reaching one cannot possibly be achieved, namely, the establishment of a community of states, subjected to a central administration with centralized executive power at its disposal, or even the establishment of a federal world-state with a world-wide administration and legislature. According to the pattern of the evolution of national law, centralization of the judiciary must precede centralization of legislative and executive power.

To be sure, a different line of development for international law is not absolutely excluded. The laws determining social evolution are not so strict as biological and physiological laws. The human will, directed to a certain end, is able to shape social life arbitrarily, but only to a limited extent. Hence it follows that a social reform has more chance of success if it follows the tendencies hitherto exhibited by social evolution. It has less chance, if it opposes these tendencies. It is, for instance, relatively easy to proceed to socialism from capitalism or even from state capitalism; but an attempt to attain the same object, starting from feudalism is impossible, even senseless. For the same reason it is probably impossible to proceed directly from the completely decentralized state of the international community of today to a federal world-state. It is perhaps possible, however, to reach an intermediate stage, that of an international community embracing many important states, and based on the principle of compulsory court jurisdiction.

Such an organization would represent tremendous progress in relation to the present situation. Political idealists, whose desires soar beyond this possibility to a world-state, should always bear in mind that their ideal is attainable only by way of the intermediate stage of compulsory international jurisdiction. Nature makes no jumps; nor can law either.

## V

The proposition that the next and most important step toward international peace is the establishment of an international court with compulsory jurisdiction is confirmed by the experiences of the League of Nations. One of the most important, if not decisive, causes of the failure of the League of Nations is a fatal fault of its construction, the fact that the authors of the Covenant placed at the center of this international organization not the Permanent Court of International Justice, but a kind of international administration, the Council of the League of Nations. The Assembly of the League—its other organ—placed beside the Council, gives the impression of an international legislature. The dualism of administration and parliament was probably more or less distinctly present in the minds of the founders, when they created two main organs of the League.

It might have been foreseen from the very beginning that a world government will not succeed if its decisions have to be taken unanimously, binding no member against his will, and if there is no centralized power to execute them. It is not to be wondered at that a world parliament, or in whatever manner the Assembly of the League of Nations may be characterized, can be of only nominal value if the principle of majority be almost completely excluded from its procedure. Yet in the sphere of international relations, the majority principle is, with one exception, without application. This exception is extremely significant, however. It is the procedure of international courts. Here, and here alone, is the majority principle generally accepted. If two or more states submit their disputes to the decision of a court of arbitration, they presuppose as a matter of course that the decision may be arrived at by a majority of votes. Subjection to the majority vote of an international court is not considered incompatible with the so-called sovereignty of the state. Subjection to a majority vote of any other organ, however, is generally rejected for the reason that such subjection is incompatible with the sovereignty of the state. If the international organ, instituted by an international treaty, has not the character of a court, the contracting states always insist upon their right to be represented on it during the procedure by which the binding norm is created, and on their right not to be bound against their will. On this point, the attitude of states toward international courts is, as a matter of fact, wholly different from their attitude toward all other international organs. In establishing an international community, this difference should be carefully taken into account. It was clearly manifested at the foundation of the League of Nations. The majority principle, systematically excluded from the procedure of the Council and the Assembly, has been introduced without any difficulty into the constitution of the Permanent Court of International Justice.

A critical analysis of the Covenant and an impartial examination of the activity of the League show that it would have been more correct to have made the principal organ an international court rather than an international administrative organ. Of all the political tasks, entrusted to the League by its constitution, only the function, stated in Articles 12 to 17, concerning the settlement of disputes, has been fulfilled with a certain degree of success. The disarmament of the member states, provided for in Articles 8 and 9, has completely failed. Article 10, guaranteeing the territorial integrity of the members against external aggression, has never been applied. Article 11 coincides in part with Articles 12 to 17 concerning the settlement of disputes. Insofar as Article 11 differs from Articles 12 to 17, by providing for the employment of essentially different means for the maintenance of peace, it has in fact never been put into practice. Article 19 was designed to make possible by legislative acts of the Assembly the modification of the legal relations among the members. But it was inapplicable from the very beginning because of technical insufficiencies in the text. Article 22, regulating the mandates, has permitted no more than sham activity. Articles 23 to 25 concern the so-called technical functions of the League, such as measures against the traffic in women, children and opium. It is just this activity of the League which has been emphasized over and over again, to make the League appear in a more favorable light. This is rather significant; for the so-called technical functions of the League are so far from its essential aims that they need not be taken into consideration in this connection. The great political apparatus in Geneva was not put in motion to fulfill tasks of such secondary importance. Besides, for the performance of these duties other international organizations already existed before the foundation of the League of Nations. Among its specific functions, it has attempted to perform only the settlement of disputes among member states. The results obtained in this field, however, are not in proportion to the extensiveness of the organization or its bureaucratic machinery. The reason is that neither an international administrative organ, such as the Council of the League of Nations, nor a sham parliament, such as the Assembly, is fitted for this task, which by its very nature can be satisfactorily performed only by an international court.

## VI

The Covenant of the League placed the Council, not the Permanent Court, at the center of its international organization, because it conferred upon the League not only the task of maintaining peace within the community, by settling disputes and by restricting the armament of the member states, but also the duty of protecting them against external aggression. This protection of member states against external aggression was all the more necessary because disarmament was set up as a main object of the League. The constitution of an international community can oblige a member state to restrict its armament to a considerable extent only if this state can reckon upon efficacious help from the community in case the state should be attacked by another state not belonging to the community and therefore not obliged to disarm. This is possible only if the disarmament of the members is accompanied by an armament of the community, if an armed force is formed, which is at the disposition of the central organ. Such a centralization of the executive power is not possible within an international-law community, and is therefore not provided by the Covenant of the League. If it is impossible to establish an armed force for the community of states, in other words, if it is not possible to establish a federal state, then the assistance, rendered by the community to a victim of external aggression, can consist only in the obligation of the other members to defend the attacked state. Under such circumstances, the duty of disarmament becomes contradictory to the necessity of defense against external aggression. Nevertheless, the Covenant of the League puts the duty of disarmament in the foreground. Disarmament is to form the first duty of the Members of the League, placed immediately after Articles 1 to 7, which deal with the organization of the League.

The duty of a state, a member of a universal international community, to defend another member state from attack by a non-member, is a very problematic one; especially if the international organization embraces many states which have no common frontier; if these states have joined in the first place for the purpose of maintaining peace among each other, and if aside from this purpose they have no political interest in common that might unite them against the external aggressor. It may be very difficult for a government to fulfill a duty to defend a member state, to enter into war against a state with which it is on good political and economic terms, especially if the aggression is based on grounds not entirely disapproved of by the public opinion of the state obliged to give it succor. The situation of Great Britain and France in the conflict between Czechoslovakia and Germany, a situation which led to the treaty of Munich, is a characteristic example. Treaties obliging the contracting parties to a joint war against third states are efficacious only if concluded between states having more interests and more important interests in common than those which form the basis of a universal international community. It is therefore not surprising that not only the provision of the League Covenant concerning disarmament has completely failed, but likewise the provision concerning mutual defense against external aggression (Article 10). The obvious violation of the territorial integrity of a member state, even the total destruction of its political independence, as the result of external aggression, was not even made a subject of deliberation within the League; and that despite the wording and the spirit of Article 10. Such was the case in regard to Austria, Czechoslovakia and Poland. Let us not forget that it was just on account of Article 10 of the Covenant that the United States of America refused to enter the League.

The duty of taking part in a military action, in a war, can be imposed upon the members of an international community, even if the only purpose is to maintain peace among the members. The duty is required to meet the case of a member state which, in violation of the constitution, resorts to war against another member state or refuses to carry out the decision of the international court instituted by the constitution. Such action has the character of a collective sanction. From the point of view of the political ideology at the basis of the international community, it is totally different from a defensive war against a non-member state. As a matter of fact, the League of Nations, in spite of its complete failure in the cases of external aggression, has at least made certain efforts to fulfill its duty in the cases of illegal aggression undertaken by member states against other member states. This was the case in regard to Manchukuo, Abyssinia, Finland.

The experiences of the League of Nations show that it is necessary to make a clear distinction between the maintenance of internal peace and protection against external aggression; and that it is hardly possible to fulfill the second task by the specific means at the disposal of a universal international organization embracing many different states. It is a task the fulfillment of which does not concern an international court. It is a function that lies beyond the possible activity of an international court, even beyond the power of a universal union of states the centralization of which does not exceed the degree compatible with its international character. As long as it is impossible to constitute this union of states as a federal state, it seems to be more correct to limit its task to the maintenance of internal peace, and to leave protection against external aggression to political alliances between the member states. The constitution of the League should not forbid alliances between member states; it should only provide that alliances between member states ought not to be directed against other member states. On the contrary, to maintain peace within the international community, its constitution should try to establish the strongest possible guaranty within the compass of international law; the submission of all disputes among member states without exception to the compulsory jurisdiction of an international court.

### V I I

The Covenant of the League conferred the main task in the settlement of disputes among members to the Council of the League, not to the Permanent Court of International Justice. It did this primarily because the authors of the Covenant could not make up their minds to establish an international court with compulsory jurisdiction for all international disputes of the members; and they could not make up their minds because they were prejudiced against such compulsory jurisdiction of an international court; and these prejudices still prevail today. To eliminate these prejudices by clearing up the true circumstances, is one of the most important tasks in preparing intellectually for future peace.

One of the main objections against an international court with compulsory jurisdiction is, that it is not possible to settle territorial conflicts between states by a judicial decision, especially if the dispute arises from a territorial claim which cannot be based on positive international law. This objection is correct, but it concerns not so much a court with compulsory jurisdiction as one of the general conditions of every union of states whose aim it is to maintain peace within the international community. It is the regulation of territorial relations of the states forming the international community I have mentioned before. The boundaries of the states within an international community must, from the beginning, be arranged in such a way that they do not violate any vital interests. Otherwise this community will have little prospect of a long-continuing existence. Vital interests, however, are not to be viewed as violated unless a considerable portion of the population is repressed, by incorporation within a particular state organization, against their wills. A satisfactory solution of the territorial problem is, therefore, possible only on the basis of the principle of self-determination, combined with an effective protection of minorities. If these claims are fulfilled, then all justified interests are protected. Disputes arising out of such a situation can very well be adjudicated by a court. For the court has—at least in principle—to apply positive law to the concrete case.

Another objection which is continually brought against the establishment of a compulsory international jurisdiction is that such jurisdiction is only possible if at the same time there is a sort of international parliament competent for the creation of law by majority vote. From the fact that it is impossible to form such a legislative body, it is concluded that a compulsory international jurisdiction is also impossible.

This argument is incorrect in every respect. As I have shown, the development of national law indicates on the contrary that the obligation to submit to the decision of the courts long precedes legislation, i.e., the conscious creation of law by a central organ. Within the individual states courts have for centuries applied a legal order which could not be changed by any legislator, but which developed, exactly like present-day international law, out of custom and agreements; and in this legal system custom was for the most part formed by the practice of the courts themselves. We have no reason to assume that international law will necessarily develop differently from national law. The court, which exercises jurisdiction by deciding all the legal disputes of those parties subject to the court, even if it is empowered by the constitution to apply only the positive law, will adapt this law in its concrete decisions gradually and imperceptibly to actual needs—in other words, the court will decide on the basis of "equity." The history of Roman and Anglo-American law shows how judicial decisions create law. But even from a purely theoretical standpoint, the assumption of an absolute opposition between legislation and judicial decision, between creation and application of law, is untenable. The opposition is in reality only very relative; every act applying law is at the same time an act creating law. One should not overlook the important fact that the law is not only and exclusively what the legislator more or less clearly sets forth or what the general rule of customary law more or less comprehensibly implies. Law is also what the courts finally decide in a concrete case. A famous professor of the Harvard University Law School, John Chipman Gray, wrote: "It has been sometimes said that the Law is composed of two parts,—legislative law and judge-made law—but, in truth, all the Law is judge-made law." [1] That goes perhaps too far. Law does not only exist in the form of concrete judicial decisions, of individual norms. Law exists also in the form of general norms created by a central legislative organ or by custom. But there is no absolute guaranty that the concrete judicial decision, the individual norm, will always correspond to the general norm which should be

[1] John Chipman Gray, *The Nature and Sources of the Law*, 2nd ed., New York, The Macmillan Company, 1927, p. 125.

applied to the concrete case. It is the legal order itself, a special general rule, according to which the concrete decision, issued by an authority of last resort, creates law for the concrete case; has force of law, even if this individual norm does not correspond to the general norm which should be applied to this case. This is the institution of *res judicata*. If one properly judges this very important institution, established by all the legal orders, then one will view the general and abstract form of law—the statute, the rule of customary law, and especially the function of legislation—in a new light. One will avoid overestimating the function of legislation, and will understand why there can be no legislator without a judge even though there can very well be a judge without a legislator.

## VIII

The incorrect assumption that there can be no compulsory jurisdiction of an international court because there is no complete and satisfactory international legal order lies at the basis of most of the arguments with which governments justify their refusal to submit all international disputes to the decision of a court. Take, for example, the ever-recurring appeal to the "gaps" in international law. An international court cannot be intrusted with the decision of all disputes because for very many cases the legal order to be applied by the court lacks any applicable norm. This argument is taken from the theory of national law and has often been refuted in that realm. It is false because it alleges the logical impossibility of a decision, although it can easily be shown that a decision is always logically possible. Either the claim raised by one state against the other in a legal dispute is justified by the legal order, because a particular legal norm obligates the defendant to act in the required way, in which case the complaint is admitted; or the claim raised cannot be justified by the legal order, since the latter contains no legal norm obligating the defendant to act in the required way. In this case the claim is to be rejected; and it is to be rejected on the basis of the positive, actually valid legal order, by application of this order which permits all its subjects to do or omit anything it does not forbid them to do or omit. This logically possible application of the legal order may be undesirable from a juridico-political, moral, or any other standpoint. But this may happen even in cases where one does not speak of "gaps" in the legal system because the complaint is allowed on the basis of the positive law. This reference to a "gap" in the legal system is only a way of expressing a desire to reform the legal system. If one knows the way in which courts exercise the function of reforming the legal order, then the argument of ostensible "gaps" in the legal system as an argument against the obligation to submit all conflicts to the decision of an international court no longer holds.

The assertion which has already become a dogma, that an international court can decide about legal disputes, but not about political conflicts, can be treated in the same way. A dispute has a "political" and not a legal character when a party to the dispute tries to justify its position by appealing not to positive law but to another normative system, and therefore desires that the conflict be decided not on the basis of a norm of positive law but on the basis of another principle, such, for instance, as natural law or justice. The distinction between political and legal disputes, and the rejection or limitation of international jurisdiction based on this distinction, are again founded on the supposed need to reform the positive law, whether or not this reform is, in fact, necessary. It has been shown from the theory and history of law that it is an essential function of the courts, which can under no conditions be withdrawn from them, to reform the law to be applied. Therefore the distinction between political conflicts and legal disputes is bound to fail in the aim for which it was originally conceived— namely, to sabotage the obligatory jurisdiction of an international court.

In this connection it should be observed that to say that positive law is from one viewpoint or another inequitable or unjust, is a subjective judgment of value. The party to a dispute whose interests in a concrete case are not protected by positive law will be easily persuaded that the law itself is inequitable, unjust, and needs to be reformed, while the other party will be convinced of the opposite. If there is any question at all the decision as to which should be withdrawn from the parties in conflict and turned over to an impartial authority, it is the question whether or not the positive law applicable to the conflict is just. An authority well fitted to fulfill this task is a court. Indeed, paradoxical as it may seem at first sight, a group of independent, experienced, and conscientious men, professionally in contact with law, not themselves involved in the particular conflict, is sometimes better qualified to decide this question than the legislator, who is always more or less committed politically; especially since the decision of the court is fundamentally limited to the special case and can therefore take account of its special character. The disinclination of governments to subject all disputes to the decision of a court can, therefore, not be justified by alleging the inability of courts, from their very nature, to adapt the law to the requirements of equity or justice. The exactly opposite seems more acceptable. It is not so much the party desiring a reform of the actually valid international law, but rather the party interested in its being kept unaltered who has cause to hold back from obligatory jurisdiction. For a court which is competent to decide all disputes within a community will give due consideration to equity and justice even if it is not explicitly empowered to do so by the constitution. Under such conditions of jurisdiction, consideration is likely to be given to questions of equity and justice in a much greater measure than in a court whose jurisdiction is limited to disputes specified by the treaty establishing the court.

## I X

The establishment of obligatory jurisdiction is, therefore, first of all a problem of confidence. Much depends on the possibility of finding a procedure by which a really independent court can be formed, able to fulfill its duties in a way satisfactory not only from a moral but from a technical point of view as well. We can as little doubt the possibility of such a procedure as that the procedure underlying the Permanent Court of International Justice at The Hague leaves much to be desired.

Here the dependence of the judges on the states to which they belong is not restricted to the utmost possible extent. A careful psychological and socio-technical investigation of all the methods fit to solve this problem and utilization of all the available experiences in this matter are further tasks in preparing the way for the future peace.

Of relatively subordinate significance is the question of whether there should be established, in addition to the court, a mediating agency with the competence to settle disputes by proposing solutions acceptable to both parties. The importance of such a mediating agency is not very great. If the normal diplomatic process does not bring about an agreement between the two parties in conflict, a special mediating and conciliating commission has little prospect of success.

On the other hand, if an international court with obligatory jurisdiction is established, another institution must be set up beside the court solely to execute its decisions if, in opposition to the fundamental law, a party to the dispute does not submit to the decision. This must be an administrative organ similar to the Council of the League of Nations; but its function is restricted to the execution of judicial decisions. This fact will facilitate considerably both its composition and particularly its procedure—especially insofar as it is necessary that its decisions be adopted according to the majority-vote principle.

If the treaty constituting the international community does not establish a central executive power, a central armed force at the disposal of the above-mentioned administrative organ, the decisions of the international court can be executed against a member state only by the other members of the community, if necessary by the use of their armed forces under the directions of the administrative organ. Such an execution of the judicial decision has the character of a collective sanction, even if performed only by one member state.

In addition to the nonfulfillment of a judicial decision by one of the parties to a dispute, there is, as I mentioned before, a second case of coercive proceedings by the community against a member who resorts to war against another member without calling upon the court. In this case also the collective sanction has the character of the enforcement of a judicial decision if the court has to be called upon either by the party affected or by the administrative organ itself to determine the illegal character of the action.

The establishment of an international court with compulsory jurisdiction—it is true—would be a considerable limitation upon so-called sovereignty of the states subjected to this jurisdiction. But experience teaches that states submit more easily to an international court than to an international government. Treaties of arbitration have proved, up to now, to be the most effective. Seldom has a state refused to execute the decision of a court which it has recognized in a treaty. The idea of law, in spite of everything, seems still to be stronger than any other ideology of power.

# THE COMMONWEALTH OF
# SCIENCE

## *by* Harold D. Lasswell

AT FIRST GLANCE the claims of science are extremely
modest. Science does not prescribe values; science implements them. If it is possible to specify the characteristics of valued events, the technique of science can disclose the conditions of their occurrence and enhance the possibility of their control.

On further examination it is evident that behind the modest
façade of science lurks a tacit claim for exemption from morals,
a claim to fulfill curiosity with no regard to the timing of
knowledge in relation to human need.

We are well acquainted with the singlemindedness that so
often sets the highly specialized man of science apart from his
fellows. Inflamed with the zest of discovery the specialist re-
sents every rival claim on his attention. If his results are used
by men for the purpose of inflicting wounds on one another,
why should he concern himself about it? Does he not rain
knowledge upon the just as well as the unjust? Can he, the
skillful instrument of truth, police his fellowmen and frisk
them for all the weapons forged by the technologies based on
science? Is there not a just division of labor according to native
talent and acquired skill?

No claim for exemption from morality can be allowed. Men
are responsible for what they do to themselves and to one another. The human consequences of science are part of the moral
responsibility of scientists.

But how can this moral responsibility be assumed if scientists are to remain scientists and not become policemen? The
answer is found in the proper organization of the division of

scientific labor. Professional associations make possible the integrated performance of many specialized operations. Men whose training has been basically scientific are specialized to teaching, educational administration, personnel management, public relations management. They protect and support the colleagues who engage in the daily pursuit of truth.

The existing division of scientific labor does not go far enough. At present the professional associations are taken up with problems common to every economic and technical association. Very little effort is devoted to the task of discovering the moral effects of science and of controlling future applications.

What is needed should not be confused with *ex cathedra* remarks on controversial public questions. Scientists often betray the spirit and the practice of science by ill-considered remarks in public. Their reputations depend upon contributions made to chemistry, physics or astronomy—contributions made after disciplined observations under strict theoretical control. When these men declare themselves on tax policy, labor policy, credit policy—without having informed themselves upon the existing state of knowledge of these subjects—they exploit the reputation gained in the field of scientific achievement as a means of impostorship in the field of public policy.

The study of public policy requires the disciplined methods of observation and analysis so brilliantly cultivated for the exploration of other segments of reality. The task of science in relation to morals is to apply its own characteristic procedures to the understanding of man's inner life, and the conditions that affect it. Many destructive moods and ideas have already attracted careful study. By observing the words and movements of individuals, physicians can distinguish melancholy, suicidal persons from suspicious murderers. These extreme patterns of inner life are not distributed evenly throughout the population; middle class families, in particular, appear to produce more deviates than the families of manual toilers. Persons whose social status has been reduced—by business failure or unemployment—display these responses more often than persons whose status has improved or remained the same. Often the occurrence of the pattern in question can be connected with contributory somatic factors.

All who make responsible decisions about other people— such as physicians, personnel administrators, policemen—are deeply concerned about the cause, treatment and prevention of these more striking forms of deviation. What we now know about human destructiveness has been made known to us very largely through the efforts of those who are confronted by extreme examples of flagrant difficulties of interpersonal adjustment.

Yet the understanding of human beings was for many years handicapped by a certain presupposition that stood in the way This presupposition was that the only significant factors in understanding man were physical movements—events that could be recorded by means of selected physical indicators. In practice, of course, words—meaning-events—were always noted; but they were treated apologetically. After all, anyone trained in physical science was accustomed to classify events of movement and not events of meaning. It was widely assumed that words should be "reduced" to "movements." It was obvious that morbid states were evidenced—and even alleviated—by words; yet so great was the prevailing "physicalistic" bias that this procedure was not frankly avowed. Meaning-events were citizens of the second class in the hierarchy of scientific data.

The physicalistic bias influenced the choice of a context to be used in determining "health" or "disease." "Disease" is a term that applies to processes destructive of wholeness. For a long time the "whole" was conceived to be the "cell bundle" comprising the body. Hence destructive (disease) processes were assumed to damage the integration of the body considered as a bundle of cells. On the basis of this expectation, scientific effort was directed to the task of connecting deviationa processes with specific lesions—with inherited defect, toxic conditions, and similar factors.

In actual practice this physicalistic conception of totality was not strictly adhered to. It was always necessary to pay some attention to the words uttered in the surrounding environment Individuals who were treated with contempt "cracked up" more often than persons who received a continuous flow of appreciation from other people. Children who were reared in families characterized by "bossy," "ambitious," and "puritanical" mothers showed a greater collection of deviational symptoms than children from more serene environments.

It was only gradually that the physicalistic bias was broken down and the interpersonal relationship was accepted as a valid whole. When the focus of attention of the scientific observer is enlarged to include the interpersonal context, the most conspicuous features are small, direct, primary group relations. Attention is centered upon family and intimate friendship groups, or upon the direct connection among groups of workers and their supervisors. One effect of the discovery of the interpersonal context is to remove the exaggerated importance that has often been assigned to physicalistic factors in the environment. In the early studies of industrial relations elaborate inventories were made of physical surroundings—such as temperature, light and color, extra meals during working hours. When the significance of interpersonal factors is clearly understood, the influence of these physicalistic details sinks into a much more minor position in the scale of importance. This has been most convincingly demonstrated in the Western Electric experiments (reported by Elton Mayo and associates). In one experiment that extended over five years, a semi-skilled test group of workers was systematically exposed to many changes in the physical environment. Throughout the entire period—up to the final months—the test group showed a constantly rising curve of output. Many physicalistic factors in the environment were modified in the meanwhile, but they had no appreciable effect upon the curve. It was not until near the end of the experimental period that the output of the group began to suffer; but this was not the result of any change in the physical surroundings of the workers. The essential change in the environment appears to have been in the flow of appreciation. During the early years of the experiment, high officials of the plant frequently visited the experimental room. Often they brought visitors with them from out of town. Wise men from the East —from Harvard—were brought in to consult on the execution of the experiment. A friendly research worker was always present to assist in integrating the social life of the group. At the very end of the experimental period a different state of affairs prevailed. The great depression had come; business executives neglected the test room and it was evident that few hopes were held out that the experiment would have beneficial results. As the great wave of unemployment engulfed the nation, limited experiments seemed singularly futile. Thus the test workers were receiving less deference from their environment—less respect—than at first; they responded by respecting what they were doing much less than at the start. The final result was the slowing up of the total level of achievement and the dulling of associated joy in effective expression.

Once the importance of these interpersonal factors has been discovered, the scientific eye is sharpened for the structural characteristics of society. The members of any community can be divided into low, middle and high respect classes. In the United States, southern Negroes occupy a low position in the respect scale of life; wealthy New Englanders, of Revolutionary ancestry, obviously occupy an extremely high position. Respect groupings are not perfectly correlated with control over income —respect is given to artists and scientists whose money income is low. Sometimes respect varies inversely with safety: in periods of general crisis those who take the most risk are treated with special consideration. Deference is not only expressed in terms of respect but in terms of power and clarity. By power is meant control over decisions; to be powerful is to be consulted in the making of important group decisions. Deference in terms of clarity is far more subtle and difficult to describe. To be clarified is to understand the probable structure of events.

It requires most meticulous observation if we are to uncover the destructive processes in interpersonal relations. Often it is comparatively easy to demonstrate the destructive consequences of certain methods of rearing children, or of directing workers. But in the intricate practices of society, many processes are illuminated only after highly technical study. Thus it is not possible to demonstrate the mechanics of the price system without arranging for the collection of enormous quantities of data.

Many observational standpoints are possible with reference to the manifold of interpersonal events. These standpoints can be conveniently classified according to the degree of intensiveness or extensiveness. The relation of the observer to a given field of events may be called "intensive" when, during a prolonged period of time, he focuses his attention upon a given career line, and makes use of a complex method of exploring the structure of events within the field. One example of a prolonged, complex procedure is the psychoanalytical interview, in which the interviewer concentrates an hour a day through several months upon his subject and encourages the use of the method of free association as a means of uncovering the personality structure before him. At the other extreme, the observer takes up a short, simple relationship to his field of observation (an "extensive" standpoint). A standard example of this relationship is the brief poll interview in which a subject is asked, "Are you for the re-election of President Roosevelt or not?"

The intensive standpoints are the most productive of understanding of how different styles of civilization bear upon the human beings who are exposed to them. No one can read the life story of southern Negroes, obtained by social-scientific observers, without experiencing a quickened sense of insight into the life of other human beings. When these case histories are selected according to a careful sampling procedure, it is possible to build up a satisfactory cross-section of the meaning of culture for personality.

Although the case history represents the most elaborate method of establishing the meaning of life in different social situations, many other procedures are quite revealing. It is possible to describe the contents of the channels of mass communication—radio, press, print—and in this way to disclose the features of the environment to which various nationalistic and class groups have been exposed. To the man who hears only vaguely of the world beyond his province or his nation, there appears a drastically different structure of reality than to the one whose attention is directed to representative incidents throughout the world. To understand the inner meaning of life to a Chinese, it is necessary to work out proper methods for describing the symbols that are brought to the focus of attention of representative Chinese at every period of life. By proper sampling procedures it is possible to describe the world of those who live in different parts of the earth and occupy determinate positions in the social structure.

Having discovered the interpersonal context, we need to decide how much of it should be taken into consideration when we isolate destructive processes. Nothing short of the world as a whole can be included in an adequate inventory. Practices in different parts of the world—in respect of the expansion of population, the acquisition of special techniques of production—cannot fail to have dynamic implications. Man is only now engaged in developing his self-observatories—as distinguished from his star observatories. The world needs to be dotted with institutes of trained specialists, capable of leaving ever more reliable records of human experience.

The need of timing should be emphasized if we are to keep abreast of the shifting relationship of details to the larger context. Details that are non-destructive in one situation may work destructively in another. Emphasis put upon the achievement of peace and order by law serves a unifying function in communities of homogeneous social structure. Yet the same emphasis upon law as an instrument of social solidarity may have destructive consequences when the problem is to bring together peoples of diverse social structure. In World War I, Anglo-American statesmen advocated the establishment of a world legal order by treaty. They said little about unifying the economic structure of the Major Powers, and building a solid foundation for legal unity. Over-preoccupied with legalism, the statesmen of the West had a disruptive effect upon the subsequent course of world affairs.

The notable expansion of physical science has created the machine; the machine, in turn, has created environmental situations of the utmost difficulty. Failure to regularize the machine has meant failure to regularize the tempo of social development; this has contributed to war, revolution, and disturbances of every kind. The machine made by science has moral consequences attributable.to science. If these consequences are to be controlled in the future, they must be understood, and that depends upon a scientific division of labor capable of revealing destructive processes.

Gradually it is becoming clear that the principal enemy of man is man's own destructiveness. Human destructiveness is of two kinds—destructive impulses; destructive practices. To some extent the process of reducing destructiveness is the task of spreading skillful methods of thought by means of which the individual can control his impulses. Such a program, however, is inadequate unless destructive practices are exposed and reduced. Both impulses and practices must be controlled in any comprehensive program.

In the commonwealth of science, scientists will apply the observational methods of science to the understanding of man, and especially to the description and control of all that makes for human destructiveness. For methodological reasons it is useful to distinguish philosophy, science and practice from one another. But the tools of methodological convenience need not be deified and invoked to evade moral consequences. In the commonwealth of science, philosophy continues to *derive* values that can only be *implemented* by science and policy. The practice of values calls for a philosophy and a science of values.

# 6. SCIENCE AND THE INDIVIDUAL

# INTELLECTUAL EVOLUTION

## *by* Jean Piaget

THE SUBJECT of our investigations is intellectual evolution—that is, the development of knowledge and of its different modes, the genesis of the forms of thought, of their adaptation to experience, and the rules which they obey.

In its point of departure this evolution raises a problem which is essentially biological; the relationship between understanding or perception and its objects is a particular case of adaptation— that is, a combination of assimilation and accommodation—which unites the organism with its external environment. The first question which the theory of the development of the understanding must investigate is how this relationship results from biological organization and adaptation. For example, it is impossible to determine how the elementary forms of spatial perception are evolved without seeing how they are related to the mode of inheritance of the organs of perception and of equilibrium, and to the different modes of organic adaptation.

But in the last analysis the evolution of individual thought is closely enmeshed in collective systems of knowledge, especially in those great systems of rational collaboration which deductive and experimental science has produced. The genetic theory of knowledge must therefore reach out into an historico-critical analysis of scientific thought, and also into genetic logic. For instance, to understand the evolution of the idea of space in the mind of a child, it is not enough to know how this idea is first born. One must also determine how the so-called "displacement groups" which form it follow one another in succession from the motor level to that of the most abstract conceptions; one must establish the respective parts of the scheme of logic and of the intuition in this formation; one must define exactly the relationship between the ideas of space and those of time, object, number, movement, speed, et cetera. In short, truly to understand the psychological aspect of the development of space, one must attack all the problems which this idea and related ideas suggest in the realm of mathematics and physics; but not from a point of view which is purely reflective and abstract, rather from one which is genetic and experimental. A comparative analysis must intervene between the psychological development of thought and the history of science.

The psychology of intellectual evolution leans therefore upon the biological theories of adaptation, the psychological theories of understanding, the sociological theories of signs and norms (the rules of socialized thought), the history of science, and upon comparative logic. One can then consider this special branch of psychology as a genetic theory of knowledge, a broad theory which must borrow its elements from a very great number of fields of research, thus partially synthesizing them, but withal an exact and well-defined theory, which has its own method, namely, the envisaging of intellectual realities only from the point of view of their development and genetic construction.

In fact, the best method for the psychological theory of the development of the understanding will always be the analysis of the intellectual evolution of the child. The thought of the child alone constitutes a continuous process which by a normal evolution links the initial sensorimotor adaptations to the socialized and scientific forms of understanding. In so far as the development of individual thought from birth to adult life can be observed directly and by experiment, and in so far as it is also open to the influences which various adult social groups have on the formation of the reason, this development forms an ideal field on which to set up all the biological, psychological, sociological, and logical problems of understanding in order to examine their genetic construction. A genetic and experimental epistemology is thus conceivable as a special branch of psychology.

We should like in what follows to give an example of this method and its results in studying—on the three planes of sensorimotor activity, egocentric thought, and rational thought—the genesis of some of those ideas of conservation (continuity) which play such a great role in scientific thought. As we trace this growth we shall also have the opportunity of following, on these three successive levels, the steps of one of the most important processes in the development of thought, namely, the passage from egocentric perception and thought to objective reasoning.

For the following hypotheses may be made in this matter. At the beginning of mental life, the world appears to the child as a series of pictures which are centered about activity and lack any intrinsic stability. The absence of permanent objects and of the objective organization of space seems thus to go hand in hand with a radical and unconscious egocentricity, so that the subject does not consider himself as one thing among many, but only conceives of things in relation to his own actions. Yet at the other extremity of the development the universe is considered as being formed of permanent objects whose movements take place in a space independent of us, and whose many relationships form a series of invariables which prolong the conservation of the object itself; invariables of number, quantity, matter, weight, et cetera. One may therefore say then that, in so far as egocentricity is reduced by the co-ordination of the individual point of view with other possible ones, the co-ordination which explains this reduction explains also the formation of logical instruments of conservation (ideas of "groups," systems of relations, et cetera) and the formation of invariables in the world of reality (ideas of the permanence of the object, of quantities, weights, et cetera).

## I. SENSORIMOTOR INTELLIGENCE

Even in the most elementary sensorimotor activities with which the intellectual development of the child begins, it is possible to discern certain of the processes of conservation. Because of the final richness of these processes, as well as their initial limitations, it is necessary to analyze them in detail.

It is evident that the reflex mechanisms (for example, sucking), the habits grafted on these reflexes (thumb sucking, et cetera), or the more complex "circular reactions" which tend to reproduce an interesting result (to swing suspended toys, et cetera) all lead essentially to repetition, and consequently imply a tendency toward persistence. On the one side these factors assume that movements are so organized that they are always capable of returning to their point of departure. From the point of view of space, these motor units form what the geometricians call "displacement groups," closed systems of operations which tend to continuance. On the other side, the elementary psychological activity which is characteristic of them is essentially an "assimilation" of external realities, so that these realities are not considered as entities in themselves, but only as functional elements (things are conceived merely as something to be sucked, something to be swung or handled, et cetera). Now this assimilation is also a factor in conservation, since it implies a certain practical recognition and a certain identifying generalization based on habitual repetition. Thus, when the baby of five or six months sees his usual rattle, or even a new plaything, dangling before him, he will swing it at once, assimilating it (by an assimilation which reproduces, recognizes, and generalizes) into the scheme of objects to be swung.

But, if these elementary sensorimotor organizations thus introduce from the very start a certain permanence into the primitive universe by constructing space in practical "groups" and by an assimilation of the things perceived into schemes of action, this conservation and this permanence emanate from the subject himself, and hence begin by presenting a purely egocentric character. In other words, there is not yet any conservation of objects as such, nor any permanence in the external world, not even in the space which forms its framework.

First of all, as far as objects are concerned, it is easy to establish the fact that, although the baby is capable of recognizing differences in things at a very early age, almost to the end of his first year he behaves as if the objects which disappeared from his field of perception momentarily ceased to exist. For instance, between the ages of five and eight months, when the child already knows enough to seize any solid objects which he sees, one has only to cover them with a cloth, or place a screen in front of them at the moment when the baby's hand is directed towards them, and he will give up looking for them and immediately lose his interest. I have even observed this in systematically hiding the bottle when my six-month-old son was about to take it. But one can see a still more curious reaction around nine or ten months, when the child is capable of seeking the object behind the screen and the notion of real exterior permanence begins to put in an appearance. For example, when the baby is placed between two pillows and he has succeeded in finding an object hidden under the right one, the object can be taken from his hands and placed under the left pillow before his very eyes, but he will look for it under the right pillow where he has already found it once before, as if the permanence of the objective were connected with the success of the former action, and not with a system of external displacements in space.

In short, the primitive world is not made up of permanent objects with autonomous trajectories, but of moving perceptive pictures which return periodically into non-existence and come back again as the functional result of the proper action. It is easy to prove still more clearly that this world is centered in the activity of the self by an analysis of the egocentric character of space which determines its configuration.

If the movements of the child are immediately capable of organization into "groups," closed and reversible systems, those "groups" are in the beginning centered entirely on the subject himself, and afford no room for any objective spatial construction. The clearest example of these egocentric "groups" is seen in the way in which a baby, before nine or ten months, rotates objects, a movement which finally forms the idea of the "wrong side" of objects. Everyone has observed a child handling things and turning them over and over to explore their various sides. Now do these rotary movements give way immediately to the formation of objective groups? A very simple experiment shows us that this is not so. One has only to give a five- or six-month-old baby his bottle with the nipple away from him, and turn it around slowly before his very eyes. If the child can see a bit of the rubber nipple at the other end of the bottle, he immediately turns the object around, but if he doesn't see the nipple, he doesn't even attempt to turn it, but sucks the wrong end! A series of other experiments with other "displacement groups" has shown the same centering on the subject and not on the object.

How then is the baby going to construct a world of permanent objects situated in a real space, and thus escape from his primitive egocentric universe? It is the work of the sensorimotor or practical intelligence, which precedes language, to set up a system of relations to co-ordinate this series of various perspectives which the baby has and thus cause him to locate himself among objects instead of illusively bringing them to him.

In other words, as the activity of the baby develops and the causal, temporal, and spatial sequences which this activity creates become more complex, objects are detached more and more from the action itself, and the body of the subject becomes one element among others in an ordered ensemble. Thus a total reversal of perspective takes place, which marks the beginning of the objectification of the external world, and of the idea of its permanence. The interplay of practical relationships in the world of reality teaches the child to shift the center of space and its objects from his action to himself, and thus locate himself at the middle point of this world which is being born. In this way the permanence of objects appears as the product of this formation of objective "groups" of displacements, and these groups themselves depend for their creation upon the way in which the sensorimotor or practical intelligence allows the child to free himself from his initial egocentricity and gives him power to act on things, thanks to a system of co-ordinated relationships.

But, if the co-ordination of practical relationships leads to a first victory over egocentricity and to the beginning of the objective idea of conservation, this external permanence remains limited to the plane of action and immediate perception, and cannot extend at once to the level of conceptual representation in general. In fact, it is in a sense an "ontological egocentricity" from which the practical intelligence delivers the individual, and not social and representative egocentricity, which will remain very important even after the appearance of language, and all through infancy. In other words, the co-ordination of practical relationships teaches the child that his body is one thing among many, and that he is thus part of a world of stable objects, whereas at the beginning the baby saw only a world of inconsistent pictures gravitating about his own activity. But the sensorimotor intelligence is not enough to teach the child that the perspective he has of this world is not absolute but relative, and must be co-ordinated with the perspectives of other people to attain a general and truly objective picture of reality.

## II. EGOCENTRIC THOUGHT

Just at the moment when the practical world of which we have been speaking has been created, the child comes into possession of language, and henceforth is called upon to adapt himself to the thoughts of others as well as to the external material world. Now on this new plane of thought which the social world creates, the child finds difficulties similar to those he has already overcome on the plane of the practical universe, and so he passes through stages similar to those of his escape from initial egocentricity and his progressive co-ordination. Hence the principles of conservation remain unchanged, only this time they are on the plane of abstract concepts. Although the child admits the permanence of concrete objects in the world of immediate experience, he really has no idea of the conservation of matter, weight, or movement, nor even any conception of logical or numerical groups. If he fails, it is because he lacks an intellectual instrument with which to construct the "invariables of groups" which are formed by physical realities. This instrument is called "the logic of relations" by the logicians, and is really the tool of co-ordination par excellence, both from the social and from the rational point of view. It is created only as it succeeds in stemming the egocentricity which constantly opposes it.

In order to make the link between the ontological egocentricity of the first sensorimotor stage and the social and logical egocentricity of the beginnings of conceptual thought perfectly clear, let us briefly turn again to the example of space. We have already seen that on the practical plane the child of two or three years is capable of using a certain number of "groups" of displacements: he knows how to turn an object over, to hide it behind one screen, or a series of two, and find it in the right place, et cetera. But what will happen when it is a question not only of acting upon the object, but of imagining distant objects, and of co-ordinating the perspective of different observers?

One of our assistants has investigated this in the following experiment: the child is placed opposite a small model of three mountains, and given a certain number of colored pictures of these mountains; he is then asked which of the pictures show the mountains from the positions occupied successively by a doll on the mountains in the model. The function of age in the development of these reactions is very clear. The little ones do not understand that the observer sees the same mountains quite differently from various points of view, and hence they consider their own perspective absolute. But the older ones gradually discover the relativity necessary to objectivity, after a number of systematic errors due to the difficulty of co-ordinating the relationships in question. Here then on this social and logical plane of the co-ordination of perspectives we have a passing from egocentricity to an objective "group" of changes, exactly parallel to the passage one has observed on the sensorimotor level in the relationships between the baby and the objects handled, only this time the necessity of considering the point of view of other people has created a new difficulty.

Now this process also influences very closely the idea of the conservation or continuity of the mechanical and physical characteristics of objects as well as of their spatial peculiarities. In fact, since the child considers a mountain as being just what it appears to be in his own perspective, it could not possibly have either form or stable dimensions—that is, no "invariables of groups" are constructed. That is actually what observation shows to be true. I have been able to determine in experimenting on my own children, by going about real mountains with them, that at about four or five years of age they still considered the apparent changes due to our own changes of position as quite real.

For every mountain they admitted the existence of changes of form and dimensions absolutely contrary to the idea of the permanence of objects. It would be easy to generalize these results for all objects in distant space (stars, clouds, et cetera).

But we must show how this preoccupation with the problem of the proper perspective—that is to say, of "immediate experience" as opposed to experience based on rational deduction—hinders the mind from co-ordinating relationships, and finally forming ideas of the permanence of matter, weight, movement, et cetera. It is clear that every principle of conservation implies a system of relationships which explains real permanence through apparent change. Now in so far as the mind is dominated by "immediate experience," it is not capable of recognizing this relativity, nor the "invariables" which it implies.

Here is an example dealing with the ideas of the conservation of matter and weight. We show children of different ages two paste balls of the same dimensions and weight. Then we change the shape of one of them to a cylinder (a sausage), and we ask if the two objects still have the same weight. Now the little ones think that the weight of the cylinder is less than that of the ball (because a ball appears to concentrate more matter in itself than an elongated cylinder), and they even state that the quantity of paste has diminished because of the change in form! But the older ones believe in the conservation of weight and matter; and between the two one finds a stage at which children think that weight alone varies with form, matter remaining constant.

In the same way, one of our pupils has shown that sugar dissolved in a glass of water is not conserved, in the minds of young children: the level which rises at the immersion of the sugar is considered as being lowered as before, after the sugar is dissolved; the sugar is conceived of as gradually vanishing, and even the sweet taste, which is all that remains of the dissolved piece, is supposed to disappear after several hours. But older children, by a series of steps it is useless to describe here, succeed in attaining the idea of the conservation of the sugar, its weight, and even the volume it occupied in the liquid. Some even go so far as to construct a kind of rude atomic theory, like that which the pre-Socratic physicists had, to account for these phenomena.

It is the same *a fortiori* in the case of more subtle ideas, such as that of the conservation of movement, or the principle of inertia. It is, indeed easy to show that the physics of the child begins by being impregnated with an animistic dynamism, which is the direct opposite of the idea of inertia. Things are endowed with active forces, spontaneous and untransmittible, formed on the model of voluntary muscular activity. Later, before arriving at more mechanistic ideas, the child passes through an intermediate period which recalls in many respects the physics of Aristotle. Thus the trajectory of a projectile is explained, not by the conservation of the impulse received, but by an ἀντιπερίστασίς in the real sense of the word, the projectile being pushed by the air it displaces in its progress. The clouds move in the same way, by the wind which their displacement arouses, et cetera.

It seems to us easy to show that all these ideas which are so contrary to the ideas of conservation are explained by the same causes, by an egocentric relationship, not yet reciprocal or rational, between the subject and the objects of the external world. On the one hand, objects are assimilated to the ego, and conceived on the model of its own activity. Hence the anthropocentric ideas of force, weight, et cetera, which are common in the physics of the little ones. On the other hand, experience remains "immediate," dominated by a series of successive impressions which have not yet been co-ordinated. It is not formed by that logic of relationships which alone will impress upon it an objective form by co-ordinating the many relationships which are perceived or conceived. Thus, in the case of the pellets which change their form, the child does not succeed in freeing his judgment from the illusions caused by habitual perceptions (we know the point at which the evaluations of weight are dependent on factors of form), that he may co-ordinate the relationships into a coherent ensemble which can support the deduction of real permanence. In short, the absence of permanence is the result of the pre-eminence of immediate experience over rational deduction, and immediate experience is the ensemble of subjective impressions, successively registered and not yet co-ordinated into a system of relationships which encloses the subject in an objective world.

## III. RATIONAL CO-ORDINATION

We saw first of all how the sensorimotor co-ordinations led the child from an unstable world centered about his own activity to an idea of the permanence of objects, based on the formation of "displacement groups" which ordered space into an objective practical universe. On the other hand, we have just established the fact that when thought and abstract concepts are imposed on this sensorimotor world, egocentricity reappears on this new plane, and the world of concepts also begins to be centered in the ego, and is thus stripped of the basic permanence which reason demands. How is the child to surmount this second group of obstacles and reach the idea of rational permanence?

The process of reasoning on this plane of conceptual thought is exactly the same as on the sensorimotor level, with this difference, that it is a question henceforth of the co-ordination of the perspectives of different individuals, as well as the co-ordination of the different aspects of individual experience. This social co-ordination, which adds a new dimension to those which are already a part of rational co-ordination, creates in the intellectual realm what one might call "logic," in contrast to the sensorimotor or practical intelligence, which makes only perceptions and motions into systems. Logic is then the "group" of operations which co-ordinates the inter-individual relationships with the intra-individual ones into a system capable of assuring the permanence which is necessary to the invariables of experience.

The essence of rational co-ordination is then to be sought in the "logic of relations"—that is, in this fundamental group of operations which assures the reciprocity of individual perspectives and the relativity of the facts of experience. To refer again to the example of space, on which we have already insisted, it is the logic of relations which makes the child come gradually to understand, between seven and eleven years, that the left and the right are not absolute, but that his own left corresponds to the right of an individual opposite him, and that an object between two others is at one and the same time at the left of the first and the right of the third. It is then the logic of relationships which permits the formation of the idea of a conceptual space by the co-ordination of the different perspectives possible, and which also allows the imposition of this upon practical space, whose relationships, however well co-ordinated they may be among themselves, are always limited to one's own perspective.

Now this logic of relations, which thus maintains on the level of thought the "groups" of operations outlined by sensorimotor intelligence, and which gradually eliminates intellectual egocentricity, finally succeeds, in the realm we are trying to analyze here, in forming invariables which represent for the reasoning mind so many principles of permanence applicable to the physical world.

In the field of the permanence of quantity, for instance, it is easy to show how the grouping of relationships involves in each case the construction of formal invariables, which, when applied to reality, correct the illusions of non-permanence which we have just described in the "immediate experience" of infancy. In the investigations into the genesis of the ideas of quantity and number, one of our assistants brought to light a number of facts which make this change clear. Here are some of them.

When one fills a large glass with some continuous substance, such as colored water, or a discontinuous one, such as beads, and then separates these into two or four small glasses, or into some narrow and elongated or short and fat ones, et cetera, the quantities appear to increase or diminish for the child below seven years of age according to whether the subject considers the level of the substance in the receptacles, their size, or their number. Moreover, when one makes two groups correspond piece by piece (for example, the beads in two rectilinear rows), the child considers at first that the two quantities are equal; but this is only an illusion, because one has only to place the elements in one of these groups nearer or farther apart (to put the beads in a heap, or make one row longer and more widely spaced than the other) and the two quantities are no longer considered as equal; a row of ten beads is conceived as increasing in number if they are spaced more widely, and a pile is considered as containing more or fewer beads according to whether one heaps it up or spreads it out before the eyes of the child, et cetera.

In short, before the age of six or seven there is no idea of the permanence of continuous quantities, nor of discontinuous groups, nor any necessary equivalence between two groups which correspond piece by piece, et cetera, whatever the active operations may be which the subject himself performs in the course of the experiments. For this reason up to this age the child has not yet formed any idea of cardinal or ordinal numbers which are capable of indefinite extension; nor has he yet elaborated any idea of classes of things in extension, which depends upon the inclusion of parts in a permanent whole. The essential forms which number and logical class give to the mind are thus, after all, bound up closely with the processes of conservation, and one might say in general that if the thought of the child remains pre-logical during infancy, it is because of the lack of these very principles of permanence.

Now how does the child proceed from this pre-logical state to the discovery of the permanence of groups and quantities? By the co-ordination of the relationships involved; that is, by those operations of "multiplication of relations" which are essential to the logic of relationships. As soon as he ceases to envisage as separate unities the level, size, and number of the columns of liquid, the length of the rows, and the space between the objects, et cetera, the child succeeds in co-ordinating these relationships, in understanding their relative positions in a system of independent variables, and thus he forms units which are capable of permanence. It is therefore the logic of relationships which transforms immediate experience, with its illusions of perception, into a rational system, the changes of which depend on necessary invariables. It would be easy to show that the idea of the permanence of matter, weight, and movement, which we were speaking of above, is the result of similar processes. In the thought of the child, as in the evolution of the sciences, rational permanence always results from the union of a deduction based on the co-ordination of relationships with an experience similarly formed; and every invariable implies a "group" which creates it—that is, a system of related and reversible changes.

But you will say that the problem is not yet solved, that there still remains the question of how this "logic of relations" which explains the genesis of the principles of conservation and of the "invariables of groups" is itself originated. Now it is first necessary to understand the espitemological character of what we call the egocentricity of the child (i.e., a quite unconscious and natural illusion of perspective, which precedes moral egoism and conscious egocentricity). Then one will understand that this process of co-ordination, at once social and intellectual, by which the child escapes from his self-centered point of view to find his place among other people, is actually the rational instrument which makes up this logic of relations. For, in any field, the faculty of knowing is a process of co-ordination in which the ego is subordinated to some objective system of references, and the logic of relationships is nothing but a tool and a result of this co-ordination; a tool in that it guides the ego in its escape from itself, and a result since it is a grouping of systematic operations and an ensemble of successive invariables.

In conclusion, one sees how the genetic analysis of any aspect of the thought of a child necessarily corresponds to the analysis of scientific thought. Indeed, the effort by which the child, by means of that social and rational instrument which the logic of relationships gives him, escapes from his egocentricity and creates a universe is the very beginning of that ever-present gigantic effort of science to free man from himself by putting him within the relativity of the objective world.

# HUMAN BEHAVIOR

## *by* Charles Gustav Jung

THE SEPARATION of psychology from the premises of biology is purely artificial, because the human psyche lives in indissoluble union with the body. And since these biological premises hold good not only for man, but for the whole world of living beings, the scientific basis on which they rest obtains a validity far exceeding that underlying a psychological judgment, which is valid only in the realm of consciousness. Therefore it is not a matter of surprise that the psychologist is often prone to reach back to the security of the biological viewpoint, and to borrow freely from physiology and the theory of instinct. Nor is it astonishing to find a widely accepted point of view which regards psychology as merely a chapter in physiology. Although psychology rightly claims autonomy in its own special field of research, it is true that it must recognize a far-reaching correspondence between its facts and the data of biology.

Among the psychic factors determining human behavior, the instincts are primarily the motivating forces of psychic events. In view of the controversy which has raged around the nature of the instincts, I should like to establish clearly what seems to me to be the relation between the instincts and the psyche and why I name instincts as psychological factors. If we started with the hypothesis that the psyche is absolutely identical with the state of being alive, then we should have to accept the existence of a psychic function even in unicellular forms. In that case, instinct would form a type of psychic organ and the hormone-producing glandular activity would have a psychic causality.

But if we look upon the appearance of the psyche as a relatively recent event in evolutionary history, and assume that the psychic function is a phenomenon accompanying a nervous system, which in some way or other has become centralized, then it would be difficult to believe that the instincts were originally psychic in nature. And since the connection of the psyche with the brain is a more probable conjecture than the psychic nature of life in general, I regard the characteristic compulsoriness of the instincts as an ecto-psychic factor. None the less, it is psychically important, because it leads to the formation of structures or patterns, which may be regarded as determinants of human behavior. Under these circumstances, the immediate, determining factor is not the ecto-psychic instinct, but that structure which results from the interaction of the instinct and the psychic situation of the moment. Thus the determining factor would be a modified instinct. The change undergone by the instinct is as significant as the differences between the color we see and the objective wave-lengths producing it. The ecto-psychic fact of instinct would play the role of a stimulus merely, while the psychic instinct-phenomenon would be an assimilation of this stimulus to a pre-existing psychic complexus. A name is needed for this process. I should term it psychification. Thus, what we call instinct offhand would be a datum already psychified, but of ecto-psychic origin.

## I. GENERAL PHENOMENOLOGY

The concept outlined above makes it possible to understand the variability of the instinctive factors within the general phenomenology. The psychified instinct forfeits its uniqueness to a certain extent, at times actually losing its most essential characteristic—compulsoriness; it is no longer an ecto-psychic, unequivocal fact, but has become instead a modification conditioned by its encounter with a psychic datum. As a determining factor, instinct is variable and therefore lends itself to different applications. Whatever the nature of the psyche may be, it is endowed with an extraordinary capacity for variation and transmutation.

For example, no matter how unequivocal the physical state of irritation called hunger may be, the psychic consequences resulting from it can be manifold. Not only can the reactions to ordinary hunger vary widely, but the hunger itself can appear as denatured, or even as metaphorical. It is not only that we use the word hunger in the most varied sense, but by combination with other factors, the hunger itself can assume the most varied forms. The originally simple and unequivocal determinant can appear transformed into pure greed, or into many aspects of boundless desire or insatiability, as for example, the lust for gain or inordinate ambition.

Hunger, as the characteristic expression of the urge to self-preservation, is without doubt one of the primary and most powerful factors influencing behavior; in fact, the lives of primitives are more affected by it, and more powerfully, than by sexuality. At this level of existence, hunger means the alpha and omega—existence itself.

The importance of the instinct of preservation of the species is obvious. However, the growth of culture having brought with it so many restrictions of a moral and a social nature, sexuality has been given, temporarily at least, an excess value comparable to that of water in a desert. Because of the premium of intense sensuous enjoyment which nature has set upon the business of reproduction, the urge towards sexual satisfaction appears in man—no longer conditioned by a mating season—as an almost separate instinct. The sexual instinct enters into combination with many feelings and aspects, with spiritual and material interest, and to such a degree that, as is well known, the attempt has even been made to trace the whole of culture to these combinations.

Sexuality, like hunger, undergoes a radical psychification, which makes it possible for the primarily purely instinctive energy to be diverted from its biological applications and turned into other channels. The fact, that the energy can be deployed into various fields, indicates the existence of still other drives strong enough to change the direction of the sexual instinct and to deflect it, at least in part, from its immediate goal.

I should like, then, to differentiate as a third group of instincts the *drive to activity*. This urge functions when the other urges are satisfied—indeed, it is perhaps only called into being after this has occurred. Under the concept of activity would fall wanderlust, love of change, restlessness, and the play-instinct.

There is another drive, different from the instinct for activity and as far as we know specifically human, which might be called the reflection-urge. Ordinarily we do not think of "reflection" as ever having been instinctive, but associate it with a conscious state of mind. *Reflexio* means bending back and, used psychologically, would express the fact that the reflex process, which conducts the stimulus over into the instinctive discharge, is interrupted by psychification. Owing to the interference of reflection taken in this automatic sense, the psychic processes exert an attraction on the impulse-to-action excited by the stimulus. Therefore, before having discharged itself in the external world, the impulse is deflected into an endo-psychic activity. *Reflexio* is a turning inward with the result that instead of an immediate *act*, various derived contents or conditions result, which may be termed reflection or deliberation. Thus in place of the compulsive act, there appears a certain amount of freedom, and in place of the predictability a relative unpredictability as to the effect of the impulse.

The richness of the human psyche and its essential character are probably determined by this reflection-urge. Reflection re-enacts the process of excitation and conducts its stimulus over into a series of images, which, if the impetus is strong enough, is finally reproduced in some form of expression. This may take place directly, for instance in speech, or may appear in the form of abstract thought, of impersonations, of ethical conduct, or again, it may be expressed in a scientific achievement, or in a work of art.

Through the reflection-urge, this stimulus is more or less wholly transformed into psychic content, that is, it becomes an experience: a natural process is transformed into a conscious content. Reflection is the cultural instinct par excellence, and its strength is shown in the power of culture to maintain itself in the face of untamed nature.

Instincts are not creative in themselves, because they have been stably organized and have therefore become automatic.

The reflection-urge is no exception to this rule, for the production of consciousness is not of itself a creative act, but may under certain conditions be a merely automatic process. It is a fact of great importance that this compulsion, so feared by civilized man, also produces that characteristic fear of becoming conscious, best observed in neurotic persons, but not in them alone.

Although in general instinct is a system of definitely organized tracks and consequently tends toward unlimited repetition, yet man has the distinctive power of creating something new in the real sense of the word, just as nature, in the course of long periods of time, succeeds in creating new forms. Though we cannot classify it with a high degree of accuracy, the creative instinct demands special mention. I do not know whether "instinct" is the correct word. We use the term "creative instinct," because this factor behaves at least dynamically, like an instinct. Like instinct it is compulsive, but it is not common, and it is not a fixed and invariably inherited organization. Therefore I prefer to designate the creative impulse as a psychic factor similar in nature to instinct, having indeed a very close relationship to the instincts, but without being identical with any one of them. Its connections with sexuality are a much discussed problem, and, furthermore, it has much in common with the activity-urge as well as with the reflection-urge. Still it can repress all of these instincts, or make them serve it to the point of the self-destruction of the individual. Creation is as much destruction as construction.

To recapitulate, I emphasize the fact that from the psychological standpoint, five main groups of instinctive factors can be differentiated: hunger, sexuality, activity, reflection, and creativity. And in the last analysis, instincts are ecto-psychic determinants.

A discussion of the dynamic factors determining human behavior is obviously incomplete without mention of the will. The part that will plays, however, is a matter of dispute, and the whole problem is bound up with philosophical considerations, which in turn are burdened with the premises of a *Weltanschauung*. If the will is posited as free, then it is not bound to causation and there is nothing more to be said about it. If it is to be taken as predetermined and placed in a relationship of dependence upon the instincts, then it is an epiphenomenal factor of secondary importance.

Different from the dynamic factors are the modalities of the psychic function, which influence human behavior in other respects. Among these I mention especially the sex, age, and hereditary disposition of the individual. These three factors are taken first as physiological facts, but they are also psychological factors inasmuch as, like the instincts, they are subjected to psychification. Anatomical masculinity, for instance, is far from being proof of the psychic masculinity of the individual. And similarly, physiological age does not always correspond with the psychological. As regards hereditary disposition, the determining factor of race or family can be suppressed by a psychological superstructure. Much that is interpreted as heredity in the narrow sense is rather a sort of psychic contagion, which consists in an adaptation of the child-psyche to the unconscious of the parents.

To these three semi-physiological modalities, I should like to add three that are psychological. Among these I wish to stress the conscious and the unconscious. It makes a great deal of difference in the behavior of the individual, whether the psyche is functioning mainly consciously or unconsciously. Naturally it is only a question of a greater or lesser degree of consciousness, because total consciousness is empirically impossible. An extreme state of unconsciousness is characterized by the predominance of compulsive instinctive processes, the result of which is either uncontrolled inhibition, or a lack of inhibition throughout. The happenings within the psyche are then contradictory and take place in terms of alternating, a-logical antitheses. In such a case, the level of consciousness is essentially that of the dream-state. In contrast to this, a high degree of consciousness is characterized by a heightened awareness, a preponderance of will, a directed, rational behavior, and an almost total absence of instinctive determinants. The unconscious is then found to be at a level definitely animal. The first state lacks intellectual and ethical accomplishment, the second naturalness.

The second modality is extraversion and introversion, and determines the direction of psychic activity, that is, it decides the question whether conscious contents refer to external objects or to the subject. Therefore, it also decides the question whether the value stressed lies without, or within the individual. This modality works so persistently that it builds up habitual attitudes, that is, types with recognizable external traits.

The third modality points, to use a metaphor, upward and downward, because it has to do with spirit and matter. It is true that matter is in general the subject of physics, but it is also a psychic quality, as the history of religion and philosophy clearly shows. And just as matter is finally to be conceived of as being merely a working hypothesis of physics, so also spirit, the subject of religion and philosophy, is a hypothetical quality in constant need of reinterpretation. The so-called reality of matter is attested in the first place by our sense-perceptions, while belief in the existence of the spirit is supported by psychic experience. Psychologically, we cannot establish anything more final with respect to either matter or spirit than the presence of certain conscious contents, some of which are labeled as having a material, and others a spiritual origin. In the consciousness of civilized peoples, it is true, there seems to exist a sharp division between the two qualities, but on the primitive level the boundaries become so blurred that matter often seems endowed with soul while spirit appears to be material. However, from the existence of these two categories, ethical, esthetic, intellectual, social, and religious systems of values eventuate, which on occasion determine how the dynamic factors in the psyche are to be finally used. Perhaps it would not be too much to say that the most crucial problems of the individual and of society turn upon the way the psyche functions toward spirit and matter.

## II. SPECIAL PHENOMENOLOGY

Let us now turn to the special phenomenology. In the first part we have differentiated five principal groups of instincts and six modalities. However, the concepts described are only academically valuable as general categories. In reality, the psyche is a complicated interplay of all these factors. Moreover, in conformity with its peculiar structure, it shows an endless individual variability on the one hand, and on the other, an equally great capacity to undergo change and differentiation. The variability is conditioned by the circumstance that the psyche is not a homogeneous structure, but apparently consists of hereditary units only loosely bound together, and for this reason it shows a very marked tendency to split into parts. The tendency to change is conditioned by influences coming both from within and from without. Functionally speaking, these tendencies are closely related to each other.

1. Let us first turn to the question of the psyche's tendency to split. Although this peculiarity is most clearly observable in psychopathology, yet fundamentally it is a normal phenomenon, which can be recognized with greatest ease in the projections made by the primitive psyche. The tendency to split means that parts of the psyche detach themselves from consciousness to such an extent that they not only appear foreign but also lead an autonomous life of their own. It need not be a question of hysterical multiple personality, or schizophrenic alterations in personality, but merely so-called complexes quite in the field of the normal. Complexes are psychic fragments, which owe their splitting off to traumatic influences or to certain incompatible tendencies. As the association experiment proves, the complexes interfere with the purposes of the will and disturb the performances of consciousness; they produce disturbances in memory and obstacles in the flow of associations; they appear and disappear according to their own laws; they obsess consciousness temporarily, or influence speech and action in an unconscious manner. In a word, complexes behave like independent beings, a fact especially evident in abnormal states of mind. In the voices heard by the insane, they even take on a personal ego-character like that of the spirits manifesting themselves through automatic writing and similar techniques. An intensification of the complex-phenomenon leads to morbid states, which are only more or less extensive multiple dissociations endowed with an invincible life of their own.

The behavior of new contents, which have been constellated

in the unconscious, but are not yet assimilated to consciousness, is similar to that of the complexes. These contents may be based on subliminal perception, or they may be creative in character. Again, so long as they are not made conscious and integrated with the life of the personality, they also lead a life of their own. In the realm of artistic and religious phenomena, these contents likewise appear at times in personified form, especially as so-called archetypal figures. Mythological research designates them as "motives"; to Lévy-Bruhl they appear as *représentations collectives;* Hubert and Mauss call them "categories of fantasy." I have employed the concept of the collective unconscious to embrace all of these archetypes. They are psychic forms which, like the instincts, are common to all mankind, and therefore their presences can be proved wherever relevant literary documents have been preserved. As factors influencing human behavior, the archetypes play no small role. The total personality can be affected by them through a process of identification. This effect is best explained by the fact that the archetypes probably represent typical situations of life. Abundant proof of such identifications with archetypes is furnished by psychological and psycho-pathological cases. The psychology of Nietzsche's *Zarathustra* also furnishes a good example. The difference between these structures and the split-off products of schizophrenia lies in the fact that the former are entities endowed with personality and fraught with meaning, whereas the latter are only fragments with vestiges of meaning—in reality they are products of disintegration. Both, however, possess to a high degree the capacity of influencing, controlling, or even suppressing the ego-personality, so that a temporary or lasting transformation of personality occurs.

2. As we have seen, the inherent tendency of the psyche to split means on the one hand dissociation into multiple structural units, on the other, however, a possibility very favorable to change and differentiation: it allows the singling out of special parts in order to train them through concentration of the will and thus bring them to their maximum development. In this way, with a conscious one-sidedness, certain capabilities, especially those promising social usefulness, can be fostered to

the neglect of others. This produces an unbalanced state similar to that caused by a dominant complex—a change in personality. It is true that we do not refer to this as obsession by a complex, but as one-sidedness. Still, the actual state is approximately the same, with this difference, that the one-sidedness lies within the intention of the individual, and is therefore furthered by all possible means, whereas the complex is felt to be injurious and disturbing. Frequently one fails to see that the consciously-willed one-sidedness is one of the most important causes of an undesirable complex, or conversely, that certain complexes cause a one-sided differentiation of doubtful value. Some degree of one-sidedness is unavoidable and, in the same measure, complexes are also unavoidable. Looked at in this light, complexes might be identified with certain modified instincts. An instinct which has undergone too much psychification can revenge itself in the form of an autonomous complex. This is the chief source of the neuroses.

It is well known that very many faculties can become differentiated in man. I do not wish to lose myself in the details of case-histories and therefore limit myself to the normal and ever-present faculties of consciousness. Consciousness is primarily an organ of orientation in a world of outer and inner facts. First and foremost, consciousness establishes the fact that something is there. I call this faculty *sensation*. By this I do not mean any specific sense activity, but perception in general. Another faculty gives the interpretation of that which is perceived; this I term *thinking*. By means of this function, the thing perceived is assimilated and the transmutation of the object of perception into a pychic content proceeds much further than in mere sensation. A third faculty establishes the value of the object. This function of evaluation I call *feeling*. The pain or pleasure reaction of feeling marks the highest degree of subjectification of the object. Feeling brings subject and object into such close relationship that the subject must choose between acceptance and rejection.

These three functions would be quite sufficient for orientation with respect to any fact, if the object in question were isolated in time and space. But, in space, every object is in endless connection with the multiplicity of objects, and, in time, the object represents merely a transition from a former condition to the succeeding one. The greater part of spatial relationship and temporal change is unavoidably unconscious at the moment of orientation, and yet, for the determination of the meaning of an object, space-time relationships are necessary. It is the fourth faculty of consciousness, namely, *intuition,* which makes possible, at least approximately, the determination of the space-time relationship. This is a function of perception which includes the subliminal, that is, the possible relationship of objects not appearing in the field of vision, and the possible changes in past and future, about which the object itself gives no clue. Intuition is an immediate awareness of relationships which could not be established by the other three functions at the moment of orientation.

I mention the orientating functions of consciousness because they can be singled out for empirical observation and are subject to differentiation. At the very outset, nature has established marked differences in their importance for different individuals. As a rule, one of the four functions is especially developed, which consequently gives the mentality as a whole its characteristic stamp. Through the predominance of one function there result typical dispositions, which can be designated as thinking types, feeling types, et cetera, as the case may be. Such a type-form is a bias like a vocation, with which a person has identified himself. Whatever has been erected into a principle or a virtue through inclination or usefulness always results in one-sidedness and a compulsion toward one-sidedness which excludes all other possibilities, and this applies to men of will and action just as much as to those whose object in life is the constant training of memory. Whatever we persist in excluding from conscious training and adaptation necessarily remains in an untrained, undeveloped, infantile or archaic state, ranging from partial to complete unconsciousness. Hence, together with the motives of consciousness and reason, unconscious influences of a primitive character are always normally present in ample measure and disturb the attention of consciousness. For it is by no means to be assumed that all those forms of activity latent in the psyche, which are suppressed or neglected by the individual, are thereby robbed of their specific energy. For instance, if a man relied wholly on the data of vision, this would not mean that he would cease to hear. And if he could be transplanted to a soundless world, he would in all probability soon satisfy his desire of hearing by indulging in auditory hallucinations.

The fact that the natural functions of the psyche cannot be stripped of their specific energy gives rise to characteristic antitheses, which can be best observed in the field of activity where these four orientating functions of consciousness come into play. The chief contrasts are those between thinking and feeling on the one hand, and between sensation and intuition on the other. The opposition between the first two is an old story and needs no comment. The opposition between the second pair becomes clear when understood as the opposition between the objective fact and the apparent possibility. Obviously anyone on the lookout for new possibilities does not rest in the actuality of the moment, but passes on beyond it as soon as possible. These contrasts are marked by their irritating nature, and this is equally true when the conflict occurs within the individual psyche or between individuals of opposite temperaments.

It is my belief that the problem of the opposites here merely hinted at, should be made the basis of a critical psychology. A critique of this sort would be of utmost importance not only for the narrow field of psychology, but also for the wider field of the cultural sciences in general.

In this essay, I have gathered together all those factors which, from the standpoint of a purely empirical psychology, play a leading role in determining human behavior. The multiplicity and variety of the aspects claiming attention are due to the nature of the psyche—the mirroring of itself in many-sided facets—and they are a measure of the difficulties confronting the investigator. The tremendous intricacy of psychic phenomenology is borne in upon us only after we see that all attempts to formulate a comprehensive theory are foredoomed to failure. The premises are always far too simple. The psyche is the starting point of all human experience, and all knowledge gained eventually leads back to it. The psyche is the beginning and the end of every realization. It is not only the object of its science, but the subject also. This lends psychology a unique place among all the other sciences: on the one hand there is a constant doubt as to the possibility of its being a science at all, while on the other, psychology gains the right to state a theoretical problem, the solution of which will be one of the most difficult tasks for a future philosophy.

# SCIENCE AND ETHICS

## *by* Edwin Grant Conklin

SCIENCE, as we all know, is tested, verifiable organized knowledge; ethics is concerned with ideals, conduct and character. Any program looking to human welfare and betterment must include both science and ethics, and there would be great gain for the world if organized religion and organized science could co-operate more effectively in the promotion of practical ethics.

Among the generalizations of science which have been charged with the weakening of ethics, first place must be given to the theory of the natural evolution of man and of ethical systems. It is a fundamental postulate of modern science that man is a part of nature and that his body, mind and social relations have undergone evolution in the long history of the human species. This is not a mere hypothesis but an established fact, if anything is a fact. There is positive evidence that in long past times there were types of human and partly human beings that were much more brutish in body, mind and social relations than the general average of the present race. There is abundant evidence that ethics has undergone evolution no less than intelligence; it has developed from its beginnings in the primitive family group, to tribal, racial, national and international relations; from the ideals and practices of savagery to those of barbarism and civilization; from the iron rule of vengeance and retribution, "an eye for an eye, a tooth for a tooth," to the ideals of love and forgiveness and that highest conception of ethics embodied in the Golden Rule. But as in physical evolution there are retarded or retrogressive individuals and races, so also in the development of ethical ideals some people and periods are far behind others and all fall short of their highest ideals.

As is well known, the distinctive principle running through the whole of Darwin's philosophy of evolution is what he called natural selection. Having studied the notable effects of human selection in the production of new breeds of domestic animals and cultivated plants, he sought for some comparable process operating in nature without human guidance. This he found in the Malthusian principle of overproduction of populations, the elimination of the less fit and the preservation of favored races in the struggle for life. In general, he regarded the environment, whether organic or inorganic, as the principal eliminator of the unfit, although he assigned a certain role to the organism itself as selector and eliminator, especially in sexual selection, while in mental, moral and social evolution this auto-selection played even a larger part in his philosophy.

I shall not at this time discuss the present status of Darwinism further than to indicate that from practically every branch of modern biology it continues to receive confirmation and extension, so that in spite of severe attacks from many sources and assurances from some excited opponents that "Darwinism is dead," it is still very much alive.

It has been charged by many humanists that Darwinism is destructive of the highest ethical ideals. It is said to be the apotheosis of cruelty and selfishness, to recognize no values except survival, no ideals except success. In this struggle for existence the weak go under, the strong survive; and this is said to justify personal and class strife and wars of conquest. Militarists and dictators have seized upon this principle as justification of their philosophy that might makes right. Conflicts and wars are said to be both the means and measure of progress, and military training to be the highest type of discipline. By both militarists and humanists Darwinism has been considered as an eternal struggle, a vast battle of living things with one another and with their environment, a grim portrayal of "nature red in tooth and claw."

This is, however, a fundamental misconception of natural selection. Darwin himself repudiated this extension of his principle to the struggle between races and nations of men. In a letter to Alfred Russell Wallace he wrote that "the struggle between races of men depends entirely on intellectual and moral qualities." Those who attempt to extend the principle of natural selection into the field of intellectual, social and moral qualities should remember that the standards of fitness are wholly different in these fields. Physically the fittest is the most viable and most capable of leaving offspring; intellectually the fittest is the most rational; socially the fittest is the most ethical. To attempt to measure intellectual or social fitness by standards of physical fitness is hopelessly to confuse the whole question, for human evolution has progressed in these three distinct paths. Man owes his unique position in nature to this three-fold evolution, and although the factors of physical, intellectual and social progress are always balanced one against another, they are not mutually exclusive. All three may and do co-operate in such manner that each strengthens the other.

And this leads to the inquiry whether human or so-called artificial selection is not also natural. If we define "natural" as that which is regular and lawful, and not arbitrary and lawless, then human selection is also natural, and this must necessarily follow if man in his entirety is the product of natural evolution. Since Darwin's day the study of the behavior of lower organisms as well as that of human beings in all stages of development from the infant to the adult has shown that selective activity is everywhere present. One-celled plants and animals respond positively to some stimuli, negatively to others, and in general, though not invariably, this selectivity of response is beneficial. For example, they avoid extremes of heat or cold, they move or grow toward certain chemical substances and away from others, they take in as food certain substances and reject others. Even germ cells show some of these same properties, and in general it may be said that all living things manifest differential sensitivity and reactivity, and that by a process of trial and error and finally trial and success they generally manage to eliminate reactions that are not satisfactory and to persist in those that are. This is the Darwinian principle extended to the reactions of organisms in which the organism itself is eliminator and selector. Intelligence in animals and man is arrived at in this same way, by many trials and failures and finally trial and success, remembering of past failures and successes, elimination of the former and persistence in the latter. A cat that by trial and error has learned to open the door of a cage, as in Thorndike's experiments, or a horse that has learned in the same way to lift a latch and open a gate is intelligent with respect to that one situation; intelligence in human beings is acquired in the same way. Indeed, intelligence is the capacity of profiting by experience, while the ability to generalize experiences and to recognize fundamental resemblances in spite of superficial differences is what we call abstract thought or reasoning.

In his famous Romanes address at Oxford in 1892 on "Evolution and Ethics" Professor Huxley maintained that ethics consists in opposing the cosmic process of natural selection by intelligent human selection and in replacing the ruthless destruction of the weak and helpless with human sympathy and co-operation. He illustrated the superiority of human selection by pointing out the fact that a cultivated garden left to nature grows up to weeds and, therefore, that human intelligence can improve on the blind processes of nature in meeting human needs.

All this is undoubtedly true; we are continually improving on nature for our own purposes; all agriculture, industry, medicine, education are improvements on nature. The notion that nature is always perfect is certainly false, and the cry, "Back to nature," is more likely to be a call to regress than to progress. But it is a mistake to suppose that human intelligence and purpose, social sympathy, co-operation and ethics in general are not also parts of nature and the products of natural evolution. In Darwin's theory the environment eliminates the unfit organism, but in individual adaptations to new conditions the organism itself eliminates many useless or injurious responses. In such cases the organism rather than the environment is the eliminator or selector, either by the hit-or-miss process of "trial and error" or by the vastly more rapid and less wasteful method of remembered experience, that is, by intelligence. Thus intelligence can improve on the blind processes of nature, because it is not blind, although it also is natural. And thus intelligence has become a prime factor in evolution. Intelligence and social co-operation have become the most important means of further human progress.

Will and purpose are similarly natural phenomena growing out of the use of intelligence in finding satisfaction. Will is not an uncaused cause but rather the product of all those bodily and mental processes, such as appetites, emotions, memory and intelligence, which stimulate, regulate or inhibit behavior. Ability thus to control activity in response to remembered experience is what we call freedom from fixed, mechanistic action. Both intelligence and freedom vary greatly in different animals and in the same individual at different stages of development. They are relatively slight in human infants, but they rise to a maximum in normal adults. However, men are never perfectly intelligent nor absolutely free, but the more intelligent they are the freer they are.

All this is pertinent to a discussion of the natural history of ethics, for social ethics assumes the ability and the responsibility of individuals to regulate behavior in accordance with ideals and codes of conduct. It, therefore, demands freedom to choose between alternatives that are offered. Without such freedom there can be no responsibility, no duty, no ethics. It has long been the creed of certain rigidly mechanistic scientists that freedom, responsibility and duty are mere delusions and that human beings are automata, thinking, feeling and doing only those things which were predetermined by their heredity and environment over which they have no control. This fatalistic creed was in large part a deduction from the determinism of nature which was revealed in mathematics, astronomy, physics and chemistry and was then extended by certain physiologists to all vital phenomena, including human life and personality. Indeed some of these "hard determinists" went so far as to maintain that the whole course of human history was predetermined in the original constitution of the universe, that nations had risen and fallen, cultures and civilizations had come and gone and that the present state of the world and its future destiny were all determined by inexorable laws. However, many biologists who investigated the behavior of animals refused to regard them as mere automata, and students of human behavior generally held that there must be some flaw or break in this logical chain that bound man helpless on the wheel of fate, some fallacy in the logic that denied all freedom and responsibility to man, some monstrous error in the conclusion that saints and sinners, philanthropists and fiends were mere pawns or puppets in a game in which they were moved by forces over which they had no control.

As a way of escape mathematicians and physicists, who were most impressed by the determinism of inanimate nature, were generally inclined to adopt some form of Cartesian dualism, which would endow living beings and especially man with an immaterial principle or soul which was not subject to this rigid determinism. But on the other hand, students of life phenomena in general could find no sufficient evidence for such dualism, and hence arose the strange anomaly of physiologists and psychologists being more rigid determinists, so far as life and man are concerned, than students of the physical sciences.

Several scientists recently have expressed the view that Heisenberg's principle of indeterminacy in the sub-atomic field can somehow be converted into the novelty, creativity and freedom manifested by living things. But, so far as I am aware, no one has shown how this can be done, since the principle of indeterminacy does not apply to molecules or masses of matter, and living things are always composed of complex aggregations of these. Furthermore, biologists generally do not admit any fundamental indeterminacy in the behavior of living beings. Novelty, creativity and freedom, wherever their origin has been traced, are found to be caused by new combinations of old factors or processes, whether these be atoms, molecules, genes, chromosomes, cells, organs, functions or even sensations, memories and ideas. By such new combinations of old elements there emerge all the new properties of chemical compounds, and by new combinations of genes and chromosomes and environmental stimuli all the novelties of heredity and development arise. There is good evidence that even psychical properties, such as intelligence, will and consciousness, emerge in the process of development because of specific combinations of physical and psychical factors. This is, indeed, the whole philosophy of evolution, namely, that the entire universe, including man and all his faculties and activities, are the results of transformation rather than of new-formation, of emergence rather than of creation *de novo*.

Freedom does not mean uncaused activity; "the will is not a little deity encapsuled in the brain," but instead it is the sum of all those physical and psychical processes, including especially reflexes, conditionings and remembered experiences, which act as stimuli in initiating or directing behavior. The will is not undetermined, uncaused, absolutely free, but is the result of the organization and experience of the organism, and in turn it is a factor in determining behavior. Therefore, we do not need to import from sub-atomic physics the uncertain principle of uncertainty in order to explain free will. The fact that man can control to a certain extent his own acts as well as phenomena outside himself requires neither a little daemon in the electron nor a big one in the man.

Just one hundred years ago the English poet, William Wordsworth, wrote:

> Man now presides
> In power where once he trembled in his weakness;
> Science advances with gigantic strides,
> But are we aught enriched in love and meekness?

These lines are much more significant today than when they were penned. The strides of science have never before been so gigantic as during the past century. So far as our knowledge of and control over natural forces and processes are concerned we live in a new world that could not have been forecast by scientists and could scarcely have been imagined by poets and seers of one hundred years ago. Within the last century we have passed from the "horse and buggy stage" to the locomotive, the automobile and the airplane era; from slow mails to the telegraph and telephone and radio, from education and music and art for the favored few to a time when these are available to untold millions. Applied scientific knowledge has made amazing advances in all the means of living; in the abundance and variety of food and clothing; in comfort, convenience and sanitation in housing; in relative freedom from degrading drudgery and a corresponding increase in leisure and opportunity for the pursuit of happiness. At the same time medical science has to a great extent removed the fear of "the pestilence that walketh in darkness"; no more do whole cities flee in panic from the black death, or yellow fever, or white plague; no more do civilized people live in dread of smallpox or typhoid fever or diphtheria; the average length of life has been greatly increased; physical pain has been reduced and comforts have been multiplied.

These are only a few of the marvelous advances of science, most of them within the memory of old persons still living. No similar progress can be found within any other century of human history. "But are we aught enriched in love and meekness?" With man's increased control over the forces of nature there has not gone increased control over human nature. Man's conquest over outer nature has outrun his conquest over his own spirit, and consequently the gifts of science, which might be unmixed blessings if properly used, become new dangers when used for evil purposes. Science is organized knowledge, and knowledge in itself is neither good nor bad but only true or false. That which gives social and moral value to science is the purpose for which men use it. If it is used for selfish advantage it may weaken or destroy social co-operation. If used for greater and more terrible wars it may end in the destruction of civilization itself.

Neither in human nature nor in social relations has progress kept pace with science. This is not the fault of science but rather of man and of society. The great advances in the applications of science have often been used for selfish purposes rather than for social welfare. Scientific progress in medicine and sanitation is far in advance of its social utilization, but not in advance of its urgent need. Rational and peaceful means of solving class conflicts and of preventing wars would be vastly less costly and more effective than strikes and armaments. Scientific control of population and the necessities of civilized life would be more humane and progressive than to leave these to the law of the jungle. The fact is that social progress has moved so much slower than science that one might say that scientific progress is matched against social stagnation. Many thoughtful persons are asking: "Will science, which has so largely made our modern civilization, end in destroying it? Has it not placed powers in the hands of ignorant and selfish men which may wreck the whole progress of the race?"

It is a fact that improvements in human nature are not keeping pace with increasing knowledge of and control over outer nature. By means of language, writing, printing, the radio and all the means of communication and conservation of knowledge each human generation transmits its acquirements to succeeding ones. Thus present-day science, culture and civilization represent the accumulated experience and knowledge of all the past, each succeeding generation standing, as it were, on the shoulders of preceding ones. Every individual, on the other hand, begins life where all his ancestors began, namely, in the valley of the germ cells; he then climbs to the summit of maturity and goes down into the valley of death. But society, gifted with continuous life, passes on with giant strides from mountain top to mountain top. And so it happens that science and civilization in general outrun individual heredity, for the learning and acquirements of each generation are not transmitted to succeeding ones through the germ cells but only through social contacts. For this reason increasing knowledge and power have greatly outrun improvements in inherent human nature, so that man is still, in the language of Raymond Fosdick, "the old savage in the new civilization."

It is impossible to halt the march of science except by destroying the spirit of intellectual and political freedom. No scientific moratorium by international agreement is possible, even if it were desirable, and any nation that undertook to halt the progress of science would be doomed to the fate of Ethiopia and China. Is there any way of escape from this perilous situation, in which knowledge and power have outrun ethics? Can world-wide ethics keep up with world-wide science? Can science itself do anything to close this widening gap between lagging human nature and the increasing responsibilities of civilization?

Eugenics has been proposed as a possible and necessary solution of this problem. Undoubtedly great improvement in human heredity could be effected, if the principles of good breeding which are used with such notable results in the improvement of domesticated animals and cultivated plants were to be used in the breeding of men. There is no doubt among students of heredity that by means of a system of selective breeding a healthier, longer-lived, more intelligent type could be developed and the prevalence of emotional instability and neuroses could be decreased. But the difficulties in the way of such a eugenical program are enormous where the human stock is so mixed, as it is in almost all races of men, and where the rules of good breeding would have to be self-administered or imposed by authorities that are influenced by social, racial or ethical prejudices. Even if these obstacles could be overcome and this program wisely and persistently followed it would take thousands of years to bring about any marked improvement in the masses of mankind, and in the present crisis of civilization we need a more quick-acting remedy, if it can be found.

Fortunately there are other and more rapidly acting remedies for this disharmony between biological and social progress. Heredity determines only the capacities and potentialities of any organism, the realization of those potentialities depends upon development, which is greatly influenced by environment, hormones, health or disease, use or disuse, conditioned reflexes or habits. In every individual there are many capacities that remain undeveloped because of lack of suitable stimuli to call them forth. Since these inherited potentialities may be social or anti-social, good or bad, it is the aim of enlightened society to develop the former and to suppress the latter. In the heredity of every human being there are many possible personalities; which one of these becomes actual depends upon developmental stimuli. Each of us might have been much better or much worse characters than we are if the conditions of our development had been different. Endocrinologists and students of nutrition are already preventing or overcoming many of the deficiencies or defects that arise in the course of development. Medicine and sanitation have notably reduced the occurrence, spread and mortality of epidemics and there is every reason to expect that the causes and cures of the most serious diseases that now afflict mankind will be discovered, that sickness and suffering will be greatly reduced and that the average length of life will be still further increased. In all these respects science is contributing greatly to human welfare and to practical ethics.

But of all the possible means of rapidly improving social conditions, ethical education is probably the most promising. Education, based upon a knowledge of the principles of development and aimed at the cultivation of better relations among all classes, races and nations is the chief hope of social progress. The most enduring effect of education is habit formation. Good education consists in large part in the formation of good habits of body, mind and morals. Heredity is original or first nature; habits are second nature, and for character formation and social value they are almost if not quite as important as heredity itself. Ethical habits especially, are dependent on education, and in all normal human beings it is possible to cultivate habits of unselfishness rather than selfishness, of sympathy rather than enmity, of co-operation rather than antagonism. To trust entirely to heredity to improve men or society is to forget that heredity furnishes capacities for evil as well as for good, and to disregard the universal experience of mankind that human nature may be improved by humane nurture. And as an educational discipline there are no other studies that distinguish so sharply truth from error, evidence from opinion, reason from emotion; none that teach a greater reverence for truth nor inspire more laborious and persistent search for it. Great is philosophy, for it is the synthesis of all knowledge, but if it is true philosophy it must be built upon science, which is tested knowledge.

> To the solid ground
> Of nature trusts the mind that builds for aye.

Education, then, which looks to the highest development of the physical, intellectual and moral capacities of men is the chief hope of human progress. Even any possible program of improvement of inherited human nature must rest upon education concerning the principles of heredity and the methods of applying them to the breeding of men. Without waiting for the slow improvement of human nature through eugenics great progress can be made toward the "good society" by the better development of the capacities we already possess. All the advances from savagery to the highest civilization have been made without any corresponding improvement in heredity. Within a few generations, through the inculcation of better social habits or fashions, there have been many improvements in human relations. The torture and execution of heretics, whether theological or political, had all but disappeared from the earth until the recent revival of intolerance under dictatorships; belief in witchcraft and demoniacal possession and methods of exorcising devils by fire or torture no longer exist; human slavery as a legal institution has been abandoned everywhere; in this country the duel is no longer regarded as the necessary way of defending one's honor. These and a hundred other improvements in social relations have come about through education and enlightened public opinion. May we not hope that class, racial and national conflicts and wars may be outmoded in the same way?

Sensations, emotions and instincts are the principal driving forces in our lives as well as in those of animals. Primitive instincts, or what we properly call the "Old Adam," may cause persons, classes and nations to disregard reason and to give way to an orgy of passion. Lawyers for the defense sometimes call this a "brain storm," but it might more truly be called a "brainless or endocrine storm," for it is the sort of behavior which one sees in decerebrate cats or in animals in which the lower centers of the emotions and reflexes are very active but are imperfectly controlled by the higher centers of intelligence and reason. One of Europe's dictators says, "We think with our blood," which is a pretty sure way "to see red." Another dubious test of truth is "to feel it in the bones," which is generally indicative of ossified thought. It is especially man's superior brain that makes him the paragon of animals. It was intelligence and not brute force that enabled primitive men to overcome great beasts of prey, and it is intelligence joined with ethical ideals that alone can guarantee future progress. Emotional behavior is highly infectious; a dog fight sets all the dogs in the neighborhood into a frenzy; an excited chimpanzee will set a whole colony of apes raging; and we know only too well how the mob spirit may spread through a peaceful community, or war psychology sweep through an entire nation. The only safety for society and advancing civilization is in learning to control these animal passions by intelligence and reason.

Throughout the period of recorded human history there has been a notable growth of freedom not only from the rigors of nature but also from the tyrannies of men. Freedom from slavery of the body, mind and spirit has been bought at a great price through long centuries of conflict and martyrdom, and one of the amazing revelations of the past few years is the compliant way in which millions of people in Europe have surrendered all freedom not only in government but also in speech, press, thought and conscience on the orders of dictators. Even in certain sciences, freedom of teaching and research has been restricted or prohibited, in spite of the fact that the advancement of science rests upon freedom to seek and test and proclaim the truth. Dictators seek to control men's thoughts as well as their bodies and so they attempt to dictate science, education and religion. But dictated education is usually propaganda, dictated history is often mythology, dictated science is pseudo-science. Free thought, free speech and free criticism are the life of science, yet at present these freedoms are stifled in certain great nations "with a cruelty more intense than anything western civilization has known in four hundred years."

In spite of a few notable exceptions it must be confessed that scientists did not win the freedom which they have generally enjoyed, and they have not been conspicuous in defending this freedom when it has been threatened. Perhaps they have lacked that confidence in absolute truth and that emotional exaltation that have led martyrs and heroes to welcome persecution and death in defense of their faith. Today as in former times it is the religious leaders who are most courageous in resisting tyranny. It was not science but religion and ethics that led Socrates to say to his accusers, "I will obey the god, rather than you." It was not science but religious conviction that led Milton to utter his noble defense of intellectual liberty, "Who ever knew truth put to the worst in a free and open encounter? For who knows not that truth is strong, next to the Almighty?" It was not science but religious patriotism that taught, "Resistance to tyrants is obedience to God." The spirit of science does not cultivate such heroism in the maintenance of freedom. The scientist realizes that his knowledge is relative and not absolute, he conceives it possible that he may be mistaken, and he is willing to wait in confidence that ultimately truth will prevail. Therefore, he has little inclination to suffer and die for his faith, but is willing to wait for the increase and diffusion of knowledge. But he knows better than others that the increase and diffusion of knowledge depend entirely upon freedom to search, experiment, criticize, proclaim. Without these freedoms there can be no science.

There is no possibility that all men can be made alike in personality, nor any reason why all races and nations should hold the same political and social ideals. But there are grounds for hoping that they may come to cherish the same ethical concepts, for the needs and satisfactions, the instincts and emotions of all men are essentially similar. Upon this fact rather than upon uniform opinions, the hope of universal ethics rests. Science is everywhere the same in aims and methods, and this fact greatly strengthens the hope that in a world bound together by science into one neighborhood there may come to be common ideals regarding fundamental ethics.

The greatest problems that confront the human race are how to promote social co-operation; how to increase loyalty to truth, how to promote justice, and a spirit of brotherhood; how to expand ethics until it embraces all mankind. These are problems for science as well as for government, education and religion. Each of these agencies has its own proper functions to perform. Instead of working at cross purposes these greatest instruments of civilization should and must co-operate if any satisfactory solution is to be found. Scientists will unanimously agree that the spirit and aims and methods of science must be followed by all these agencies if any permanent progress is to be achieved; they will unanimously agree that science should co-operate to the fullest extent with government and education, but unfortunately there is no such unanimity of opinion when it comes to co-operation with religion. The memory of the many conflicts between science and theology in the past and the knowledge of the existing antagonism of many religious bodies to science have generated a reciprocal antagonism on the part of many scientists to all religion. If the humanitarian aims of both science and religion could be viewed in the spirit of sweet reasonableness it would be seen that the differences between them are not such as to prevent fruitful co-operation in promoting human welfare.

Science as well as religion consists of both faith and works, principles and practice, ideals and their realization. The faith, ideals and ethics of science constitute a form of natural religion. Scientists generally would agree, I think, that the faith and ideals of science include the following: (1) Belief in the universality of that system of law and order known as nature. (2) Confidence that nature is intelligible and that by searching our knowledge of it may be increased. (3) Recognition of the fact that knowledge is relative, not absolute, and that only gradually do we arrive at truth concerning nature. (4) Realization that there is no way to avoid temporary error, since in unexplored fields we learn largely by trial and error. (5) The necessity of freedom, openmindedness and sincerity in seeking truth. (6) Confidence that truth is mighty and will prevail and that even unwelcome truth is better than cherished error. (7) Realization that truth cannot be established by compulsion nor error permanently overcome by force. (8) Belief that the long course of evolution which has led to man and society, intelligence and ethics, is not finished, and that man can now take an intelligent part in his future progress. In these articles the faith of science does not differ essentially from that of enlightened religions.

The ethics of science regards the search for truth as one of the highest duties of man; it regards noble human character as the finest product of evolution; it considers the service of all mankind as the universal good; it teaches that both human nature and humane nurture may be improved, that reason may replace unreason, co-operation supplement competition and the progress of the human race through future ages be promoted by intelligence and good will.

In its practical aspects the ethics of science includes everything that concerns human welfare and social relations; it includes eugenics and all possible means of improving human heredity through the discovery and application of the principles of genetics; it is concerned with the population problem and the best means of attaining and maintaining an optimum population; it includes all those agencies which make for improved health and development, such as experimental biology and medicine, endocrinology, nutrition and child study; it includes the many scientific aspects of economics, politics and government; it is concerned especially with education of a kind that establishes habits of rational thinking, generous feeling and courageous doing. In spite of notable advances of our knowledge of these subjects we still know too little about human nature and the causes of social disorders. The extension of the methods of experimental science into this field is bound to be one of the major advances of the future. The ills of society, like the diseases of the body, have natural causes and they can be cured only by controlling those causes.

Shakespeare said: "If to do were as easy as to know what were good to do, chapels had been churches and poor men's cottages princes' palaces." Or in the language of Mark Twain, "To be good is noble, but to tell others to be good is noble and no trouble." This is the age-long problem with which religion and ethics have struggled, namely, how can men be induced to live up to the best they know? How can they be brought to substitute the spirit of service for selfishness, love for hate, reason for unreason? The long efforts of past centuries show that there is no rapid solution of this great problem. But in the co-operation of science, education and religion there is hope for the future.

The ethics of great scientists is essentially similar to that taught by great religious leaders. A scientist not friendly to organized religion has said that the *Decalogue* of Moses might be accepted as the Decalogue of Science if the word "Truth" were substituted for the word "God." Ivan Pavlov, the great Russian physiologist, left an ethical bequest to the scientific youth of his country, which reads like the warnings of the ancient prophets. Over the tomb of Pasteur in the Pasteur Institute in Paris are inscribed these words of his: "Happy is he who carries a God within him, an ideal of beauty to which he is obedient, an ideal of art, an ideal of science, an ideal of the fatherland, an ideal of the virtues of the Gospel." John Tyndall, no friend of the church, pronounced this eulogy of Michael Faraday, one of the greatest experimental scientists who ever lived: "The fairest traits of a character, sketched by Paul, found in him perfect illustration. For he was 'blameless, vigilant, sober, of good behavior, apt to teach, not given to filthy lucre.' I lay my poor garland on the grave of this

Just and Faithful Knight of God."

As scientists we are inheritors of a noble ethical tradition; we are the successors of men who loved truth and justice and their fellow-men more than fame or fortune or life itself. The profession of the scientist, like that of the educator or religious teacher, is essentially altruistic and should never be prostituted to unethical purposes. To us the inestimable privilege is given to add to the store of knowledge, to seek truth not only for truth's sake but also for humanity's sake, and to have a part in the greatest work of all time, namely, the further progress of the human race through the advancement of both science and ethics.

# THE SCIENCE OF VALUE AND THE VALUE OF SCIENCE

## by Ralph Barton Perry

THE PRESENT discussion grows out of the situation which has prevailed in the world during the last twenty-five years. The victors of the first World War have been challenged by revolutionary forces and by revolutionary creeds; while at the same time they have felt deep misgivings concerning the validity of their own traditional creed, and concerning its power of survival. That we of the western democracies should suffer disillusionment and even despair, implies that we have cherished a certain fundamental aspiration which we have agreed to call "democracy" or "civilization." We are not prepared to accept the totalitarian good as the equivalent of our good, and to acknowledge that its gain offsets our loss; but we measure the total outcome by our own standard.

Nor do we, as a rule, take the position of frank partisanship, and prefer our good simply because it is ours. We take the view that our side is the better side—that democracy is better than totalitarianism, or civilization than barbarism. We say, in effect, that our good is really or truly good, whereas the enemy's good despite the enemy's equal and opposite conviction is, in fact, evil. Both parties are haunted by the suspicion, and in moments of exceptional candor publicly avow, that their claims are purely partisan, but in the next breath they defend their partisanships, and claim a superiority of principle as well as of force.

Out of these confused assumptions and conflicting claims arises the question, as old as the dialogues of Plato, concerning the relativity or absoluteness of moral preference. What kind of knowledge is knowledge of the good? Or, in what sense, if any, is there a science of value?

Periods of disillusionment and despair tend to be periods of recrimination. It is easier to find scape-goats than remedies. During the last decade the western European peoples—the so-called democracies which have been waging war, defensive or offensive, against the so-called totalitarian or Axis powers—have been searching within themselves for something on which to place the blame. At the same time that they have fearfully denounced the enemy powers as evil they have been contemptuously denounced by the enemy powers as witless and weak. In the course of this self-accusation and mutual accusation almost every element of modern civilization has been indicted,—Semitism, racial decadence, liberalism, plutocracy, imperialism, capitalism, socialism, Christianity—and even science, the chief pride and glory of the modern world.

Among the democracies science is criticized for having itself neglected, or for having encouraged the neglect of, the "values" of life. There are those among us who say that our fault lies in not being scientific enough, or in our failure to extend science to human and social behavior as well as to the physical world. More familiar, however, is the opinion that we have been too scientific, and should now turn to non-science or anti-science, that is, to action, emotion, faith, or artistic appreciation. Meanwhile, the totalitarian powers, who are notable for their deeds, as well as for their words, have already destroyed the autonomy of science; having subordinated pure science to the technical arts, and science as a whole to the cult of nationalism or racism.

This situation calls for a re-examination of the old question of the value of science in human life. We are compelled again to ask, as, beginning with Socrates, has been asked at the dawn of every new epoch in European thought, "What is the good of knowledge?"

The present essay attempts to deal in turn with these two questions: the science of value, and the value of science. I shall mingle dogmatism and argument—I hope, judiciously. It is clearly out of the question to defend every thesis that I advance, but I shall hope in any case to make my meaning clear. I begin with the problem of the science of value. What is value and how is it known?

The meanings of the term value, and of other terms such as good, evil, right, wrong and obligation, all stem from the presence in man of attitudes of favor and disfavor, of for and against, or of positive and negative interest. Under this broad conception may be subsumed a great variety of emotions, feelings or activities: positive interest being represented by liking, enjoying, desiring, seeking, wishing, hoping, needing, resolving, loving; negative interest by disliking, avoiding, dreading, rejecting, hating, resenting. These attitudes may be relatively simple, as are the liking of pleasure and the repugnance to pain; or they may be relatively complex, as are the sentiments of patriotism and moral obligation. A world devoid of attitudes of interest would be a world devoid of values. When these attitudes occur, their objects possess value. If the attitude is positive, its object is good; and if the attitude is negative, the object is bad —in the broad, generic senses of these terms. There are many derivative senses of the terms good, bad and value. The character of value is extended from the object of interest itself to the causes, conditions, or instances of the object.

The noun "value" is used in two senses: to mean an object having value, or to mean the interest which invests it with value; and values may therefore be classified either objectively or subjectively. Values considered as objects having value may be classified in any manner in which the objects are classified; thus one may speak of physical values or mental values, of natural values, or artificial values, of mundane and celestial values. Values considered as interests may be classified in any way in which interests are classified—as simple and complex, as inherited or acquired, as affective or conative. The expression "social values" is ambiguous, since it may refer to social entities or agencies such as the state, which have value; or to social forms of interest, such as patriotism, which give value. Esthetic values are so named with reference to a subjective attitude or form of appreciation, while the arts are commonly named for their objects, such as painting, sculpture or architecture. Moral values are distinguished objectively from other values by their reference to conduct and character, subjectively by their reference to approbation and conscience. But whether values are classified objectively or subjectively, the other term of the relationship is always implied. Objects having value are assumed to be directly or indirectly objects of interest, while interests are assumed to have their corresponding and appropriately qualified objects.

If values are such as I have affirmed them to be, then values are facts. This does not mean that the object which has value is necessarily a fact, but that it is a fact that the object has value. Thus at the moment when these words are written both the Germans and the British seek victory, and victory has value; but victory is not a fact. The victory of Britain over Germany may occur in the future, and when it does occur it will be enjoyed by the British. In that event the object having value will also be a fact. But in the feelings of the British a victory over Germany has value now, and it is a fact that such is the case despite the present non-existence of the object.

Stated in general terms this means that either simpler facts, or non-existent, ideal objects may be constituents of a complex fact. There is nothing peculiar or paradoxical in this. It is characteristic of all mental acts that they have objects which may or may not exist. It is essential to the character of certain mental acts, such as dreaming, imagination or abstract thought, that their objects should not exist. Such participation of non-existence in existence is not even peculiar to mind. To the conceptual or mathematical factor in physical science there must be some corresponding non-existent factor in physical nature.

Once it is granted that values are facts there can be no radical difference between the knowledge of physical or psychical nature, and the knowledge of values. If we focus attention on the objects having value, such as maxims, codes, ideals, goals of endeavor, and visions or counsels of perfection, we are exploring realms of non-existent entities and their logical relations. But the same is the case when the physicist resorts to mathematics, frames theories, and makes deductions from hypotheses. The fact that peace derives value from the longings of a war-ridden world, or through its promise of happiness to destitute and frustrated men, is just as solid a fact as the fact that gases obey the laws of probability, or atoms the differential calculus. There is the same gap between the concrete particulars of immediate experience and the sharp outlines and logical texture of conceptual thought—in the one case as in the other.

Values, then, are facts, or the non-factual derivatives and components of facts. Their aspect of non-factuality does not distinguish them from other natural facts, nor does it entail any fundamental difference in the methods by which they can be known. There is no justification for the antithesis between science and values, any more than there would be justification for an antithesis between science and motion, or science and heat, or science and life, or science and human behavior. Values constitute the subject-matter of a branch of knowledge, which in proportion as it is systematized in a manner appropriate to this subject-matter is entitled to the name of science. This analysis prepares the ground for what will, no doubt, be considered the crucial problem, namely, as to how values can be ranked, so that one set of values can be known to be superior to another set of values—democracy, for example, superior to totalitarianism, or civilization superior to barbarism.

In dealing with this question I lay down an initial assumption which to some will seem a begging of the question, but which I do not know how to avoid. I assume that every answerable question will contain in itself a reference to the evidence which will be accepted as conclusive. In discussing the question of the superiority or supremacy of one set of values, I shall, therefore, endeavor to put the question in a manner that seems to me to permit of an answer.

The question of superiority can be asked regarding the object of interest, or regarding the interest itself. One object may be deemed superior to another when it is preferred by a given interest, or when it more effectively promotes the object of a given interest. Thus one coffee can be said to be superior to another coffee, when lovers of coffee, having tasted both, prefer the first to the second. Or one drug may be considered as superior to another when it is more soporific, sleep being desired. Superiority in both of these senses is proved conclusively when the fact of preference or the fact of comparative efficacy is established by experiment. The question of superiority is in each case associated with a *test* of superiority, recognized and accepted by all who consider the question. Superiority of the first sort is as universal as the interest involved; in other words, grades of coffee are as universal as the taste for coffee. Superiority of the second sort, such as more soporific, is as universal as natural causation.

The question of the relative superiority of interests can be similarly construed. One interest may be deemed superior to another when any individual having both interests sets one above another in the order of his personal preference, as when he prefers his vocation to his avocation. Or one interest, such as golf, may be considered as superior to another interest, such as bridge, on the ground that it is more efficacious in promoting the interest in health. Here, again, the universality of the ranking of interest would depend on two factors: the existence of an identical order of preference among all men, or within any group of men; the natural causation by which interests affect one another, whether as co-operative, conflicting or compatible.

Is there or is there not any one interest to which all men do actually subordinate every other interest? Is there a single ultimate goal to which every will is by nature inclined? Everyone who is familiar with the history of philosophy knows that this thesis has been repeatedly affirmed. It has been claimed for the Platonic Good, for the love of God, for pleasure and for self-preservation. Everyone who is familiar with the history of philosophy should also know that these claims are invalid. There is no supreme end of which it can be claimed that all men prefer it either actually, or "virtually," in the sense that all men would seek it if they were perfectly enlightened. This negative conclusion I take to be a simple matter of fact, as I would the opposite conclusion if it were true.

There are, then, many orders of preference, and they cannot be reduced to any one of their number. It is, however, a common error to suppose that there is nothing to be *said for* one order of preference that cannot be said for all. Since orders of preference differ, they can be compared. In order to explain this question further I shall define a certain order of preference and set forth its characteristics.

It is a matter of fact that interests sometimes conflict: one interest cannot run its course to satisfaction without robbing or impeding another. No one would deny, least of all in this period of human history, that this is a fundamental and widely pervasive feature of human life. Out of this conflict there arises the maxim of prudence which teaches that an individual should, in the pursuit of each of his interests, take account of its effects upon his other interests, or upon the interests of other persons. Out of this conflict arises also the maxim of self-love, or self-realization, the maxim, namely, of the fullest possible development of the person's capacities and the richest possible fulfillment of his interests.

There is a third maxim which presupposes prudence and self-realization, but introduces the principle of benevolence. It recommends prudence and self-realization in behalf of all interests inclusively. In order to have a name that will be short enough to be convenient and long enough to be descriptive, I propose to call it the maxim of reflective agreement.

In constructing this maxim of reflective agreement I conceive of a person as the agent of a set of interests that are called "his,"—interests that are implanted in him as dispositions, and that actually motivate his conduct. I conceive of him as reflecting upon these his interests with a view to their aggregate realization, and as being actually governed, in some degree, by this integral purpose. I further conceive that this person possesses the faculty of sympathy by which he can feel, and be concerned for, the interests of other persons. In so far as his sympathies are universal, through a specific concern for the interests of those he knows personally, and through a generalized concern for family, neighborhood, nation or mankind, his governing purpose will tend to coincide with those of others, since their sympathies in turn embrace him. As we ascend from the family to the neighborhood, the nation, the family of nations and the broad historical stream of human life, there is a vastly increasing complexity, which requires a series of subordinate units of organization. But the principle remains the same, whether the end be domestic felicity or the harmonious happiness of all mankind.

The maxim of reflective agreement is an actual maxim in the following senses:

1. It is conceptually definable.
2. It is consistent with human capacity, and can be implanted by education.
3. It does in some instances, and in some degree, operate as a goal and direction of effort.
4. It is a norm by which conduct can be, and often is, measured, and approved or condemned.

The above are characteristics which the maxim of reflective agreement shares with many other actual maxims. There are, however, certain characteristics which it possesses uniquely. Of these I shall single out seven for explicit mention.

(1) It is the only maxim which has some appeal to everybody. In this specific sense it satisfies the requirement of universality.

(2) It is of all maxims the maxim best suited to be agreed on, both practically and theoretically, and thus to realize the possibility of agreement which is commonly presupposed in moral discussion.

(3) The maxim of reflective agreement alone satisfies the requirement of disinterestedness or impartiality. It escapes relativity and attains absoluteness by embracing within itself all the relativities of special interests.

(4) If, and only if, the terms "higher" and "highest" are taken to mean more or most inclusive, can the question of higher and highest, or any such comparative or superlative judgments, have a meaning as between one man and another, and thus satisfy the requirements of commensurability.

(5) The maxim of reflective agreement alone gives clear and verifiable meaning to such expressions as the Golden Rule, "the general good," and "the public interest"; and it should therefore be accepted by those who employ those expressions.

(6) The maxim of reflective agreement is a conscious ex-

pression and explicit formulation of that curb or scruple which is called the "social conscience."

(7) The maxim of reflective agreement defines the intent and the norm of certain major human institutions, such as the law, the state and the economic system.

And now that these characteristics have been set forth, the tale is ended. I am quite aware that this ending will seem abrupt, and disappointing. I can only ask those who want additional proof to ask themselves what it is that they want. Let me try to answer this question in their behalf, assuming that they are adherents of the maxim of reflective agreement, and of its end of harmonious happiness.

(1) They may want to have it shown that all wills do, in fact, will the harmonious happiness of mankind. This fact cannot, as a matter of fact, be substantiated.

(2) They may want some ulterior meaning of such terms as good, right or ought, so that it may be truly asserted *simpliciter*, that harmonious happiness is good and right, or that it ought to be. Whether there is or is not such a meaning is a question of fact, which I can only answer in the negative.

(3) They may want to have it shown that the harmonious happiness of mankind coincides with the order of the universe. This is a question of metaphysics, which I should be compelled to answer in the negative; and if I could answer it in the affirmative I should think no better of harmonious happiness. If I knew that the universe had the opposite design I should think less of the universe, but not less of harmonious happiness.

(4) They may want to have it shown that harmonious happiness is commanded by God. This is a question of religion on which I am at least doubtful. If I believed it to be the case I should praise God for it. I should not feel that harmonious happiness itself deserved a higher place in my esteem, though I might now consider it more prudent to conform.

(5) They may want to have it shown that the maxim of reflective agreement cannot be rejected without self-contradiction. Kant attempted this sort of proof, but succeeded only in showing that the maxim of reflective agreement contradicted other maxims, and that the person who at the same time af-

firmed this maxim and one of its contradictories contradicted himself.

(6) Finally, there are those who expect the maxim of reflective agreement, or whatever be the preferred maxim, to exercise an irresistible compulsion on the will. But there is no judgment whatever the bare utterance and grasping of which can be guaranteed to incite action, or even to win acceptance.

It does not follow, however, that the advocates of the code of reflective agreement cannot "commend" that code. Such unique characteristics as have been set forth above will commend it and will commend it uniquely. To characterize any object will commend it to interests which are sensitized to its characteristics. Seeing the object in the light of these characteristics, some men will be attracted to it—some, perhaps, for the first time. Some will be attracted to it as a novel means to old ends; some will be attracted to it as an interpretation of old maxims; some as affording a specific and clarified expression of generalized sentiments. It lies within the range of possibility that a code such as that of reflective agreement should possess the characteristics qualifying it for universal adoption, and that these characteristics should be so set forth, and so presented to existing human interests, as to bring about its universal adoption.

We turn to our second major question. What is the value of science? We should now be prepared to answer this question in terms of what we know about value. The value of science, in short, is a special theorem in the science of value, or of moral value, in general. It follows from our previous conclusions that for science to have value means that it is itself a matter of interest or operates in such wise as to promote interest.

There are, in the first place, certain interests of which science itself is the object, so that science would still have value even if it were not useful. There is an esthetic attractiveness in the form of scientific theory, an immediate interest in the processes of thinking and speculation, and also a specific interest in truth, an impulse of curiosity which extends all the way from the interest in one's neighbor's affairs, or in the contents of a sealed letter, to the interest in laws by which events can be systematically predicted.

So much for pure science, or science for the sake of science. Pure science is "pure" by virtue not of its abstractness or rigor, but by virtue of its single-minded devotion to theoretic interests. We turn now from the intrinsic values of science to its extrinsic, contributory, or instrumental values.

The utility of science has in recent years been emphasized to the almost total exclusion of its primary values. And it may well be emphasized. The values which theoretical interests generate are contributory to every other interest. There is no interest that is not furthered by knowing more. However completely he may ignore other interests, the man of knowledge serves them none the less. In fact the indirect fruitfulness of the theoretic interest is proportional to its disinterestedness, or purity. In so far as the scientist is true to his calling he achieves laws and theories which are directly applicable to no actual situation, and indirectly applicable to an infinite number of hypothetical situations.

While the value of ends, or the immediate objects of interest, depends on their being known as what they are, the value of means depends on the knowledge of causal relations. Within this type of cognitive value falls the whole vast domain of technology, from the simplest rules of thumb to the most refined and elaborate techniques. This is a matter that requires no elucidation and no emphasis in an age in which the tools of life have been so multiplied and so widely distributed that there is scarcely a man who does not acknowledge science as his benefactor.

We turn now to the moral values of science—the moral limitations of its intrinsic values, and the moral limitations of its instrumental values. The intrinsic theoretic values of science have, on the one hand, a certain universality and, on the other hand, a certain narrowness, and it is in these terms that we must appraise their moral value. For moral value lies in the relation of one interest to another, as judged by the standard of harmonious happiness.

First, theoretic interests have a certain universality and are on that account morally praiseworthy. Truth is true for every-body. It is characteristic of theoretic pursuits that they are non-acquisitive and non-competing. They are peculiarly suited to a life of harmonious happiness. They belong to that universal culture which intersects the nations of the earth and the epochs of history. They serve as a model and as a nucleus for the development of a unified humanity. Science possesses what it is customary to call "disinterestedness." Its very detachment and neutrality enable science to bring obscure or neglected interests to light and to recognize the claims of each. Science extends knowledge beyond the narrow bounds of existing sympathies: morality may then extend sympathy to the wider bounds of knowledge. Finally, pure science can flourish only provided it is free from social, political, religious, economic or institutional pressure. Hence in so far as he is aware of the social conditions of his vocation the scientist is the partisan of tolerance and liberty.

But the intrinsic theoretic values have, on the other hand, a certain narrowness. The special theoretic interests which pure science represents play an intermittent and comparatively slight role in human life. The scientist, in proportion as he is preoccupied with his vocation, tends to be selfish. This does not mean that he is self-interested, but that he lacks benevolence. When, as in biology, psychology or the social sciences, the interests of others become the objects of his investigation he does not feel and share them but describes them. The love of persons is an interest the satisfaction of which entails the satisfaction of other persons. The love of truth, even the truth about persons, entails no satisfaction save the satisfaction of the scientist himself.

Morality, although as seeking the maximum realization of the aggregate of all interests it may be said to be of a higher order, is nevertheless itself an interest; and the moral man is its partisan. But the scientist *qua* scientist rejects moral bias, along with every other bias. In his studies of human life and of society he does, it is true, deal with bias, and even with moral bias, but it is his business to know it and not to be governed by it. The cult of science thus works against morality through its very dispassionateness. Where interests are concerned the scientist treats them alike, being the observer of all and the champion of none. He feels himself superior to passion because he stands outside of it: he feels none of its heat and takes none of its risks. To the scientist as such any partisan seems child-like, naive or even contemptible; and he is disposed to overlook that moral passion to which no human interest or purpose is contemptible, and which unites the breadth of the scientist with the ardor and courage of the partisan.

We turn, next, to the moral appraisal of the instrumental values of science. They are embraced within technology, which, taken as a body of knowledge, consists of specific scientific truths, deduced from the broader generalizations of pure science, and selected for their specific usefulness. But general technology taken as the aggregate of all such specific technologies, is like pure science, all things to all interests. It differs only in that while pure science is in no camp, technology is in all camps. General technology is not fastidious in its choice of clients. The technologist is a consultant in the art of success—anybody's success, success in anything, no questions asked.

The widely prevalent belief that the utilities of science are morally benign is due to the existence of certain human institutions and professions in which technology is linked with a moral purpose. Medical science affords a good example. The physician is devoted to the prevention and remedy of disease, and is governed by a strict professional code. In the pursuit of his humanitarian end the physician utilizes the results of science—of physics, chemistry and biology. In his hands these technologies are humane, but in themselves they are quite indifferent to humanity. They lend themselves as readily to the propagation of disease as to its prevention or remedy, as readily to toxic as to therapeutic uses.

Despite its promiscuity, technology as a whole casts a certain weight against morality. Its great successes lie in the control of physical forces. Here it multiplies its most efficient instruments. But they have multiplied in advance of their moral uses, and have tended to create their own uses. For men are disposed to do what they can do easily and efficiently. The development of physical technology prompts men to do what they are thereby peculiarly equipped to do, namely, to create material goods. Those demands which can be satisfied by material goods tend to be affirmed and developed. Men also tend to shift their interest from the end to the means, and this transference of value is facilitated when the means is being continually perfected, so as to give at one and the same time a sense of novelty and of smooth execution.

A decade or so ago it was said that the cure for human ills lay in the development of a technology of human nature that should parallel the development of physical technology. We now know enough of the possibilities of such a development to shudder at the thought of its success. If we are not ready for the right use of physical technology, still less are we ready for the right use of psychological technology.

We tend to do the things that we know how to do, instead of trying to do the things that we ought to do. Unhappily the things most worth doing are the things it is most difficult to do. High attainment in the fine arts is difficult, high attainment in piety is difficult: there is no consulting technologist who can guarantee success in either of these fields of activity. It is less difficult to manufacture goods and improve their quality than it is to distribute them justly. The supreme economic difficulties do not lie in industrial or even financial processes, but in the region of general social policy. It is easier to manufacture an improved type of electric refrigerator than to raise the general standard of living or achieve economic democracy. And so we tend to devote our energies to the manufacture of electric refrigerators, and to the enjoyment of them and their contents.

It is easier to wage war than it is to achieve peace. There is a technology of war, but no technology of peace. Hence we tend to do what we know how to do: to be interested in war-making and in those results, such as conquest, which can be achieved by war.

A man who has certain techniques at his disposal may devote them to the indirect possession of other techniques. There are methods by which one can without acquiring techniques in one's own person acquire them vicariously in the persons of others. There are two of these keys to control, money and position. He who has them can through them buy or intimidate men with other techniques, and so work his will with nature or with society. But he may have no will except the will to be able to do what he can. He may use his will only to prove to himself and to others the fact that he can do what he wills. This will, which is the consummate practical expression of a technology without moral allegiance, is called the love of power, which bears to technology the same relation that cynicism bears to pure science.

There remains the question of the moral value of the science of moral value. Does it make men better to have an ethics—a moral philosophy, an idea which they set above all other ideas, which they define, for which they argue, and to which they win converts? Americans in facing the present crisis are seeking to define and prove their creed, believing that this is a condition both of survival and of fitness to survive. I accept this belief.

The ideal of harmonious happiness is a union of passion with enlightenment. It is the function of the science of that ideal to define its meaning, to illuminate its characteristics, to commend it to such human interests and sympathies as are sensitized to these characteristics, and to discover whatever laws of nature will enable men both to achieve agreement and to realize the ends in which they agree.

Let us sum up the positive values of science. Being morally neutral in its own motivation science occupies a place of peculiar eminence in a morally organized society. Requiring liberty for the exercise of its own function, it is the natural ally of libertarian institutions. Being non-acquisitive it is tolerant of other interests. What is given to science does not have to be taken away. Science presents no problems of competition—it makes no enemies. Finally, it has something to give to every interest and presents no problem of over-production. It can be misused, but it may be well used. It is the source of enlightenment by which interests find their true objects, and by which new objects evoke new interests and enrich old. In revealing the natural relations of object to object it provides the means to ends and the means to means through the long series of intermediaries by which interests, personal and social, may engage in far-flung enterprises. By revealing the natural relations of interest to interest it provides the method by which interests may be fruitfully organized, and it thus serves the peculiar art of morals—the making of the well-ordered personal life and the well-ordered social life.

The science of morals defines the supreme end, exhibits that end, and commends it for adoption by disclosing its peculiar characteristics. It provides the guiding principles for moral education, as psychology provides its subordinate technique. The science of morals defines the standard by which conduct is praised or condemned, and by which social policy is rationalized. But it is only as good as the end which it serves, and its good will be realized in the world only in so far as that end is chosen and adhered to by the wills of men.

# 7. CONCLUSION

# MAN, THE MICROCOSM

## *by* Ruth Nanda Anshen

SO OUR story ends. And what may the moral of the tale be said to be? The moral is the power of Reason and its decisive influence on the life of humanity. This book is an epitome of an endeavor to point out the disastrous dehumanization inherent in modern science when Man and Reason are abandoned, to indicate the ineluctable necessity of surrendering the individual will to an immanent and common Reason. It is a concerted effort to show that the methodological procedure of science, if it is taken as replacing philosophy, becomes intolerant and exclusive, that it fixes attention on a definite group of abstractions, neglects everything else, and elicits every vestige of information and theory which is relevant to what it has retained. We trust that we have succeeded in proving that this method is gloriously triumphant provided that the abstractions are judicious. But however triumphant, the triumph is always within limits and the refusal to recognize these limits produces catastrophic results. The anti-rationalism of science is in part justified, as a preservation of its expedient methodology. On the other hand we have attempted to point out that much of it is irrational prejudice. In the final analysis, the atomistic method is the only legitimate one for obtaining facts, but the criterion of relevance must be sought by other means.

Nineteenth Century materialism closed the mind of man to what is above him. Twentieth Century psychology opened the mind of man to what is beneath him. The reader will judge whether we, even though of the twentieth Century, have fulfilled our desire so to correlate, synthesize and clarify the vast abundance of contemporary knowledge pertaining to science and to Man (knowledge which has been rendered comparatively ineffectual by virtue of its dispersion) that the consciousness of

Man has been awakened to what is above, beneath, around and within him; awakened to the necessity of returning logic to ontology, the tragic separation of which is so eloquently exemplified in Spinoza and Hegel.

Ever since the Middle Ages the modern world has lost an integrating principle. There has been a futile effort to substitute scientific explanation for metaphysical meaning. The medieval thinkers, for example, were warmly aware that the community is based upon the guiding and the shaping power of a spiritual value and in the adaptation of the laws of nature. This transcending and shaping power is not contained either in the idea of scientific empiricism, moral empiricism, in the idea of bourgeois society or in the concepts of some collective consciousness. All lack the concrete substance, the existential value of an idea which is capable of integrating life beyond the borders of the subordination of ends to means. The substitution of the idea of progress, especially of scientific progress, for the idea of meaning and purpose has resulted in a metaphysical agnosticism, an educational secularism and a bourgeois humanism which has left the soul of man bewildered and full of fear.

There is, however, a growing, if embryonic, awareness of, and at times even an insistence upon, the indispensability of purpose, of ends in the evaluation of the nature of man since there is an increasing recognition that the emphasis on ends is ultimately the expression of the essential relationship between time and eternity, and there is a growing awakening, also, to the fact that the immanence of transcendental and spiritual values within human existence is an ontological truth which cannot be explained by any scientific atomization, or by the romantic irrationalism which seems to have engulfed the world. For the blind devotion to scientific expression and experience is nothing more than a fatal belief in continuous progress as the result of a growing enlightenment,—a profound danger to mankind when the unshakable trust in the productivity of the *methods* of science is so apotheosized; when materialism is raised to the rank of a metaphysical principle. If the craftsmen in ideas have a belief in the potentialities of human society and an awareness of the dignity of the human person, this will be the best bulwark of those ultimate standards of validity that we call science and truth, for it is not sense data, nor logical universals that we require, but a *tertium quid*, i.e., a status of values.

The contributors to this endeavor to clarify the problem of Man and science have furthermore attempted to emphasize either explicitly or implicitly the inevitable interrelationship of the processes of the human mind. They have for the most part proclaimed their dedication and devotion to eternal and abiding principles, to a concept of absolute values as being indispensable since there is an inalienable precedence of transcendent ideals over transient and ephemeral values. Anaxagoras was the first to emphasize the supremacy of mind and spirit over matter, but later, even from the period of the early Renaissance, mystical and voluntaristic tendencies prevented the full rationalization of the spirit, and Cartesian dualism definitely brought on the loss of the idea of spirit and even of the word "spirit" until spirit finally became synonymous with intellect—a pathetic distortion from which much of contemporary thought now suffers. Slowly, oh, too slowly we begin to realize that spirit is essentially power *and* mind, life *and* reason. In order to obtain a complete understanding of man, we must return to the dynamic unity of power and mind, universality and personality, in our concept of the nature of man—a concept which has too long been replaced by the static atomization of natural science.

Science and Man are the consciously determined pursuit of Truth and Being. In them the finite consciousness of humanity appropriates as its own the infinite fecundity of nature, and preserves through its conscious and subconscious experience the sources of harmony and balance. Our concern in this book has been to indicate how to combine the scientific spirit with the free moral and spiritual life of Man; how to combine secular initiative and pragmatic judgment with a tenable detachment; how to combine the visible inequalities of the naturalistic human being with the invisible equalities implied in the ontological interpretation of Man.

Science which promised so much for the amelioration of Man's lot on earth has itself produced a sense of insecurity and uncertainty because Man no longer has any faith to which to cling, and this precariousness of life has been made the basis of an educational philosophy. We have attempted to show that there is a profound thirst for some life-giving water which seems suddenly to have failed. There is in this dichotomy between science and Man, a dichotomy which we hope may be overcome, an attitude analogous to some Euripidean irony but without a *deus ex machina* to solve the difficulties. There is something of the invectives of the prophets but without their hopes for salvation in a return to God.

It has been the purpose of this book to indicate the dark, serious and perilous risks inherent in the general conceptions introduced by science into modern thought, conceptions which cannot be separated from the philosophical situation as expressed by Descartes. I refer to the assumption of bodies and minds as independent individual substances, each existing in its own right apart from any necessary reference to each other. The resultant moral discipline has emphasized the intrinsic value of the individual entity. This doctrine of minds, as independent substances, has led precipitously not merely to private worlds of experience, but also to private worlds of morals. Aristotle, meditating on the very roots of the nature of Man, poignantly understood that a solitary, separated individual could not be a man but must be either a beast or a god. And such geniuses as Aristotle, or Archimedes, or Roger Bacon being endowed with the full scientific mentality, instinctively maintained that all things great and small are conceivable only as exemplifications of general, universal principles which reign throughout the order of nature. Science cannot be said to be engaged in erecting a sublime, truly objective world in such pure material as Democritus employed, above the Slough of Despondency in which our daily life is placed. It simply endeavors to prolong a certain important line already laid out in the structure of our practical world.

There are reflections in this volume also of a quite different kind. Values, history, social acts with which it deals, point in still other directions and these also admit of a similar prolongation. For it is not sufficient to search for truth, and ultimately to find it, or to find part of it, or to approach it more closely. Whatever is found must be kept fresh and pure, it must be nourished like other truths—friendship and love, let us say— lest it perish, and this can be accomplished only at the price of incessant and generous efforts. The achievement and the preservation of truth postulate infinite devotion and fidelity— there is then no greater service which Man can render to science and to Man.

There is almost complete unanimity among the authors of this book recognizing it to be a sin, as Thomas Aquinas so elo- quently and convincingly points out, against the intelligence to wish to proceed in an identical manner in the typically different domains—physical, mathematical, and metaphysical—of specu- lative knowledge. We have striven to indicate that if science is not to be condemned to a degeneration into a confusion of *ad hoc* hypotheses, if man is to find his way out of the moral chaos, the moral wilderness, of this age, science must embrace philosophy and must establish a penetrating criticism of its own foundations. The faith in the order of nature which has made possible the growth of science is a pregnant illustration of a more profound faith. To experience this faith is to know that in being ourselves we are more than ourselves; it is to know that our experience, an experience which includes intuition, nebulous and fragmen- tary though it is, touches the utmost depths of reality; it is to know that segregated details merely in order to be themselves demand that they should exist in a system of things; it is to know that this system includes the equilibrium and harmony of logical reason, and the equilibrium and harmony of esthetic achievement and moral perception, that eternal equilibrium and harmony of Being which is the noetic and guiding principle of life, the inspiring ideal beckoning one to subtler issues. Whether one is Christian, Jew, or Mohammedan, one must admit that, in the words of Jacques Maritain, "the intellect *sees* . . . , that it is precisely the activity of the intellect which disengages from this experience and brings to the fire of immaterial visibility in act, the objects which sense cannot decipher in things and which the intellect sees. . . ."

We trust we have succeeded in demonstrating that while the human race endures the images of sense can never lose their validity; they will forever yield the personal and classical interpretation of nature. No matter what abstruse deductions science may make about them, the stars will remain visible stars; earth, water, fire and air will confront the spirit and survive the atomization and disintegration to which the science of chemistry may subject them. And in the final analysis, the authority of science will depend upon the analogy of objects and events and upon the evidence of sense and intuition. We have attempted to warn that effort must be expended to sharpen the distinction between description based upon intuition and speculation based upon some criterion established by the philosophers or scientists. This is an essential part of genuine philosophy and of science as it has been maintained from Plato's critique of sophistry to Kant's critique of dogmatic metaphysics—and cannot be abandoned unless man indeed is

> . . . proud man,
> Drest in a little brief authority,
> Most ignorant of what he's most assur'd.

This and much more we have endeavored to point out and finally and above all the ancient truth of Parmenides that thought and Being are one—that human beings if they are to retain their humanity, if they are to retain their liberty which is so rudely being eliminated from the experience of mankind, must not forget that they are members of the universe with all the responsibility which this membership implies, and that,

> They wanted yet the master work, the end
> Of all yet done; a creature who, not prone
> And brute as other creatures, but endowed
> With sanctity of reason, might erect
> His stature, and upright with front serene
> Govern the rest, self-knowing, and from thence
> Magnanimous to correspond with Heav'n.

And thus a new freedom will arise, wiser and stronger than the freedom destroyed by the atomizations of science, and a new concept of Man, noble and with serenity of mind and spirit, Man who may not again experience the disappointment of Job in realizing the impossibility of achieving first principles—Man who is Man only when he is considered as a complete Being, the microcosm, a totality concerning whom any form of segregation is artificial and destructive, for to subdivide Man is to execute him, whereas to recognize his unity is to resurrect him.

# LIST OF CONTRIBUTORS

**RUTH NANDA ANSHEN**
Editor of the *Science of Culture Series*

**ALEŠ HRDLIČKA**
Curator, United States National Museum, Smithsonian Institution

**REINHOLD NIEBUHR**
William E. Dodge, Jr., Professor of Applied Christianity, Union Theological Seminary, New York

**JACQUES MARITAIN**
Former Professor of Philosophy, Catholic Institute of Paris; Professor of Philosophy, Institute of Medieval Studies of Toronto, Princeton University, and Columbia University

**ALFRED E. COHN**
Member, Rockefeller Institute for Medical Research

**ARTHUR H. COMPTON**
Chairman of the Department of Physics and Dean of the Division of Physical Science, The University of Chicago

**WALDEMAR KAEMPFFERT**
Science Editor of *The New York Times*

**JAMES T. SHOTWELL**
Bryce Professor of the History of International Relations, Columbia University; Director of the Division of Economics and History of the Carnegie Endowment for International Peace

**HAROLD C. UREY**
Professor of Chemistry, Columbia University

**K. KOFFKA**

Late Professor of Psychology, Smith College

**BRAND BLANSHARD**

Professor of Philosophy, Swarthmore College

**BRONISLAW MALINOWSKI**

Former Professor of Anthropology, University of London; Professor of Anthropology, Yale University

**CARL L. BECKER**

Professor of Sociology, Cornell University

**JULIAN HUXLEY**

Secretary, Zoological Society of London; Vice-President, Eugenics Society, London

**WALTER B. CANNON**

George Higginson Professor of Physiology, Medical School, Harvard University

**KARL T. COMPTON**

President, Massachusetts Institute of Technology

**FRANK H. KNIGHT**

Professor of Economics, The University of Chicago

**LEWIS MUMFORD**

Author

**PHILIP C. JESSUP**

Professor of International Law, Columbia University; Director, Division of International Law, Carnegie Endowment for International Peace

**HANS KELSEN**

Professor of International Law, Harvard University

**HAROLD D. LASSWELL**

Chief of the Experimental Division for Study of Wartime Communication

**JEAN PIAGET**

Professor of Child Psychology and of the History of Scientific Thought, University of Geneva

**CHARLES GUSTAV JUNG**

Professor of Analytic Psychology, Technische Hochschule, Zurich

**EDWIN GRANT CONKLIN**

Professor Emeritus of Biology, Princeton University

**RALPH BARTON PERRY**

Professor of Philosophy, Harvard University

# INDEX

Achievements of modern technology (Mumford), 346
Acosmic mysticism (Niebuhr), 50
Acquired characteristics (Hrdlicka), 36
Action (Anshen), 9; (Niebuhr), 44
Acton, Lord, (Mumford), 347
Adams, Henry, (Cohn), 111; Samuel, (Cohn), 113
Adaptation (Hrdlicka), 20; (Piaget), 409
Adolescent of today (Hrdlicka), 38
Age of dissipation (Urey), 169, 170
Agriculture (Huxley), 270
Albert the Great (Maritain), 89
Alexander (Becker), 257
America (Kaempffert), 141
American: Christianity (Niebuhr), 64; civilization (Compton, Arthur H.), 121; technological society (Compton, Arthur H.), 121; thought and science (Compton, Arthur H.), 129
American Federation of Labor (Compton, Karl T.), 316
Anatomy of idolatry (Niebuhr), 47
Anaxagoras (Anshen), 474; (Becker), 252; (Compton, Arthur H.), 126
Anaximander (Becker), 251
Animals (Hrdlicka), 27, 28, 29
Animism (Becker), 248
Anonymous group working (Huxley), 280
Anthropocentric humanism (Maritain), 85
Anthropologist (Malinowski), 209
Anthropology (Malinowski), 208
Anthropomorphism (Niebuhr), 48
Anti-rationalism of science (Anshen), 472
Apperception (Hrdlicka), 28

Applied science (Huxley), 286
Aquinas, Thomas, (Anshen), 476; (Maritain), 84, 86, 88, 90
Archimedes (Anshen), 475
Aristotle (Anshen), 10, 475; (Becker), 255, 256, 261, 265; (Cohn), 100, 101, 113; (Maritain), 66, 69, 72, 80, 89; (Mumford), 356; (Niebuhr), 51; (Piaget), 418
Arkwright (Kaempffert), 143; (Shotwell), 152
Artificial textiles and fabrics (Urey), 168
Assyrians (Compton, Karl T.), 310
Athens (Becker), 257
Atomic system (Becker), 252
Atomism of methods (Anshen), 12
Aurelius, Marcus, (Becker), 258
Authority of metaphysics (Maritain), 74
Autonomy of mind (Blanshard), 203
Averroism (Maritain), 90

Bach (Cohn), 113; (Kaempffert), 136
Bacon, Francis, (Compton, Arthur H.), 133
Bacon, Roger, (Anshen), 3, 475; (Huxley), 271; (Maritain), 72, 89
Baconian prophecy (Anshen), 3
Balance (Mumford), 356
Basic needs (Malinowski), 216, 217
Beethoven (Cohn), 113
Being (Anshen), 13, 477; (Maritain), 68, 88
Behaviorism (Blanshard), 191, 192; (Koffka), 172
Belief (Malinowski), 231
Bell, Alexander Graham, (Kaempffert), 136, 140